## INTRODUCTION TO HAZCHEM LIST 10

i.    This list cancels List No. 9 and subsequent amendments to that list.

ii.    This list is primarily for use by the emergency services and **must not** be used to determine the placarding of vehicles conveying hazardous substances.

iii.    The fact that a United Nations number and emergency action code (E.A.C.) for a given substance are shown in this document does not necessarily mean they may be used for the marking of road tankers or tank containers used for the carriage of that substance. To determine the placarding required reference must be made to the Health & Safety Commission's Approved Carriage List (The Approved List).

iv.    This document contains all items listed by the United Nations and contained in their publication "Transport of Dangerous Goods" with the exception of substances in UN Class 1, i.e. explosives. In order to accommodate as much information as possible in one comprehensive document the headings to each column have been abbreviated where necessary. These headings and the information and guidance provided in each column are explained in the following clauses.

## 1.    UNITED NATIONS NUMBER (UN)

1.1    The identification number shown in the first column of the list is generally that allocated by the United Nations and contained in the publication referred to in paragraph iv. of the introduction. Certain of the entries can also be found in the "The Approved Carriage List" issued by the Health and Safety Commission under The Carriage of Dangerous Goods by Road Regulations 1996.

1.2    It will be noted that against certain United Nations numbers more than one entry has been made, each with a differing emergency action code, e.g. UN. 1866 and UN 1986. In these cases the substances are carried in various forms whose properties pose different hazards and therefore require separate emergency action codes.

1.3    It will also be noted that against many United Nations numbers is the abbreviation 'N.O.S'. This abbreviation denotes 'not otherwise specified'. These numbers are used for substances which do not have a discrete entry in the list of UNs and represent the hazard or hazards the substance or article possesses e.g. UN 2929 'Toxic Liquid, Flammable, Organic, N.O.S'.

1.4    The List on pages 3 to 101 is set out in UN number order. If only the substance name is known, the UN number can be found by reference to the alphabetical list of substances on pages 104 to 156.

## 2.    SUBSTANCE

2.1    The names of substances in the second column of the list are by 'Proper Shipping Names'.

2.2    There is an alphabetical list of substances on pages 104 to 156 of this document which show the appropriate UN number for that substance. Substances shown in bold capital type in this list indicate the proper shipping name. Normal type indicates an alternative name with the appropriate UN number under which the substance will appear in the main list.

## 3.    EMERGENCY ACTION CODE (EAC)

3.1    Emergency Action Codes (commonly known as Hazchem codes), which appear in the third column of the list, have been assigned with the agreement of the Health and Safety Executive. The codes are designed to be used in conjunction with the Emergency Action Scale Cards, which are intended to be carried by emergency service personnel. The cards indicate the action that may be necessary (except additional personal protection (A.P.P.) and the use of alcohol resistant foam) **during the first few minutes** of an incident. Set out below is an example of an Emergency Action Scale Card.

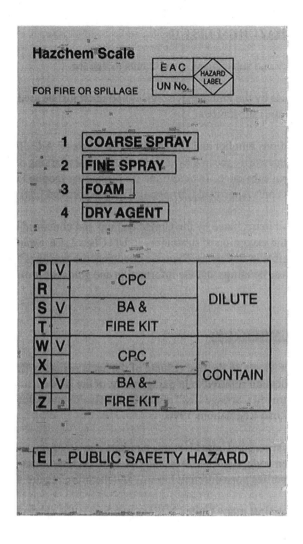

**Note:** **Emergency Action Scale Cards are available from The Stationery Office and will for the time being continue to show reverse letters which should be ignored.**

3.2     The codes allocated and shown in the list apply to the transport in bulk (i.e. 3,000 litres or more) of the single substance by road or rail. These codes will not necessarily apply in cases where loads are carried in quantities below 3,000 litres or for non-transport incidents although they may be used to provide some indication of the action that may be necessary. In the case of mixed loads of substances the appropriate code to be displayed is determined by reference to the code chart contained in the Health & Safety Commission's Approved Carriage List.

3.3     Substances in Class 7, i.e. radioactive substances, although included in the list have not been allocated emergency action codes.

### 3.2     Interpretation of Emergency Action Code

### 3.2.1     Extinguishing Media

3.2.1.1     The firefighting extinguishing media is determined by reference to the first character of the emergency action code as follows:

1     denotes **coarse spray**
2     denotes **fine spray**
•2    denotes **alcohol resistant foam** but, if not available, fine spray can be used
3     denotes **normal foam** i.e. protein type foam that is not alcohol resistant
•3    denotes **alcohol resistant foam** but, if not available, normal foam can be used
4     denotes **dry agent** - water <u>MUST NOT</u> be allowed to come into contact with substance

Issued under the authority of the Home Office
(Fire and Emergency Planning Directorate)

# HAZCHEM
# List 10
# 1999

HM Fire Service Inspectorate

Publications Section          London:  The Stationery Office

First published 1999

ISBN 0 11 341223 1

**Note: Any higher number than the one shown can be used but a lower number <u>must not</u> be used.**

3.2.1.2 •2 and •3 have been included where polar solvents (water miscible, flammable liquids e.g. alcohols) MAY cause breakdown of protein foams and where alcohol resistant foam may offer more effective extinguishing properties than protein foam or water spray.

**Note: •2 and •3 are not displayed on the vehicle placards or on the Emergency Action Scale Cards and will only be shown as 2 and 3 respectively. This information can therefore only be obtained by reference to this document or another appropriate source.**

### 3.2.2    <u>Personal protection</u>

3.2.2.1 Where the second character of the EAC is S, T, Y or Z self-contained open circuit positive pressure compressed air breathing apparatus conforming to BS EN 137 should be worn in combination with fire kit, consisting of tunic and overtrousers conforming to BS EN 469 and firefighters' gloves conforming to BS EN 659 should be worn.

3.2.2.2 Where the second character of an EAC is P, R, W or X liquid-tight chemical protective clothing conforming to BS EN 466 part 2 (when available)* in combination with the breathing apparatus specified in clause 3.2.2.1 should be used. This will ensure protection for up to 30 minutes.

**\*Note:   At the time of publication BS EN 466 part 2 has yet to be agreed. In the interim period chemical protective clothing is available whose performance is based on the draft standard for EN 466 part 2.**

### <u>Violent Reaction</u>

3.2.3   Where the second character of the EAC is a P, S, W or Y there is a danger that the substance can be violently or explosively reactive. This danger exists for all flammable gases and flammable liquids with a flash point below 61°C as well as for many other reactive substances.

### <u>Contain/dilute</u>

3.2.4.   Where the second character of an emergency action code is W, X, Y or Z spillages should be prevented from entering drains and watercourses. Where the second character of the code is P, R, S or T spillages may be washed to drains with large quantities of water. Due care must however still be exercised to avoid unnecessary pollution of watercourses.

**Note 1:   In order to mitigate the effects of environmental pollution by Fire Service operations and to improve liaison between the Fire Service and the Environment Agency a consistent set of arrangements and standards for dealing with incidents has been established and set out in a Memorandum of Understanding (MOU).**

**Note 2:   Ideally all contamination and decontamination run-off should be contained. However, the Environment Agency accepts that this will not always be practical for normal Fire Service operations and that life saving operational procedures must take precedence over other considerations at the scene of an incident. Nevertheless, all steps that are reasonably practicable should be taken to contain contaminants and the Fire Service should always inform the Environment Agency as soon as possible so that appropriate advice can be given.**

**Note 3:   The Offences of causing pollution outlined in the Environment Act 1995 apply equally to the Fire Service as to other organisations. Potentially polluting substances, even apparently harmless substances such as food and beverages, can cause serious problems if discharged into a watercourse e.g. 250 litres of a soft drink or beer would constitute a pollutant as it can lead to deoxygenation of the water. Firefighting foams are also a potential source of pollution and their entry into watercourses and drainage systems should be prevented whenever possible.**

**Note 4:   Helpful guidance on run-off can also be found in the Health and Safety Executive's Guidance Note EH70 "Control of fire-water run-off from CIMAH sites to prevent environmental damage".**

### E "Public Safety Hazard"

3.2.5   An 'E' following the first two characters of an EAC indicates that there may be a public safety hazard and that the following actions should be taken:

i.      People should be warned to stay indoors with all doors and windows closed, preferably in rooms upstairs and facing away from the incident. Ignition sources should be eliminated and any ventilation stopped.

ii.     Effects may spread beyond the immediate vicinity. All non-essential personnel should be instructed to move at least 250 metres away from the incident.

iii.    Police and Fire Service incident commanders should consult each other and with a product expert, or with a source of product expertise.

iv.     THE POSSIBLE NEED FOR SUBSEQUENT EVACUATION SHOULD BE CONSIDERED, BUT IT SHOULD BE REMEMBERED THAT IN MOST CASES IT WILL BE SAFER TO REMAIN IN A BUILD-ING THAN TO EVACUATE.

**SITUATIONS WHERE EVACUATION MAY BE NECESSARY INCLUDE THE FOLLOWING:**

| EXAMPLES | ASSESSMENT |
|---|---|
| 1.i.  Smoke from bulk or packaged product fire which is allowed to burn out. (Often safest and least environmentally damaging option.) | 1.  Nuisance effects will last several hours. Smoke or gas concentrations in open air are unpleasant but short-term exposure is not likely to be dangerous. |
| ii.   Small long lasting toxic emission. | |
| 2.    A larger long lasting toxic gas emission which will be carried towards an inhabited area after a predicted wind change not due for at least two hours. | 2.  Area considered for evacuation will not be exposed to significant danger for at least an hour, preferably longer. |
| 3.    Evacuation of people from an isolated house in the country may be feasible, possibly using additional BA sets. | 3.  Downwind area is very sparsely populated and resources are available to protect people during their evacuation. |
| 4.i.  Righting a loaded tanker, especially a liquefied gas carrier. | 4.  Area considered for evacuation could be exposed to danger as a result of actions necessary to restore normality at a time determined by the recovery team. |
| ii.   Recovering or clearing petrol from drains. | |

## 4.   ADVICE ON ADDITIONAL PERSONAL PROTECTION (A.P.P.)

4.1     Advice on A.P.P. is shown in the fourth column of the list. These codes appear as A, B or AB in the List; they do not appear on vehicle placards or on the Emergency Action Scale Cards. Whenever an APP code is assigned to a substance further information must be sought.

4.2     **Code letter A** means that thermal protective clothing consisting of tunic and overtrousers conforming to BS EN 469 together with firefighters' gloves conforming to BS EN 659 should be worn in combination with liquid-tight chemical protective clothing (see clause 3.2.2.2) to protect against one of the following additional hazards:

i.      The possibility that the substance may penetrate chemical protective clothing within 10 minutes under continuous exposure conditions, or

ii.     that the substance is carried above 100°C, or

iii     that the substance is carried below -20°C.

4.3 Where a **code letter B** appears gas-tight chemical protective clothing should be worn. Gas-tight chemical protective clothing conforming to BS EN 943 part 2 (when available)* in combination with the breathing apparatus specified in clause 3.2.2.1 will ensure the required level of protection for up to 30 minutes.

**\*Note: At the time of publication BS EN 943 part 2 has yet to be agreed. In the interim period gas-tight chemical protective clothing is available whose performance is based on the draft standard for EN 943 part 2.**

4.4 Where the **code letters AB** appear the thermal protection specified in clause 4.2 in combination with gas-tight chemical protective clothing as specified in clause 4.3 should be worn. This combination will ensure the required level of protection against both cold and hot substances and will give a degree of protection against substances that may penetrate the chemical protective clothing.

## HAZARDS

7. The fifth column of the list has been sub-divided to show the primary hazard of the substance and, where appropriate, the subsidiary risks in descending order of priority. The classifications referred to are those adopted by the United Nations Committee of Experts on the Transport of Dangerous Goods and are as follows:

| Class | | | |
|---|---|---|---|
| | 1 | - | Explosives |
| | 2.1 | - | Flammable gases |
| | 2.2 | - | Non-flammable, non-toxic gases |
| | 2.3 | - | Toxic gases |
| | 3 | - | Flammable liquids |
| | 4.1 | - | Flammable solids |
| | 4.2 | - | Substances liable to spontaneous combustion |
| | 4.3 | - | Substances which in contact with water emit flammable gases |
| | 5.1 | - | Oxidising substances other than organic peroxides |
| | 5.2 | - | Organic peroxides |
| | 6.1 | - | Poisonous (toxic) substances |
| | 6.2 | - | Infectious substances |
| | 7 | - | Radioactive substances |
| | 8 | - | Corrosives |
| | 9 | - | Miscellaneous dangerous substances |

**Note: In this column the number following a decimal point always indicates a sub-division of a class.**

## 8. ADR HAZARD IDENTIFICATION NUMBER (HIN)

8.1 For United Kingdom internal transport operations there are two forms of hazard identification permitted under The Carriage of Dangerous Goods by Road Regulations, 1996. These both include the hazard warning diamond and, if in the "Approved List", the UN number. Vehicles must also display one of two additional identification numbers.

- UK registered vehicle on domestic journeys must also display the emergency action (Hazchem) code

- All other vehicles must display the ADR HIN.

8.2 The advice contained in the ADR Code (HIN) should be interpreted as follows:
The HIN consists of two or three figures. In general, the figures indicate the following hazards:

2       Emissions of gas due to pressure or to chemical reaction

3       Flammability of liquids (vapours) and gases or self-heating liquids

4.      Flammability of solids or self-heating solids

5.      Oxidizing (fire-intensifying) effect

| | |
|---|---|
| 6 | Toxicity (or risk of infection) |
| 7. | Radioactivity |
| 8. | Corrosivity |
| 9 | Risk of spontaneous, violent reaction |

**Note:** **Spontaneous violent reactions within the meaning of figure 9 include the possibility following from the nature of a substance of a risk of explosion, disintegration and polymerization reaction following the release of considerable heat or flammable and/or toxic gases.**

8.3     Doubling of a figure indicates an intensification of that particular hazard.

8.4     Where the hazard associated with a substance can be adequately indicated by a single figure, this is followed by zero.

8.5     The following combinations of figures have a special meaning: 22, 323, 333, 362, 382, 423, 44, 446, 462, 482, 539, 606, 623, 642, 823, 842 and 90, see below.

8.6     If the letter 'X' prefixes a hazard identification number, this indicates that the substance will react dangerously with water. For these substances, water may only be used with the approval of experts.

8.7     The hazard identification numbers have the following meanings:

| | |
|---|---|
| 20 | Asphyxiant gas or gas with no subsidiary risk |
| 22 | Refrigerated liquefied gas, Asphyxiant |
| 223 | Refrigerated liquefied gas, flammable |
| 225 | Refrigerated liquefied gas, oxidising (fire intensifying) |
| 23 | Flammable gas |
| 239 | Flammable gas, which can spontaneously lead to violent reaction |
| 25 | Oxidising (fire-intensifying) gas |
| 26 | Toxic gas |
| 263 | Toxic gas, flammable |
| 265 | Toxic gas, oxidising (fire-intensifying) |
| 268 | Toxic gas, corrosive |
| 30 | Flammable liquid (flash-point between 23° C and 61°C inclusive) or flammable liquid or solid in the molten state with a flash point above 61°C, heated to a temperature equal to or above its flash point, or self-heating liquid |
| 323 | Flammable liquid which reacts with water, emitting flammable gases |
| X323 | Flammable liquid which reacts dangerously with water, emitting flammable gases* |
| 33 | Highly flammable liquid (flash-point below 23°C) |
| 333 | Pyrophoric liquid |
| X333 | Pyrophoric liquid, which reacts dangerously with water* |
| 336 | Highly flammable liquid, toxic |
| 338 | Highly flammable liquid, corrosive |
| X338 | Highly flammable liquid, corrosive, which reacts dangerously with water* |
| 339 | Highly flammable liquid which can spontaneously lead to violent reaction. |
| 36 | Flammable liquid (flash-point between 23°C and 61°C inclusive), slightly toxic or self-heating liquid toxic. |
| 362 | Flammable liquid, toxic, which reacts with water, emitting flammable gases |
| X362 | Flammable liquid, toxic, which reacts dangerously with water, emitting flammable gases* |
| 368 | Flammable liquid, toxic, corrosive |
| 38 | Flammable liquid (flash-point between 23°C and 61°C inclusive), corrosive |
| 382 | Flammable liquid, corrosive, which reacts with water, emitting flammable gases |
| X382 | Flammable liquid, corrosive, which reacts dangerously with water, emitting flammable gases |
| 39 | Flammable liquid, which can spontaneously lead to violent reaction |
| 40 | Flammable solid, or self-reactive substance, or self heating substance |
| 423 | Solid which reacts with water, emitting flammable gases |
| X423 | Flammable solid which reacts dangerously with water, emitting flammable gases* |

| | |
|---|---|
| 43 | Spontaneously flammable (Pyrophoric) solid |
| 44 | Flammable solid, in the molten state at an elevated temperature |
| 446 | Flammable solid, toxic, in the molten state, at an elevated temperature |
| 46 | Flammable or self-heating solid, toxic |
| 462 | Toxic solid which reacts with water, emitting flammable gases |
| X462 | Solid which reacts dangerously with water, emitting toxic gases |
| 48 | Flammable or self-heating solid, corrosive |
| 482 | Corrosive solid which reacts with water, emitting corrosive gases |
| X482 | Solid which reacts dangerously with water, emitting corrosive gases |
| 50 | Oxidising (fire-intensifying) substance |
| 539 | Flammable organic peroxide |
| 55 | Strongly oxidising (fire-intensifying) substance |
| 556 | Strongly oxidising (fire-intensifying) substance, toxic |
| 558 | Strongly oxidising (fire-intensifying) substance, corrosive |
| 559 | Strongly oxidising (fire-intensifying) substance, which can spontaneously lead to violent reaction |
| 56 | Oxidising substance (fire-intensifying), toxic |
| 568 | Oxidising substance (fire-intensifying), toxic, corrosive |
| 58 | Oxidising substance (fire-intensifying), corrosive |
| 59 | Oxidising substance (fire-intensifying) which can spontaneously lead to violent reaction |
| 60 | Toxic or slightly toxic substance |
| 606 | Infectious substance |
| 623 | Toxic liquid, which reacts with water, emitting flammable gases |
| 63 | Toxic substance, flammable (flash-point between 23°C and 61°C inclusive) |
| 638 | Toxic substance, flammable (flash-point between 23°C and 61°C inclusive), corrosive |
| 639 | Toxic substance, flammable (flash-point not above 61°C ), which can spontaneously lead to violent reaction |
| 64 | Toxic solid, flammable or self-heating |
| 642 | Toxic solid, which reacts with water, emitting flammable gases |
| 65 | Toxic substance, oxidising (fire-intensifying) |
| 66 | Highly toxic substance |
| 663 | Highly toxic substance, flammable (flash-point not above 61°C) |
| 664 | Highly Toxic substance, flammable or self-heating |
| 665 | Highly toxic substance, oxidising (fire-intensifying) |
| 668 | Highly toxic substance, corrosive |
| 669 | Highly toxic substance which can spontaneously lead to a violent reaction |
| 68 | Toxic substance, corrosive |
| 69 | Toxic or slightly toxic substance, which can spontaneously lead to violent reaction |
| 70 | Radioactive material |
| 72 | Radioactive gas |
| 723 | Radioactive gas, flammable |
| 73 | Radioactive liquid, flammable (flash-point not above 61°C) |
| 74 | Radioactive solid, flammable |
| 75 | Radioactive material oxidising (fire-intensifying) |
| 76 | Radioactive material, toxic |
| 78 | Radioactive material, corrosive |
| 80 | Corrosive or slightly corrosive substance |
| X80 | Corrosive or slightly corrosive substance, which reacts dangerously with water* |
| 823 | Corrosive liquid which reacts with water, emitting flammable gases |
| 83 | Corrosive or slightly corrosive substance, flammable (flash-point between 23°C and 61°C inclusive) |
| X83 | Corrosive or slightly corrosive substance, flammable (flash-point between 23°C and 61°C inclusive), which reacts dangerously with water* |
| 839 | Corrosive or slightly corrosive substance, flammable (flash-point between 23°C and 61°C inclusive), which can spontaneously lead to violent reaction |
| X839 | Corrosive or slightly corrosive substance, flammable (flash-point between 23°C and 61°C inclusive), which can spontaneously lead to violent reaction and which reacts dangerously with water* |
| 84 | Corrosive solid, flammable or self-heating |
| 842 | Corrosive solid which reacts with water, emitting flammable gases |

| 85 | Corrosive or slightly corrosive substance, oxidising (fire-intensifying) |
| 856 | Corrosive or slightly corrosive substance, oxidising (fire-intensifying) and toxic |
| 86 | Corrosive or slightly corrosive substance, toxic |
| 88 | Highly corrosive substance |
| X88 | Highly corrosive substance, which reacts dangerously with water* |
| 883 | Highly corrosive substance, flammable (flash point between 23°C and 61°C inclusive) |
| 884 | Highly corrosive solid, flammable or self-heating |
| 885 | Highly corrosive substance, oxidising (fire-intensifying) |
| 886 | Highly corrosive substance, toxic |
| X886 | Highly corrosive substance, toxic which reacts dangerously with water* |
| 89 | Corrosive or slightly corrosive substance, which can spontaneously lead to violent reaction |
| 90 | Environmentally hazardous substance; miscellaneous dangerous substances |
| 99 | Miscellaneous dangerous substance carried at an elevated temperature |

*Water not to be used except by approval of experts

8.8     The Hazard Identification Numbers shall be shown on the plate (40cm wide by min 30cm high) as indicated below:

Hazard Identification Number (HIN)
(2 or 3 figures, 10cm height)

United Nations (UN) number of substance
(4 figures, 10cm height)

Background orange.
Border, horizontal line and figures black,
15mm thickness.

Home Office
Fire and Emergency Planning Directorate

# NUMERICAL LIST OF

# DANGEROUS SUBSTANCES

| UN | Substance | EAC | APP | Hazards | | ADR |
| | | | | Class | Sub Risks | HIN |
|---|---|---|---|---|---|---|
| 1001 | ACETYLENE, DISSOLVED | 2SE | | 2.1 | | 239 |
| 1002 | AIR, COMPRESSED | 2T | | 2.2 | | 20 |
| 1003 | AIR, REFRIGERATED LIQUID | 2PE | A | 2.2 | 5.1 | 225 |
| 1004 | UN No. not used | | | | | |
| 1005 | AMMONIA, ANHYDROUS | 2RE | AB | 2.3 | 8 | 268 |
| 1006 | ARGON, COMPRESSED | 2T | | 2.2 | | 20 |
| 1007 | UN No. not used | | | | | |
| 1008 | BORON TRIFLUORIDE, COMPRESSED | 2WE | B | 2.3 | 8 | 268 |
| 1009 | BROMOTRIFLUOROMETHANE (REFRIGERANT GAS R13B1) | 2RE | A | 2.2 | | 20 |
| 1010 | BUTADIENES, INHIBITED | 2WE | | 2.1 | | 239 |
| 1011 | BUTANE | 2WE | | 2.1 | | 23 |
| 1012 | BUTYLENE | 2WE | | 2.1 | | 23 |
| 1013 | CARBON DIOXIDE | 2RE | A | 2.2 | | 20 |
| 1014 | CARBON DIOXIDE AND OXYGEN MIXTURE, COMPRESSED | 2S | | 2.2 | 5.1 | 25 |
| 1015 | CARBON DIOXIDE AND NITROUS OXIDE MIXTURE | 2RE | A | 2.2 | | 20 |
| 1016 | CARBON MONOXIDE, COMPRESSED | 2SE | | 2.3 | 2.1 | 263 |
| 1017 | CHLORINE | 2XE | AB | 2.3 | 8 | 268 |
| 1018 | CHLORODIFLUOROMETHANE (REFRIGERANT GAS R22) | 2RE | A | 2.2 | | 20 |
| 1019 | UN No. not used | | | | | |
| 1020 | CHLOROPENTAFLUOROETHANE (REFRIGERANT GAS R115) | 2RE | A | 2.2 | | 20 |
| 1021 | 1-CHLORO-1,2,2,2,-TETRAFLUOROETHANE (REFRIGERANT GAS R124) | 2RE | | 2.2 | | 20 |
| 1022 | CHLOROTRIFLUOROMETHANE (REFRIGERANT GAS R13) | 2RE | A | 2.2 | | 20 |

| UN | Substance | EAC | APP | Hazards | | ADR |
| | | | | Class | Sub Risks | HIN |
|---|---|---|---|---|---|---|
| 1023 | **COAL GAS, COMPRESSED** | 2SE | | 2.3 | 2.1 | 263 |
| 1024 | *UN No. not used* | | | | | |
| 1025 | *UN No. not used* | | | | | |
| 1026 | **CYANOGEN** | 2WE | AB | 2.3 | 2.1 | 263 |
| 1027 | **CYCLOPROPANE** | 2WE | A | 2.1 | | 23 |
| 1028 | **DICHLORODIFLUOROMETHANE (REFRIGERANT GAS R12)** | 2RE | A | 2.2 | | 20 |
| 1029 | **DICHLOROFLUOROMETHANE (REFRIGERANT GAS R21)** | 2RE | | 2.2 | | 20 |
| 1030 | **1,1-DIFLUOROETHANE (REFRIGERANT GAS R152a)** | 2WE | | 2.1 | | 23 |
| 1031 | *UN No. not used* | | | | | 23 |
| 1032 | **DIMETHYLAMINE, ANHYDROUS** | 2PE | | 2.1 | | 23 |
| 1033 | **DIMETHYL ETHER** | 2WE | A | 2.1 | | 23 |
| 1034 | *UN No. not used* | | | | | 23 |
| 1035 | **ETHANE** | 2PE | A | 2.1 | | 23 |
| 1036 | **ETHYLAMINE** | 2PE | | 2.1 | | 23 |
| 1037 | **ETHYL CHLORIDE** | 2WE | | 2.1 | | 23 |
| 1038 | **ETHYLENE, REFRIGERATED LIQUID** | 2WE | A | 2.1 | | 223 |
| 1039 | **ETHYL METHYL ETHER** | 2PE | | 2.1 | | 23 |
| 1040 | **ETHYLENE OXIDE** *or* **ETHYLENE OXIDE WITH NITROGEN** *up to a total pressure of 1MPa (10bar) at 50°C* | 2PE | B | 2.3 | 2.1 | 263 |
| 1041 | **ETHYLENE OXIDE AND CARBON DIOXIDE MIXTURE** *with more than 9 % but not more than 87 % ethylene oxide* | 2PE | | 2.1 | | 239 |
| 1042 | *UN No, not used* | | | | | |
| 1043 | **FERTILIZER AMMONIATING SOLUTION** *with free ammonia* | 2PE | | 2.2 | | |

| UN | Substance | EAC | APP | Hazards | | ADR |
| | | | | Class | Sub Risks | HIN |
|---|---|---|---|---|---|---|
| 1044 | **FIRE EXTINGUISHERS** *with compressed or liquefied gas* | + | | 2.2 | | |
| 1045 | **FLUORINE, COMPRESSED** | 2PE | B | 2.3 | 5.1 8 | |
| 1046 | **HELIUM, COMPRESSED** | 2T | | 2.2 | | 20 |
| 1047 | *UN No. not used* | | | | | |
| 1048 | **HYDROGEN BROMIDE ANHYDROUS** | 2RE | AB | 2.3 | 8 | 268 |
| 1049 | **HYDROGEN, COMPRESSED** | 2SE | | 2.1 | | 23 |
| 1050 | **HYDROGEN CHLORIDE, ANHYDROUS** | 2RE | AB | 2.3 | 8 | 268 |
| 1051 | **HYDROGEN CYANIDE, STABILIZED** *containing less than 3% water* | 2WE | B | 6.1 | 3 | |
| 1052 | **HYDROGEN FLUORIDE, ANHYDROUS** | 2XE | B | 8 | 6.1 | 886 |
| 1053 | **HYDROGEN SULPHIDE** | 2WE | AB | 2.3 | 2.1 | 263 |
| 1054 | *UN No. not used* | | | | | |
| 1055 | **ISOBUTYLENE** | 2WE | | 2.1 | | 23 |
| 1056 | **KRYPTON, COMPRESSED** | 2T | | 2.2 | | 20 |
| 1057 | **LIGHTERS** *or* **LIGHTER REFILLS (cigarettes)**, *containing flammable gas* | + | | 2.1 | | |
| 1058 | **LIQUEFIED GASES, non-flammable,** *charged with nitrogen, carbon dioxide or air* | 2RE | A | 2.2 | | 20 |
| 1059 | *UN No. not used* | | | | | |
| 1060 | **METHYL ACETYLENE AND PROPADIENE MIXTURE, STABILIZED** | 2WE | A | 2.1 | | 239 |
| 1061 | **METHYLAMINE, ANHYDROUS** | 2PE | | 2.1 | | 23 |
| 1062 | **METHYL BROMIDE** | 2XE | B | 2.3 | | 26 |
| 1063 | **METHYL CHLORIDE (REFRIGERANT GAS R40)** | 2WE | A | 2.1 | | 23 |
| 1064 | **METHYL MERCAPTAN** | 2WE | B | 2.3 | 2.1 | 263 |
| 1065 | **NEON, COMPRESSED** | 2T | | 2.2 | | 20 |
| 1066 | **NITROGEN, COMPRESSED** | 2T | | 2.2 | | 20 |

| UN | Substance | EAC | APP | Hazards | | ADR |
| | | | | Class | Sub Risks | HIN |
|---|---|---|---|---|---|---|
| 1067 | DINITROGEN TETROXIDE, (NITROGEN DIOXIDE) | 2PE | B | 2.3 | 5.1 8 | 265 |
| 1068 | *UN No. not used* | | | | | |
| 1069 | NITROSYL CHLORIDE | 2RE | B | 2.3 | 8 | |
| 1070 | NITROUS OXIDE | 2P | A | 2.2 | 5.1 | 25 |
| 1071 | OIL GAS, COMPRESSED | 2SE | | 2.3 | 2.1 | 263 |
| 1072 | OXYGEN, COMPRESSED | 2S | | 2.2 | 5.1 | 25 |
| 1073 | OXYGEN, REFRIGERATED LIQUID | 2PE | A | 2.2 | 5.1 | 225 |
| 1074 | *UN No. not used* | | | | | |
| 1075 | PETROLEUM GASES, LIQUEFIED | 2WE | | 2.1 | | 23 |
| 1076 | PHOSGENE | 2XE | B | 2.3 | 8 | 268 |
| 1077 | PROPYLENE | 2WE | | 2.1 | | 23 |
| 1078 | REFRIGERANT GAS, N.O.S. | 2RE | A | 2.2 | | 20 |
| 1079 | SULPHUR DIOXIDE | 2RE | B | 2.3 | 8 | 268 |
| 1080 | SULPHUR HEXAFLUORIDE | 2RE | A | 2.2 | | 20 |
| 1081 | TETRAFLUOROETHYLENE, INHIBITED | 2PE | A | 2.1 | | |
| 1082 | TRIFLUOROCHLOROETHYLENE, INHIBITED | 2WE | AB | 2.3 | 2.1 | 263 |
| 1083 | TRIMETHYLAMINE, ANHYDROUS | 2PE | | 2.1 | | 23 |
| 1084 | *UN No. not used* | | | | | |
| 1085 | VINYL BROMIDE, INHIBITED | 2WE | | 2.1 | | 239 |
| 1086 | VINYL CHLORIDE, INHIBITED *or* VINYL CHLORIDE, STABILIZED | 2WE | | 2.1 | | 239 |
| 1087 | VINYL METHYL ETHER, INHIBITED | 2WE | | 2.1 | | 239 |
| 1088 | ACETAL | ●3YE | | 3 | | 33 |
| 1089 | ACETALDEHYDE | ●2YE | | 3 | | 33 |
| 1090 | ACETONE | ●2YE | | 3 | | 33 |

| UN | Substance | EAC | APP | Hazards | | ADR |
| | | | | Class | Sub Risks | HIN |
|---|---|---|---|---|---|---|
| 1091 | **ACETONE OILS** | ●3YE | | 3 | | 33 |
| 1092 | **ACROLEIN, INHIBITED** | ●2WE | B | 6.1 | 3 | 663 |
| 1093 | **ACRYLONITRILE, INHIBITED** | ●3WE | | 3 | 6.1 | 336 |
| 1094 to 1097 | *UN Nos. not used* | | | | | |
| 1098 | **ALLYL ALCOHOL** | ●2WE | B | 6.1 | 3 | 663 |
| 1099 | **ALLYL BROMIDE** | 2WE | | 3 | 6.1 | 336 |
| 1100 | **ALLYL CHLORIDE** | 3WE | | 3 | 6.1 | 336 |
| 1101 to 1103 | *UN Nos. not used* | | | | | |
| 1104 | **AMYL ACETATES** | ●3Y | | 3 | | 30 |
| 1105 | **PENTANOLS,** *flash point less than 23°C* | ●3YE | | 3 | | 33 |
| 1105 | **PENTANOLS,** *flash point 23°C or above* | ●3Y | | 3 | | 30 |
| 1106 | **AMYLAMINE** *flash point less than 23°C* | ●2WE | | 3 | 8 | 338 |
| 1106 | **AMYLAMINE** *flash point 23°C or above* | ●2W | | 3 | 8 | 38 |
| 1107 | **AMYL CHLORIDE** | 3YE | | 3 | | 33 |
| 1108 | **1 - PENTENE (n-AMYLENE)** | 3YE | | 3 | | 33 |
| 1109 | **AMYL FORMATES** | 3Y | | 3 | | 30 |
| 1110 | **n-AMYL METHYL KETONE** | ●3Y | | 3 | | 30 |
| 1111 | **AMYL MERCAPTAN** | 3WE | | 3 | | 33 |
| 1112 | **AMYL NITRATE** | 3Y | | 3 | | 30 |
| 1113 | **AMYL NITRITE** | ●3YE | | 3 | | 33 |
| 1114 | **BENZENE** | 3WE | | 3 | | 33 |
| 1115 to 1119 | *UN Nos. not used* | | | | | |

| UN | Substance | EAC | APP | Hazards | | ADR |
| | | | | Class | Sub Risks | HIN |
|---|---|---|---|---|---|---|
| 1120 | **BUTANOLS** <br> *flash point less than 23°C* | ●2YE | | 3 | | 33 |
| 1120 | **BUTANOLS** <br> *flash point 23°C or above* | ●2Y | | 3 | | 30 |
| 1121 | *UN No. not used* | | | | | |
| 1122 | *UN No. not used* | | | | | |
| 1123 | **BUTYL ACETATES,** *flash point less than 23°C* | ●3YE | | 3 | | 33 |
| 1123 | **BUTYL ACETATES,** *flash point 23°C or above* | ●3Y | | 3 | | 30 |
| 1124 | *UN No. not used* | | | | | |
| 1125 | **n-BUTYLAMINE** | ●2WE | | 3 | 8 | 338 |
| 1126 | **1-BROMOBUTANE** | 2YE | | 3 | | 33 |
| 1127 | **CHLOROBUTANES** | 3YE | | 3 | | 33 |
| 1128 | **n-BUTYL FORMATE** | ●3YE | | 3 | | 33 |
| 1129 | **BUTYRALDEHYDE** | ●3WE | | 3 | | 33 |
| 1130 | **CAMPHOR OIL** | 3Y | | 3 | | 30 |
| 1131 | **CARBON DISULPHIDE** | 3WE | | 3 | 6.1 | 336 |
| 1132 | *UN No. not used* | | | | | |
| 1133 | **ADHESIVES,** *containing flammable liquid,* <br> *flash point less than 23°C* | ●3YE | | 3 | | 33 |
| 1133 | **ADHESIVES,** *containing flammable liquid,* <br> *flash point 23°C or above* | ●3Y | | 3 | | 30 |
| 1134 | **CHLOROBENZENE** | 2Y | | 3 | | 30 |
| 1135 | **ETHYLENE CHLOROHYDRIN** | ●2W | B | 6.1 | 3 | 663 |
| 1136 | **COAL TAR DISTILLATES, FLAMMABLE,** <br> *flash point less than 23°C* | 3WE | | 3 | | 33 |
| 1136 | **COAL TAR DISTILLATES, FLAMMABLE,** <br> *flash point 23°C or above* | 3W | | 3 | | 30 |
| 1137 | *UN No. not used* | | | | | |
| 1138 | *UN No. not used* | | | | | |

| UN | Substance | EAC | APP | Hazards | | ADR |
| | | | | Class | Sub Risks | HIN |
|---|---|---|---|---|---|---|
| 1139 | **COATING SOLUTION** *flash point less than 23°C* | ●3YE | | 3 | | 33 |
| 1139 | **COATING SOLUTION** *flash point 23°C or above* | ●3Y | | 3 | | 30 |
| 1140 to 1142 | *UN Nos. not used* | | | | | |
| 1143 | **CROTONALDEHYDE, STABILIZED** | ●2WE | B | 6.1 | 3 | 663 |
| 1144 | **CROTONYLENE** | 3YE | | 3 | | 339 |
| 1145 | **CYCLOHEXANE** | 3YE | | 3 | | 33 |
| 1146 | **CYCLOPENTANE** | 3YE | | 3 | | 33 |
| 1147 | **DECAHYDRONAPHTHALENE** | 3Y | | 3 | | 30 |
| 1148 | **DIACETONE ALCOHOL,** *flash point less than 23°C* | ●2YE | | 3 | | 33 |
| 1148 | **DIACETONE ALCOHOL,** *flash point 23°C or above* | ●2Y | | 3 | | 30 |
| 1149 | **DIBUTYL ETHERS** | 3Y | | 3 | | 30 |
| 1150 | **1,2-DICHLOROETHYLENE** | 3YE | | 3 | | 33 |
| 1151 | *UN No. not used* | | | | | |
| 1152 | **DICHLOROPENTANES** | 3Y | | 3 | | 30 |
| 1153 | **ETHYLENE GLYCOL DIETHYL ETHER** | ●3Y | | 3 | | 30 |
| 1154 | **DIETHYLAMINE** | ●2WE | | 3 | 8 | 338 |
| 1155 | **DIETHYL ETHER** (ETHYL ETHER) | ●3YE | | 3 | | 33 |
| 1156 | **DIETHYL KETONE** | ●3YE | | 3 | | 33 |
| 1157 | **DIISOBUTYL KETONE** | 3Y | | 3 | | 30 |
| 1158 | **DIISOPROPYLAMINE** | ●3WE | | 3 | 8 | 338 |
| 1159 | **DIISOPROPYL ETHER** | 3YE | | 3 | | 33 |
| 1160 | **DIMETHYLAMINE SOLUTION** | ●2PE | | 3 | 8 | 338 |
| 1161 | **DIMETHYL CARBONATE** | 3YE | | 3 | | 33 |
| 1162 | **DIMETHYLDICHLOROSILANE** | 4WE | | 3 | 8 | X338 |

| UN | Substance | EAC | APP | Hazards | | ADR |
|---|---|---|---|---|---|---|
| | | | | Class | Sub Risks | HIN |
| 1163 | **DIMETHYLHYDRAZINE, UNSYMMETRICAL** | ●2WE | B | 6.1 | 3 8 | 663 |
| 1164 | **DIMETHYL SULPHIDE** | 3YE | | 3 | | 33 |
| 1165 | **DIOXANE** | ●2YE | | 3 | | 33 |
| 1166 | **DIOXOLANE** | ●2WE | | 3 | | 33 |
| 1167 | **DIVINYL ETHER, INHIBITED** | 3YE | | 3 | | 339 |
| 1168 | *UN No. not used* | | | | | |
| 1169 | **EXTRACTS, AROMATIC, LIQUID,** *flash point less than 23°C* | 3YE | | 3 | | 33 |
| 1169 | **EXTRACTS, AROMATIC, LIQUID,** *flash point 23°C or above* | 3Y | | 3 | | 30 |
| 1170 | **ETHANOL (ETHYL ALCOHOL)** *or* **ETHANOL SOLUTION** | ●2YE | | 3 | | 33 |
| 1170 | **ETHANOL (ETHYL ALCOHOL)** *or* **ETHANOL SOLUTION,** | ●2Y | | 3 | | 30 |
| 1171 | **ETHYLENE GLYCOL MONOETHYL ETHER** | ●2Y | | 3 | | 30 |
| 1172 | **ETHYLENE GLYCOL MONOETHYL ETHER ACETATE** | ●2Y | | 3 | | 30 |
| 1173 | **ETHYL ACETATE** | ●3YE | | 3 | | 33 |
| 1174 | *UN No. not used* | | | | | |
| 1175 | **ETHYLBENZENE** | 3YE | | 3 | | 33 |
| 1176 | **ETHYL BORATE** | ●2YE | | 3 | | 33 |
| 1177 | **ETHYLBUTYL ACETATE** | 3Y | | 3 | | 30 |
| 1178 | **2-ETHYLBUTYRALDEHYDE** | 3YE | | 3 | | 33 |
| 1179 | **ETHYL BUTYL ETHER** | 3YE | | 3 | | 33 |
| 1180 | **ETHYL BUTYRATE** | 3Y | | 3 | | 30 |
| 1181 | **ETHYL CHLOROACETATE** | 2WE | | 6.1 | 3 | 63 |
| 1182 | **ETHYL CHLOROFORMATE** | ●2WE | B | 6.1 | 3 8 | 663 |

| UN | Substance | EAC | APP | Hazards | | ADR |
|----|-----------|-----|-----|---------|---|-----|
| | | | | Class | Sub Risks | HIN |
| 1183 | ETHYLDICHLOROSILANE | 4WE | | 4.3 | 3 8 | X338 |
| 1184 | ETHYLENE DICHLORIDE | 2YE | | 3 | 6.1 | 336 |
| 1185 | ETHYLENEIMINE, INHIBITED | ●2WE | B | 6.1 | 3 | 663 |
| 1186 | UN No. not used | | | | | |
| 1187 | UN No. not used | | | | | |
| 1188 | ETHYLENE GLYCOL MONOMETHYL ETHER | ●2Y | | 3 | | 30 |
| 1189 | ETHYLENE GLYCOL MONOMETHYL ETHER ACETATE | ●2Y | | 3 | | 30 |
| 1190 | ETHYL FORMATE | ●3YE | | 3 | | 33 |
| 1191 | OCTYL ALDEHYDES | 3Y | | 3 | | 30 |
| 1192 | ETHYL LACTATE | ●3Y | | 3 | | 30 |
| 1193 | ETHYL METHYL KETONE (METHYL ETHYL KETONE) | ●2YE | | 3 | | 33 |
| 1194 | ETHYL NITRITE SOLUTION | ●2YE | | 3 | 6.1 | 336 |
| 1195 | ETHYL PROPIONATE | ●3YE | | 3 | | 33 |
| 1196 | ETHYLTRICHLOROSILANE | 4WE | | 3 | 8 | X338 |
| 1197 | EXTRACTS, FLAVOURING, LIQUID, *flash point less than 23°C* | 3YE | | 3 | | 33 |
| 1197 | EXTRACTS, FLAVOURING, LIQUID, *flash point 23°C or above* | 3Y | | 3 | | 30 |
| 1198 | FORMALDEHYDE SOLUTION, FLAMMABLE | ●2YE | | 3 | 8 | 38 |
| 1199 | FURALDEHYDES | ●2W | | 6.1 | 3 | 63 |
| 1200 | UN No. not used | | | | | |
| 1201 | FUSEL OIL, *flash point less than 23°C* | ●3YE | | 3 | | 33 |
| 1201 | FUSEL OIL, *flash point 23°C or above* | ●3Y | | 3 | | 30 |
| 1202 | GAS OIL *or* DIESEL FUEL *or* HEATING OIL, LIGHT | 3Z | | 3 | | 30 |
| 1203 | MOTOR SPIRIT *or* GASOLINE *or* PETROL | 3YE | | 3 | | 33 |

| UN | Substance | EAC | APP | Hazards | | ADR |
| | | | | Class | Sub Risks | HIN |
|---|---|---|---|---|---|---|
| 1204 | **NITROGLYCERIN SOLUTION IN ALCOHOL,** *with not more than 1 % Nitroglycerin* | ●2YE | | 3 | | |
| 1205 | *UN No. not used* | | | | | |
| 1206 | **HEPTANES** | 3YE | | 3 | | 33 |
| 1207 | **HEXALDEHYDE** | 3Y | | 3 | | 30 |
| 1208 | **HEXANES** | 3YE | | 3 | | 33 |
| 1209 | *UN No. not used* | | | | | |
| 1210 | **PRINTING INK,** *flammable, flash point less than 23°C* | ●3YE | | 3 | | 33 |
| 1210 | **PRINTING INK,** *flammable, flash point 23°C or above* | ●3Y | | 3 | | 30 |
| 1211 | *UN No. not used* | | | | | |
| 1212 | **ISOBUTANOL** (ISOBUTYL ALCOHOL) | ●3Y | | 3 | | 30 |
| 1213 | **ISOBUTYL ACETATE** | 3YE | | 3 | | 33 |
| 1214 | **ISOBUTYLAMINE** | ●2WE | | 3 | 8 | 338 |
| 1215 | *UN No. not used* | | | | | |
| 1216 | **ISOOCTENE** | ●3YE | | 3 | | 33 |
| 1217 | *UN No. not used* | | | | | |
| 1218 | **ISOPRENE, INHIBITED** | 3YE | | 3 | | 339 |
| 1219 | **ISOPROPANOL** (ISOPROPYL ALCOHOL) | ●2YE | | 3 | | 33 |
| 1220 | **ISOPROPYL ACETATE** | ●3YE | | 3 | | 33 |
| 1221 | **ISOPROPYLAMINE** | ●2WE | | 3 | 8 | 338 |
| 1222 | **ISOPROPYL NITRATE** | 3YE | | 3 | | |
| 1223 | **KEROSENE** | 3Y | | 3 | | 30 |
| 1224 | **KETONES, LIQUID, N.O.S.,** *flash point less than 23°C* | ●3YE | | 3 | | 33 |
| 1224 | **KETONES, LIQUID, N.O.S.,** *flash point 23°C or above* | ●3Y | | 3 | | 30 |
| 1225 to 1227 | *UN Nos. not used* | | | | | |

| UN | Substance | EAC | APP | Hazards | | ADR |
|---|---|---|---|---|---|---|
| | | | | Class | Sub Risks | HIN |
| 1228 | MERCAPTANS, LIQUID, FLAMMABLE, TOXIC, N.O.S., *or* MERCAPTAN MIXTURE, LIQUID, FLAMMABLE, TOXIC, N.O.S. | 3WE | | 3 | 6.1 | 336/ 36 |
| 1229 | MESITYL OXIDE | ●3W | | 3 | | 30 |
| 1230 | METHANOL | ●2WE | | 3 | 6.1 | 336 |
| 1231 | METHYL ACETATE | ●2YE | | 3 | | 33 |
| 1232 | *UN No. not used* | | | | | |
| 1233 | METHYLAMYL ACETATE | 3Y | | 3 | | 30 |
| 1234 | METHYLAL | ●2YE | | 3 | | 33 |
| 1235 | METHYLAMINE, AQUEOUS SOLUTION | ●2WE | | 3 | 8 | 338 |
| 1236 | *UN No. not used* | | | | | |
| 1237 | METHYL BUTYRATE | ●3YE | | 3 | | 33 |
| 1238 | METHYL CHLOROFORMATE | 3WE | B | 6.1 | 3 8 | 663 |
| 1239 | METHYL CHLOROMETHYL ETHER | 3WE | B | 6.1 | 3 | 663 |
| 1240 | *UN No. not used* | | | | | |
| 1241 | *UN No. not used* | | | | | |
| 1242 | METHYLDICHLOROSILANE | 4WE | | 4.3 | 3 8 | X338 |
| 1243 | METHYL FORMATE | ●2YE | | 3 | | 33 |
| 1244 | METHYLHYDRAZINE | ●2WE | B | 6.1 | 3 8 | 663 |
| 1245 | METHYL ISOBUTYL KETONE | ●3YE | | 3 | | 33 |
| 1246 | METHYL ISOPROPENYL KETONE, INHIBITED | 3WE | | 3 | | 339 |
| 1247 | METHYL METHACRYLATE MONOMER, INHIBITED | ●3YE | | 3 | | 339 |
| 1248 | METHYL PROPIONATE | 3YE | | 3 | | 33 |
| 1249 | METHYL PROPYL KETONE | ●3YE | | 3 | | 33 |
| 1250 | METHYLTRICHLOROSILANE | 4WE | | 3 | 8 | X338 |

| UN | Substance | EAC | APP | Hazards | | ADR |
|---|---|---|---|---|---|---|
| | | | | Class | Sub Risks | HIN |
| 1251 | **METHYL VINYL KETONE, STABILIZED** | ●2WE | B | 6.1 | 3 8 | 639 |
| 1252 to 1258 | *UN Nos. not used* | | | | | |
| 1259 | **NICKEL CARBONYL** | 2WE | B | 6.1 | 3 | 663 |
| 1260 | *UN No. not used* | | | | | |
| 1261 | **NITROMETHANE** | ●2Y | | 3 | | |
| 1262 | **OCTANES** | 3YE | | 3 | | 33 |
| 1263 | **PAINT** or, **PAINT RELATED MATERIAL** *flash point less than 23°C* | ●3YE | | 3 | | 33 |
| 1263 | **PAINT, or PAINT RELATED MATERIAL** *flash point 23°C or above* | ●3Y | | 3 | | 30 |
| 1264 | **PARALDEHYDE** | ●2Y | | 3 | | 30 |
| 1265 | **PENTANES,** *liquid* | 3YE | | 3 | | 33 |
| 1266 | **PERFUMERY PRODUCTS** *with flammable solvents, flash point less than 23°C* | ●3YE | | 3 | | 33 |
| 1266 | **PERFUMERY PRODUCTS** *with flammable solvents, flash point 23°C or above* | ●3Y | | 3 | | 30 |
| 1267 | **PETROLEUM CRUDE OIL,** *flash point less than 23°C* | 3WE | | 3 | | 33 |
| 1267 | **PETROLEUM CRUDE OIL,** *flash point 23°C or above* | 3W | | 3 | | 30 |
| 1268 | **PETROLEUM DISTILLATES N.O.S.** *or* **PETROLEUM PRODUCTS, N.O.S.** *flash point less than 23°C* | 3YE | | 3 | | 33 |
| 1268 | **PETROLEUM DISTILLATES N.O.S.** *or* **PETROLEUM PRODUCTS, N.O.S.** *flash point 23°C or above* | 3Y | | 3 | | 30 |
| 1269 to 1271 | *UN Nos., not used* | | | | | |
| 1272 | **PINE OIL** | 3Y | | 3 | | 30 |
| 1273 | *UN No, not used* | | | | | |

| UN | Substance | EAC | APP | Hazards | | ADR |
|----|-----------|-----|-----|---------|---|-----|
| | | | | Class | Sub Risks | HIN |
| 1274 | **n-PROPANOL (NORMAL PROPYL ALCOHOL)**, *flash point less than 23°C* | ●2YE | | 3 | | 33 |
| 1274 | **n-PROPANOL (NORMAL PROPYL ALCOHOL)**, *flash point 23°C or above* | ●2Y | | 3 | | 30 |
| 1275 | **PROPIONALDEHYDE** | ●2YE | | 3 | | 33 |
| 1276 | **n-PROPYL ACETATE** | ●3YE | | 3 | | 33 |
| 1277 | **PROPYLAMINE** | ●2WE | | 3 | 8 | 338 |
| 1278 | **PROPYL CHLORIDE** | 3YE | | 3 | | 33 |
| 1279 | **1,2-DICHLOROPROPANE** | 2YE | | 3 | | 33 |
| 1280 | **PROPYLENE OXIDE** | ●2WE | | 3 | | 339 |
| 1281 | **PROPYL FORMATES** | ●3YE | | 3 | | 33 |
| 1282 | **PYRIDINE** | ●2WE | | 3 | | 33 |
| 1283 to 1285 | *UN Nos., not used* | | | | | |
| 1286 | **ROSIN OIL,** *flash point less than 23°C* | 3YE | | 3 | | 33 |
| 1286 | **ROSIN OIL,** *flash point 23°C or above* | 3Y | | 3 | | 30 |
| 1287 | **RUBBER SOLUTION,** *flash point less than 23°C* | 3YE | | 3 | | 33 |
| 1287 | **RUBBER SOLUTION,** *flash point 23°C or above* | 3Y | | 3 | | 30 |
| 1288 | **SHALE OIL,** *flash point less than 23°C* | 3WE | | 3 | | 33 |
| 1288 | **SHALE OIL,** *flash point 23°C or above* | 3W | | 3 | | 30 |
| 1289 | **SODIUM METHYLATE SOLUTION** *in alcohol, flash point less than 23°C* | ●2WE | | 3 | 8 | 338 |
| 1289 | **SODIUM METHYLATE SOLUTION** *in alcohol, flash point 23°C or above* | ●2W | | 3 | 8 | 38 |
| 1290 | *UN No, not used* | | | | | |
| 1291 | *UN No, not used* | | | | | |
| 1292 | **TETRAETHYL SILICATE** | 3Y | | 3 | | 30 |
| 1293 | **TINCTURES MEDICINAL,** *flash point less than 23°C* | ●2YE | | 3 | | 33 |

| UN | Substance | EAC | APP | Hazards | | ADR |
| | | | | Class | Sub Risks | HIN |
|---|---|---|---|---|---|---|
| 1293 | **TINCTURES MEDICINAL,** *flash point 23°C or above* | ●2Y | | 3 | | 30 |
| 1294 | **TOLUENE** | 3YE | | 3 | | 33 |
| 1295 | **TRICHLOROSILANE** | 4WE | | 4.3 | 3 8 | X338 |
| 1296 | **TRIETHYLAMINE** | ●3WE | | 3 | 8 | 338 |
| 1297 | **TRIMETHYLAMINE, AQUEOUS SOLUTION,** *not more than 50% trimethylamine, by mass* | ●2PE | | 3 | 8 | 338 |
| 1297 | **TRIMETHYLAMINE, AQUEOUS SOLUTION,** *not more than 50% trimethylamine, by mass* | ●2P | | 3 | 8 | 38 |
| 1298 | **TRIMETHYLCHLOROSILANE** | 4WE | | 3 | 8 | X338 |
| 1299 | **TURPENTINE** | 3Y | | 3 | | 30 |
| 1300 | **TURPENTINE SUBSTITUTE,** *flash point less than 23°C* | 3YE | | 3 | | 33 |
| 1300 | **TURPENTINE SUBSTITUTE,** *flash point 23°C or above* | 3Y | | 3 | | 30 |
| 1301 | **VINYL ACETATE, INHIBITED** | ●3YE | | 3 | | 339 |
| 1302 | **VINYL ETHYL ETHER, INHIBITED** | 3YE | | 3 | | 339 |
| 1303 | **VINYLIDENE CHLORIDE, INHIBITED** | 3YE | | 3 | | 339 |
| 1304 | **VINYL ISOBUTYL ETHER, INHIBITED** | ●3YE | | 3 | | 339 |
| 1305 | **VINYLTRICHLOROSILANE, INHIBITED** | 4WE | | 3 | 8 | X338 |
| 1306 | **WOOD PRESERVATIVES, LIQUID,** *flash point less than 23°C* | ●3YE | | 3 | | 33 |
| 1306 | **WOOD PRESERVATIVES, LIQUID,** *flash point 23°C or above* | ●3Y | | 3 | | 30 |
| 1307 | **XYLENES,** *flash point less than 23°C* | 3YE | | 3 | | 33 |
| 1307 | **XYLENES,** *flash point 23°C or above* | 3Y | | 3 | | 30 |
| 1308 | **ZIRCONIUM SUSPENDED IN A FLAMMABLE LIQUID,** *flash point less than 23°C* | 3YE | | 3 | | 33 |
| 1308 | **ZIRCONIUM SUSPENDED IN A FLAMMABLE LIQUID,** *flash point 23°C or above* | 3Y | | 3 | | 30 |
| 1309 | **ALUMINIUM POWDER, COATED** | 4Z | | 4.1 | | 40 |

| UN | Substance | EAC | APP | Hazards | | ADR |
| | | | | Class | Sub Risks | HIN |
|---|---|---|---|---|---|---|
| 1310 | **AMMONIUM PICRATE, WETTED** *with not less than 10% water, by mass* | 1W | | 4.1 | | |
| 1311 | *UN No. not used* | | | | | |
| 1312 | **BORNEOL** | 1Z | | 4.1 | | 40 |
| 1313 | **CALCIUM RESINATE** | 1Z | | 4.1 | | 40 |
| 1314 | **CALCIUM RESINATE, FUSED** | 1Z | | 4.1 | | 40 |
| 1315 to 1317 | *UN Nos., not used* | | | | | |
| 1318 | **COBALT RESINATE, PRECIPITATED** | 1Z | | 4.1 | | 40 |
| 1319 | *UN No. not used* | | | | | |
| 1320 | **DINITROPHENOL, WETTED** *with not less than 15% water, by mass* | 1W | | 4.1 | 6.1 | |
| 1321 | **DINITROPHENOLATES, WETTED** *with not less than 15% water, by mass* | 1W | | 4.1 | 6.1 | |
| 1322 | **DINITRORESCORCINOL, WETTED** *with not less than 15% water, by mass* | 1W | | 4.1 | | |
| 1323 | **FERROCERIUM** | 4Z | | 4.1 | | 40 |
| 1324 | **FILMS, NITROCELLULOSE BASE,** *gelatin coated, except scrap* | 1Z | | 4.1 | | |
| 1325 | **FLAMMABLE SOLID, ORGANIC, N.O.S.** | 1Z | | 4.1 | | 40 |
| 1326 | **HAFNIUM POWDER, WETTED** *with not less than 25% water* | 1Z | | 4.1 | | 40 |
| 1327 | *UN No. not used* | | | | | |
| 1328 | **HEXAMETHYLENETETRAMINE** | 1Z | | 4.1 | | 40 |
| 1329 | *UN No. not used* | | | | | |
| 1330 | **MANGANESE RESINATE** | 1Z | | 4.1 | | 40 |
| 1331 | **MATCHES, "STRIKE ANYWHERE"** | + | | 4.1 | | |
| 1332 | **METALDEHYDE** | 1Z | | 4.1 | | 40 |
| 1333 | **CERIUM,** *slabs, ingots or rods* | IZ | | 4.1 | | |

| UN | Substance | EAC | APP | Hazards | | ADR |
| | | | | Class | Sub Risks | HIN |
|---|---|---|---|---|---|---|
| 1334 | **NAPHTHALENE, CRUDE** or **NAPHTHALENE, REFINED** | 2Z | | 4.1 | | 40 |
| 1335 | *UN No. not used* | | | | | |
| 1336 | **NITROGUANIDINE (PICRITE), WETTED** *with not less than 20% water, by mass* | 1W | | 4.1 | | |
| 1337 | **NITROSTARCH, WETTED** *with not less than 20% water, by mass* | 1W | | 4.1 | | |
| 1338 | **PHOSPHORUS, AMORPHOUS** | 2WE | | 4.1 | | 40 |
| 1339 | **PHOSPHORUS HEPTASULPHIDE,** *free from yellow and white phosphorus* | 4YE | | 4.1 | | 40 |
| 1340 | **PHOSPHORUS PENTASULPHIDE,** *free from yellow and white phosphorus* | 4W | | 4.3 | 4.1 | 423 |
| 1341 | **PHOSPHORUS SESQUISULPHIDE,** *free from yellow and white phosphorus* | 1Y | | 4.1 | | 40 |
| 1342 | *UN No. not used* | | | | | |
| 1343 | **PHOSPHORUS TRISULPHIDE,** *free from yellow and white phosphorus* | 4YE | | 4.1 | | 40 |
| 1344 | **TRINITROPHENOL, WETTED** *with not less than 30% water, by mass* | 1W | | 4.1 | | |
| 1345 | **RUBBER SCRAP** or **RUBBER SHODDY** | 1Z | | 4.1 | | 40 |
| 1346 | **SILICON POWDER, AMORPHOUS** | 1Z | | 4.1 | | 40 |
| 1347 | **SILVER PICRATE, WETTED,** *with not less than 30% water, by mass* | 1W | | 4.1 | | |
| 1348 | **SODIUM DINITRO-ortho-CRESOLATE, WETTED** *with not less than 15% water, by mass* | 1W | | 4.1 | 6.1 | |
| 1349 | **SODIUM PICRAMATE, WETTED** *with not less than 20% water, by mass* | 1W | | 4.1 | 4.3 | |
| 1350 | **SULPHUR** | 1Z | | 4.1 | | 40 |
| 1351 | *UN No. not used* | | | | | |
| 1352 | **TITANIUM POWDER, WETTED** *with not less than 25% water* | 1Z | | 4.1 | | 40 |
| 1353 | **FIBRES** or **FABRICS IMPREGNATED WITH WEAKLY NITRATED CELLULOSE, N.O.S.** | + | | 4.1 | | |

| UN | Substance | EAC | APP | Hazards | | ADR |
| | | | | Class | Sub Risks | HIN |
|---|---|---|---|---|---|---|
| 1354 | **TRINITROBENZENE, WETTED** *with not less than 30% water, by mass* | 1W | 4.1 | | | |
| 1355 | **TRINITROBENZOIC ACID, WETTED** *with not less than 30% water, by mass* | 1W | | 4.1 | | |
| 1356 | **TRINITROTOLUENE, WETTED** *with not less than 30% water, by mass* | 1W | | 4.1 | | |
| 1357 | **UREA NITRATE, WETTED** *with not less than 20% water, by mass* | 1W | | 4.1 | | |
| 1358 | **ZIRCONIUM POWDER, WETTED** *with not less than 25% water* | 1Z | | 4.1 | | 40 |
| 1359 | *UN No. not used* | | | | | |
| 1360 | **CALCIUM PHOSPHIDE** | 4W | | 4.3 | 6.1 | |
| 1361 | **CARBON,** *animal or vegetable origin* | 1Z | | 4.2 | | 40 |
| 1362 | **CARBON, ACTIVATED** | 1Z | | 4.2 | | 40 |
| 1363 | **COPRA** | 1Z | | 4.2 | | 40 |
| 1364 | **COTTON WASTE, OILY** | 1Z | | 4.2 | | 40 |
| 1365 | **COTTON , WET** | 1Z | | 4.2 | | 40 |
| 1366 | **DIETHYLZINC** | 4WE | | 4.2 | | X333 |
| 1367 | *UN No. not used* | | | | | |
| 1368 | *UN No. not used* | | | | | |
| 1369 | **p-NITROSODIMETHYLANILINE** | 2X | | 4.2 | | 40 |
| 1370 | **DIMETHYLZINC** | 4WE | | 4.2 | 4.3 | X333 |
| 1371 | UN No. not used | | | | | |
| 1372 | UN No. not used | | | | | |
| 1373 | **FIBRES** or **FABRICS, ANIMAL** or **VEGETABLE** or **SYNTHETIC, N.O.S.** *with oil* | 1Z | | 4.2 | | 40 |
| 1374 | **FISH MEAL (FISH SCRAP), UNSTABILIZED** | + | | 4.2 | | |
| 1375 | *UN No. not used* | | | | | |
| 1376 | **IRON OXIDE, SPENT,** *or* **IRON SPONGE, SPENT** | 4Y | | 4.2 | | 40 |

| UN | Substance | EAC | APP | Hazards | | ADR |
| --- | --- | --- | --- | --- | --- | --- |
| | | | | Class | Sub Risks | HIN |
| 1377 | *UN No. not used* | | | | | |
| 1378 | **METAL CATALYST, WETTED** *with a visible excess of liquid* | 2Y | | 4.2 | | 40 |
| 1379 | **PAPER, UNSATURATED OIL TREATED** *incompletely dried (includes carbon paper)* | 1Z | | 4.2 | | 40 |
| 1380 | **PENTABORANE** | 4W | | 4.2 | 6.1 | 333 |
| 1381 | **PHOSPHORUS, WHITE** *or* **YELLOW, DRY** *or* **UNDER WATER** *or* **IN SOLUTION** | 2WE | | 4.2 | 6.1 | 46 |
| 1382 | **POTASSIUM SULPHIDE, ANHYDROUS** *or* **POTASSIUM SULPHIDE** *with less than 30% water of crystallisation* | 2X | | 4.2 | | 40 |
| 1383 | **PYROPHORIC METAL, N.O.S.** *or* **PYROPHORIC ALLOY, N.O.S.** | 4Y | | 4.2 | | |
| 1384 | **SODIUM DITHIONITE** (SODIUM HYDROSULPHITE) | 1S | | 4.2 | | 40 |
| 1385 | **SODIUM SULPHIDE ANHYDROUS** *or* **SODIUM SULPHIDE** *with less than 30% water of crystallisation* | 2X | | 4.2 | | 40 |
| 1386 | **SEED CAKE** *with more than 1.5% oil and not more than 11% moisture* | 1Z | | 4.2 | | 40 |
| 1387 | *UN No. not used* | | | | | |
| 1388 | *UN No. not used* | | | | | |
| 1389 | **ALKALI METAL AMALGAM** | 4W | | 4.3 | | X423 |
| 1390 | **ALKALI METAL AMIDES** | 4W | | 4.3 | | 423 |
| 1391 | **ALKALI METAL DISPERSION** *or* **ALKALINE EARTH METAL DISPERSION** | 4W | | 4.3 | | X423 |
| 1392 | **ALKALINE EARTH METAL AMALGAM** | 4W | | 4.3 | | X423 |
| 1393 | **ALKALINE EARTH METAL ALLOY, N.O.S.** | 4W | | 4.3 | | 423 |
| 1394 | **ALUMINIUM CARBIDE** | 4Y | | 4.3 | | 423 |
| 1395 | **ALUMINIUM FERROSILICON POWDER** | 4Y | | 4.3 | 6.1 | 462 |
| 1396 | **ALUMINIUM POWDER, UNCOATED** | 4Y | | 4.3 | | 423 |
| 1397 | **ALUMINIUM PHOSPHIDE** | 4W | | 4.3 | 6.1 | |

| UN | Substance | EAC | APP | Hazards | | ADR |
| --- | --- | --- | --- | --- | --- | --- |
| | | | | Class | Sub Risks | HIN |
| 1398 | ALUMINIUM SILICON POWDER, UNCOATED | 4Y | | 4.3 | | 423 |
| 1399 | *UN No. not used* | | | | | |
| 1400 | BARIUM | 4W | | 4.3 | | 423 |
| 1401 | CALCIUM | 4W | | 4.3 | | 423 |
| 1402 | CALCIUM CARBIDE | 4YE | | 4.3 | | 423 |
| 1403 | CALCIUM CYANAMIDE *with more than 0.1% of calcium carbide* | 4YE | | 4.3 | | 423 |
| 1404 | CALCIUM HYDRIDE | 4W | | 4.3 | | |
| 1405 | CALCIUM SILICIDE | 4Y | | 4.3 | | 423 |
| 1406 | *UN No. not used* | | | | | |
| 1407 | CAESIUM | 4WE | | 4.3 | | X423 |
| 1408 | FERROSILICON, *with 30% or more but less than 90% silicon* | 4Y | | 4.3 | 6.1 | 462 |
| 1409 | METAL HYDRIDES, WATER-REACTIVE, N.O.S. | 4W | | 4.3 | | 423 |
| 1410 | LITHIUM ALUMINIUM HYDRIDE | 4W | | 4.3 | | |
| 1411 | LITHIUM ALUMINIUM HYDRIDE, ETHEREAL | 4WE | | 4.3 | 3 | |
| 1412 | *UN No. not used* | | | | | |
| 1413 | LITHIUM BOROHYDRIDE | 4W | | 4.3 | | |
| 1414 | LITHIUM HYDRIDE | 4W | | 4.3 | | |
| 1415 | LITHIUM | 4W | | 4.3 | | X423 |
| 1416 | *UN No. not used* | | | | | |
| 1417 | LITHIUM SILICON | 4Y | | 4.3 | | 423 |
| 1418 | MAGNESIUM POWDER *or* MAGNESIUM ALLOYS POWDER | 4Y | | 4.3 | 4.2 | 423 |
| 1419 | MAGNESIUM ALUMINIUM PHOSPHIDE | 4W | | 4.3 | 6.1 | |
| 1420 | POTASSIUM METAL ALLOYS | 4WE | | 4.3 | | X423 |
| 1421 | ALKALI METAL ALLOY, LIQUID, N.O.S. | 4WE | | 4.3 | | X423 |

| UN | Substance | EAC | APP | Hazards | | ADR |
| | | | | Class | Sub Risks | HIN |
|---|---|---|---|---|---|---|
| 1422 | **POTASSIUM SODIUM ALLOYS** | 4WE | | 4.3 | | X423 |
| 1423 | **RUBIDIUM** | 4W | | 4.3 | | X423 |
| 1424 | *UN No. not used* | | | | | |
| 1425 | *UN No. not used* | | | | | |
| 1426 | **SODIUM BOROHYDRIDE** | 4X | | 4.3 | | |
| 1427 | **SODIUM HYDRIDE** | 4W | | 4.3 | | |
| 1428 | **SODIUM** | 4W | | 43 | | X423 |
| 1429 | *UN No. not used* | | | | | |
| 1430 | *UN No. not used* | | | | | |
| 1431 | **SODIUM METHYLATE** | 2W | | 4.2 | 8 | 48 |
| 1432 | **SODIUM PHOSPHIDE** | 4W | | 4.3 | 6.1 | |
| 1433 | **STANNIC PHOSPHIDES** | 4W | | 4.3 | 6. 1 | |
| 1434 | *UN No. not used* | | | | | |
| 1435 | **ZINC ASHES** | 4Y | | 4.3 | | 423 |
| 1436 | **ZINC POWDER** *or* **ZINC DUST** | 4Y | | 4.3 | 4.2 | 423 |
| 1437 | **ZIRCONIUM HYDRIDE** | 2Z | | 4.1 | | 40 |
| 1438 | **ALUMINIUM NITRATE** | 1Y | | 5.1 | | 50 |
| 1439 | **AMMONIUM DICHROMATE** | 2X | | 5.1 | | 50 |
| 1440 | *UN No. not used* | | | | | |
| 1441 | *UN No. not used* | | | | | |
| 1442 | **AMMONIUM PERCHLORATE** | 1Y | | 5.1 | | 50 |
| 1443 | *UN No. not used* | | | | | |
| 1444 | **AMMONIUM PERSULPHATE** | 2W | | 5.1 | | 50 |
| 1445 | **BARIUM CHLORATE** | 2YE | | 5.1 | 6.1 | 56 |
| 1446 | **BARIUM NITRATE** | 2W | | 5.1 | 6.1 | 56 |
| 1447 | **BARIUM PERCHLORATE** | 2W | | 5.1 | 6.1 | 56 |

| UN | Substance | EAC | APP | Hazards | | ADR |
| --- | --- | --- | --- | --- | --- | --- |
| | | | | Class | Sub Risks | HIN |
| 1448 | BARIUM PERMANGANATE | 2X | | 5.1 | 6.1 | 56 |
| 1449 | BARIUM PEROXIDE | 2Y | | 5.1 | 6.1 | 56 |
| 1450 | BROMATES, INORGANIC, N.O.S. | 1YE | | 5.1 | | 50 |
| 1451 | CAESIUM NITRATE | 1Z | | 5.1 | | 50 |
| 1452 | CALCIUM CHLORATE | 1YE | | 5.1 | | 50 |
| 1453 | CALCIUM CHLORITE | 1Y | | 5.1 | | 50 |
| 1454 | CALCIUM NITRATE | 1Z | | 5.1 | | 50 |
| 1455 | CALCIUM PERCHLORATE | 1Y | | 5.1 | | 50 |
| 1456 | CALCIUM PERMANGANATE | 1Y | | 5.1 | | 50 |
| 1457 | CALCIUM PEROXIDE | 1Y | | 5.1 | | 50 |
| 1458 | CHLORATE AND BORATE MIXTURE | 1Y | | 5.1 | | 50 |
| 1459 | CHLORATE AND MAGNESIUM CHLORIDE MIXTURE | 1Y | | 5.1 | | 50 |
| 1460 | UN No. not used | | | | | |
| 1461 | CHLORATES, INORGANIC, N.O.S. | 1YE | | 5.1 | | 50 |
| 1462 | CHLORITES, INORGANIC, N.O.S. | 2WE | | 5.1 | | 50 |
| 1463 | CHROMIUM TRIOXIDE, ANHYDROUS | 2W | | 5.1 | 8 | 58 |
| 1464 | UN No. not used | | | | | |
| 1465 | DIDYMIUM NITRATE | 1Z | | 5.1 | | 50 |
| 1466 | FERRIC NITRATE | 1Z | | 5.1 | | 50 |
| 1467 | GUANIDINE NITRATE | 1Y | | 5.1 | | 50 |
| 1468 | UN No. not used | | | | | |
| 1469 | LEAD NITRATE | 2Y | | 5.1 | 6.1 | 56 |
| 1470 | LEAD PERCHLORATE | 2Y | | 5.1 | 6.1 | 56 |
| 1471 | LITHIUM HYPOCHLORITE, DRY or LITHIUM HYPOCHLORITE MIXTURE | 2WE | | 5.1 | | 50 |
| 1472 | LITHIUM PEROXIDE | 2W | | 5.1 | | 50 |

| UN | Substance | EAC | APP | Hazards | | ADR |
| --- | --- | --- | --- | --- | --- | --- |
| | | | | Class | Sub Risks | HIN |
| 1473 | **MAGNESIUM BROMATE** | 1YE | | 5.1 | | 50 |
| 1474 | **MAGNESIUM NITRATE** | ÍZ | | 5.1 | | 50 |
| 1475 | **MAGNESIUM PERCHLORATE** | 1Y | | 5.1 | | 50 |
| 1476 | **MAGNESIUM PEROXIDE** | 1Y | | 5.1 | | 50 |
| 1477 | **NITRATES, INORGANIC, N.O.S.** | 1Z | | 5.1 | | 50 |
| 1478 | *UN No. not used* | | | | | |
| 1479 | **OXIDISING SOLID, N.O.S.** | 1Y | | 5.1 | | 50 |
| 1480 | *UN No. not used* | | | | | |
| 1481 | **PERCHLORATES, INORGANIC, N.O.S.** | 2WE | | 5.1 | | 50 |
| 1482 | **PERMANGANATES, INORGANIC, N.O.S.** | 1Y | | 5.1 | | 50 |
| 1483 | **PEROXIDES, INORGANIC, N.O.S.** | 2W | | 5.1 | | 50 |
| 1484 | **POTASSIUM BROMATE** | 1YE | | 5.1 | | 50 |
| 1485 | **POTASSIUM CHLORATE** | 1YE | | 5.1 | | 50 |
| 1486 | **POTASSIUM NITRATE** | 1Z | | 5.1 | | 50 |
| 1487 | **POTASSIUM NITRATE AND SODIUM NITRITE MIXTURE** | 1Z | | 5.1 | | 50 |
| 1488 | **POTASSIUM NITRITE** | 1Z | | 5.1 | | 50 |
| 1489 | **POTASSIUM PERCHLORATE** | 2W | | 5.1 | | 50 |
| 1490 | **POTASSIUM PERMANGANATE** | 1Y | | 5.1 | | 50 |
| 1491 | **POTASSIUM PEROXIDE** | 1W | | 5.1 | | |
| 1492 | **POTASSIUM PERSULPHATE** | 2W | | 5.1 | | 50 |
| 1493 | **SILVER NITRATE** | 2X | | 5.1 | | 50 |
| 1494 | **SODIUM BROMATE** | 1YE | | 5.1 | | 50 |
| 1495 | **SODIUM CHLORATE** | 1YE | | 5.1 | | 50 |
| 1496 | **SODIUM CHLORITE** | 2X | | 5.1 | | 50 |
| 1497 | *UN No. not used* | | | | | |

| UN | Substance | EAC | APP | Hazards | | ADR |
|---|---|---|---|---|---|---|
| | | | | Class | Sub Risks | HIN |
| 1498 | **SODIUM NITRATE** | 1Z | | 5.1 | | 50 |
| 1499 | **SODIUM NITRATE AND POTASSIUM NITRATE MIXTURE** | 1Z | | 5.1 | | 50 |
| 1500 | **SODIUM NITRITE** | 1Z | | 5.1 | 6.1 | 56 |
| 1501 | *UN No. not used* | | | | | |
| 1502 | **SODIUM PERCHLORATE** | 2W | | 5.1 | | 50 |
| 1503 | **SODIUM PERMANGANATE** | 1Y | | 5.1 | | 50 |
| 1504 | **SODIUM PEROXIDE** | 1W | | 5.1 | | |
| 1505 | **SODIUM PERSULPHATE** | 2W | | 5.1 | | 50 |
| 1506 | **STRONTIUM CHLORATE** | 1YE | | 5.1 | | 50 |
| 1507 | **STRONTIUM NITRATE** | 1Z | | 5.1 | | 50 |
| 1508 | **STRONTIUM PERCHLORATE** | 1Y | | 5.1 | | 50 |
| 1509 | **STRONTIUM PEROXIDE** | 1Y | | 5.1 | | 50 |
| 1510 | **TETRANITROMETHANE** | 2WE | | 5.1 | 6.1 | 559 |
| 1511 | **UREA HYDROGEN PEROXIDE** | 2W | | 5.1 | 8 | 58 |
| 1512 | **ZINC AMMONIUM NITRITE** | 1Y | | 5.1 | | 50 |
| 1513 | **ZINC CHLORATE** | 1YE | | 5.1 | | 50 |
| 1514 | **ZINC NITRATE** | 1Y | | 5.1 | | 50 |
| 1515 | **ZINC PERMANGANATE** | 1Y | | 5.1 | | 50 |
| 1516 | **ZINC PEROXIDE** | 1Y | | 5.1 | | 50 |
| 1517 | **ZIRCONIUM PICRAMATE, WETTED** *with not less than 20% water, by mass* | 1W | | 4.1 | | |
| 1518 to 1540 | *UN Nos. not used* | | | | | |
| 1541 | **ACETONE CYANOHYDRIN STABILIZED** | ●2XE | B | 6.1 | | 66 |
| 1542 | *UN No. not used* | | | | | |
| 1543 | *UN No. not used* | | | | | |

| UN | Substance | EAC | APP | Hazards | | ADR |
| | | | | Class | Sub Risks | HIN |
|---|---|---|---|---|---|---|
| 1544 | **ALKALOIDS, SOLID, N.O.S.** *or* **ALKALOID SALTS, SOLID, N.O.S.** | 2X | | 6.1 | | 66/ 60 |
| 1545 | **ALLYL ISOTHIOCYANATE, INHIBITED** | 3WE | | 6.1 | 3 | 639 |
| 1546 | **AMMONIUM ARSENATE** | 2X | | 6.1 | | 60 |
| 1547 | **ANILINE** | ●3X | | 6.1 | | 60 |
| 1548 | **ANILINE HYDROCHLORIDE** | 2Z | | 6.1 | | 60 |
| 1549 | **ANTIMONY COMPOUND, INORGANIC, SOLID, N.O.S.** | 2X | | 6.1 | | 60 |
| 1550 | **ANTIMONY LACTATE** | 2Z | | 6.1 | | 60 |
| 1551 | **ANTIMONY POTASSIUM TARTRATE** | 2X | | 6.1 | | 60 |
| 1552 | *UN No. not used* | | | | | |
| 1553 | **ARSENIC ACID, LIQUID** | 2X | B | 6.1 | | 66 |
| 1554 | **ARSENIC ACID, SOLID** | 2X | | 6.1 | | 60 |
| 1555 | **ARSENIC BROMIDE** | 2X | | 6.1 | | 60 |
| 1556 | **ARSENIC COMPOUND, LIQUID, INORGANIC, N.O.S.** *including: Arsenates, n.o.s., Arsenites, n.o.s., Arsenic sulphides, n.o.s.* | 2X | B | 6.1 | | 66 |
| 1556 | **ARSENIC COMPOUND, LIQUID, INORGANIC, N.O.S.** *including: Arsenates, n.o.s., Arsenites, n.o.s., Arsenic sulphides, n.o.s.* | 2X | | 6.1 | | 60 |
| 1557 | **ARSENIC COMPOUND, SOLID, INORGANIC, N.O.S.** *including: Arsenates, n.o.s., Arsenites, n.o.s., Arsenic sulphides, n.o.s.* | 2X | | 6.1 | | 66/ 60 |
| 1558 | **ARSENIC** | 2Z | | 6.1 | | 60 |
| 1559 | **ARSENIC PENTOXIDE** | 2X | | 6.1 | | 60 |
| 1560 | **ARSENIC TRICHLORIDE** | 2X | B | 6.1 | | 66 |
| 1561 | **ARSENIC TRIOXIDE** | 2Z | | 6.1 | | 60 |
| 1562 | **ARSENICAL DUST** | 2X | | 6.1 | | 60 |
| 1563 | *UN No. not used* | | | | | |
| 1564 | **BARIUM COMPOUND, N.O.S.** | 2Z | | 6.1 | | 60 |

| UN | Substance | EAC | APP | Hazards | | ADR |
| | | | | Class | Sub Risks | HIN |
|------|-----------|-----|-----|-------|-----------|-----|
| 1565 | **BARIUM CYANIDE** | 2X | | 6.1 | | 66 |
| 1566 | **BERYLLIUM COMPOUND, N.O.S.** | 2X | | 6.1 | | 60 |
| 1567 | **BERYLLIUM POWDER** | 2X | | 6.1 | 4.1 | 64 |
| 1568 | *UN No. not used* | | | | | |
| 1569 | **BROMOACETONE** | 2WE | | 6.1 | 3 | 63 |
| 1570 | **BRUCINE** | 2X | | 6.1 | | 66 |
| 1571 | **BARIUM AZIDE, WETTED** <br> *with not less than 50% water, by mass* | 1X | | 4.1 | 6.1 | |
| 1572 | **CACODYLIC ACID** | 2X | | 6.1 | | 60 |
| 1573 | **CALCIUM ARSENATE** | 2X | | 6.1 | | 60 |
| 1574 | **CALCIUM ARSENATE AND CALCIUM ARSENITE MIXTURE, SOLID** | 2X | | 6.1 | | 60 |
| 1575 | **CALCIUM CYANIDE** | 2X | | 6.1 | | 66 |
| 1576 | *UN No. not used* | | | | | |
| 1577 | **CHLORODINITROBENZENES** | 2W | | 6.1 | | 60 |
| 1578 | **CHLORONITROBENZENES** | 2X | | 6.1 | | 60 |
| 1579 | **4-CHLORO-o-TOLUIDINE HYDROCHLORIDE** | 2X | | 6.1 | | 60 |
| 1580 | **CHLOROPICRIN** | 2XE | B | 6.1 | | 66 |
| 1581 | **CHLOROPICRIN AND METHYL BROMIDE MIXTURE** | 2XE | B | 2.3 | | 26 |
| 1582 | **CHLOROPICRIN AND METHYL CHLORIDE MIXTURE** | 2WE | AB | 2.3 | | 26 |
| 1583 | **CHLOROPICRIN MIXTURE, N.O.S.** | 2XE | B | 6.1 | | 66 |
| 1583 | **CHLOROPICRIN MIXTURE, N.O.S.** | 2X | | 6.1 | | 60 |
| 1584 | *UN No. not used* | | | | | |
| 1585 | **COPPER ACETOARSENITE** | 2Z | | 6.1 | | 60 |
| 1586 | **COPPER ARSENITE** | 2Z | | 6.1 | | 60 |
| 1587 | **COPPER CYANIDE** | 2X | | 6.1 | | 60 |

| UN | Substance | EAC | APP | Hazards | | ADR |
|---|---|---|---|---|---|---|
| | | | | Class | Sub Risks | HIN |
| 1588 | CYANIDES, INORGANIC, SOLID, N.O.S. | 2X | | 6.1 | | 66/60 |
| 1589 | CYANOGEN CHLORIDE, INHIBITED | 2XE | B | 2.3 | 8 | |
| 1590 | DICHLOROANILINES | 2X | | 6.1 | | 60 |
| 1591 | o-DICHLOROBENZENE | 2Z | | 6.1 | | 60 |
| 1592 | UN No. not used | | | | | |
| 1593 | DICHLOROMETHANE | 2Z | | 6.1 | | 60 |
| 1594 | DIETHYL SULPHATE | 2X | | 6.1 | | 60 |
| 1595 | DIMETHYL SULPHATE | ●2XE | B | 6.1 | 8 | 668 |
| 1596 | DINITROANILINES | 2W | | 6.1 | | 60 |
| 1597 | DINITROBENZENES | 2W | | 6.1 | | 60 |
| 1598 | DINITRO-o-CRESOL | 2W | | 6.1 | | 60 |
| 1599 | DINITROPHENOL SOLUTION | 3WE | | 6.1 | | 60 |
| 1600 | DINITROTOLUENES, MOLTEN | 2W | A | 6.1 | | 60 |
| 1601 | DISINFECTANT, SOLID, TOXIC, N.O.S. | 2X | | 6.1 | | 66/60 |
| 1602 | DYE, LIQUID, TOXIC, N.O.S., or DYE, INTERMEDIATE, LIQUID, TOXIC, N.O.S. | 2X | B | 6.1 | | 66 |
| 1602 | DYE, LIQUID, TOXIC, N.O.S., or DYE, INTERMEDIATE, LIQUID, TOXIC, N.O.S. | 2X | | 6.1 | | 60 |
| 1603 | ETHYL BROMOACETATE | 2WE | | 6.1 | 3 | 63 |
| 1604 | ETHYLENEDIAMINE | ●2W | | 8 | 3 | 83 |
| 1605 | ETHYLENE DIBROMIDE | 2XE | B | 6.1 | | 66 |
| 1606 | FERRIC ARSENATE | 2Z | | 6.1 | | 60 |
| 1607 | FERRIC ARSENITE | 2Z | | 6.1 | | 60 |
| 1608 | FERROUS ARSENATE | 2Z | | 6.1 | | 60 |
| 1609 | UN No. not used | | | | | |
| 1610 | UN No. not used | | | | | |

| UN | Substance | EAC | APP | Hazards | | ADR |
| | | | | Class | Sub Risks | HIN |
| --- | --- | --- | --- | --- | --- | --- |
| 1611 | **HEXAETHYL TETRAPHOSPHATE** | 2X | | 6.1 | | 60 |
| 1612 | **HEXAETHYL TETRAPHOSPHATE AND COMPRESSED GAS MIXTURE** | 2RE | B | 2.3 | | 26 |
| 1613 | **HYDROCYANIC ACID, AQUEOUS SOLUTION (HYDROGEN CYANIDE, AQUEOUS SOLUTION)** *with not more than 20% hydrogen cyanide* | 2WE | B | 6.1 | | 663 |
| 1614 | **HYDROGEN CYANIDE, STABILIZED,** *containing less then 3% water and absorbed in a porous inert material* | 2X | | 6.1 | | |
| 1615 | *UN No. not used* | | | | | |
| 1616 | **LEAD ACETATE** | 2Z | | 6.1 | | 60 |
| 1617 | **LEAD ARSENATES** | 2Z | | 6.1 | | 60 |
| 1618 | **LEAD ARSENITES** | 2Z | | 6.1 | | 60 |
| 1619 | *UN No. not used* | | | | | |
| 1620 | **LEAD CYANIDE** | 2X | | 6.1 | | 60 |
| 1621 | **LONDON PURPLE** | 2X | | 6.1 | | 60 |
| 1622 | **MAGNESIUM ARSENATE** | 2Z | | 6.1 | | 60 |
| 1623 | **MERCURIC ARSENATE** | 2X | | 6.1 | | 60 |
| 1624 | **MERCURIC CHLORIDE** | 2X | | 6.1 | | 60 |
| 1625 | **MERCURIC NITRATE** | 2X | | 6.1 | | 60 |
| 1626 | **MERCURIC POTASSIUM CYANIDE** | 2X | | 6.1 | | 66 |
| 1627 | **MERCUROUS NITRATE** | 2Z | | 6.1 | | 60 |
| 1628 | *UN No. not used* | | | | | |
| 1629 | **MERCURY ACETATE** | 2X | | 6.1 | | 60 |
| 1630 | **MERCURY AMMONIUM CHLORIDE** | 2X | | 6.1 | | 60 |
| 1631 | **MERCURY BENZOATE** | 2X | | 6.1 | | 60 |
| 1632 | *UN No. not used* | | | | | |
| 1633 | *UN No. not used* | | | | | |
| 1634 | **MERCURY BROMIDES** | 2X | | 6.1 | | 60 |

| UN | Substance | EAC | APP | Hazards | | ADR |
| | | | | Class | Sub Risks | HIN |
| --- | --- | --- | --- | --- | --- | --- |
| 1635 | *UN No. not used* | | | | | |
| 1636 | **MERCURY CYANIDE** | 2X | | 6.1 | | 60 |
| 1637 | **MERCURY GLUCONATE** | 2X | | 6.1 | | 60 |
| 1638 | **MERCURY IODIDE** | 2X | | 6.1 | | 60 |
| 1639 | **MERCURY NUCLEATE** | 2X | | 6.1 | | 60 |
| 1640 | **MERCURY OLEATE** | 2X | | 6.1 | | 60 |
| 1641 | **MERCURY OXIDE** | 2Z | | 6.1 | | 60 |
| 1642 | **MERCURY OXYCYANIDE, DESENSITIZED** | 2WE | | 6.1 | | 60 |
| 1643 | **MERCURY POTASSIUM IODIDE** | 2X | | 6.1 | | 60 |
| 1644 | **MERCURY SALICYLATE** | 2Z | | 6.1 | | 60 |
| 1645 | **MERCURY SULPHATE** | 2X | | 6.1 | | 60 |
| 1646 | **MERCURY THIOCYANATE** | 2Z | | 6.1 | | 60 |
| 1647 | **METHYL BROMIDE AND ETHYLENE DIBROMIDE MIXTURE, LIQUID** | 2XE | B | 6.1 | | 66 |
| 1648 | **ACETONITRILE** | ●2WE | | 3 | | 33 |
| 1649 | **MOTOR FUEL ANTI-KNOCK MIXTURE** | 2WE | B | 6.1 | | 66 |
| 1650 | **beta-NAPHTHYLAMINE** | 2X | | 6.1 | | 60 |
| 1651 | **NAPHTHYLTHIOUREA** | 2Z | | 6.1 | | 60 |
| 1652 | **NAPHTHYLUREA** | 2Z | | 6.1 | | 60 |
| 1653 | **NICKEL CYANIDE** | 2X | | 6.1 | | 60 |
| 1654 | **NICOTINE** | 2X | | 6.1 | | 60 |
| 1655 | **NICOTINE COMPOUND, SOLID, N.O.S.** *or* **NICOTINE PREPARATION, SOLID, N.O.S.** | 2X | | 6.1 | | 66/ 60 |
| 1656 | **NICOTINE HYDROCHLORIDE** *or* **NICOTINE HYDROCHLORIDE SOLUTION** | 2X | | 6.1 | | 60 |
| 1657 | **NICOTINE SALICYLATE** | 2X | | 6.1 | | 60 |
| 1658 | **NICOTINE SULPHATE, SOLID** *or* **NICOTINE SULPHATE SOLUTION** | 2X | | 6.1 | | 60 |

| UN | Substance | EAC | APP | Hazards | | ADR |
| | | | | Class | Sub Risks | HIN |
|---|---|---|---|---|---|---|
| 1659 | NICOTINE TARTRATE | 2X | | 6.1 | | 60 |
| 1660 | NITRIC OXIDE, COMPRESSED | 2PE | B | 2.3 | 5.1 8 | |
| 1661 | NITROANILINES (o-,m-,p-) | 2X | | 6.1 | | 60 |
| 1662 | NITROBENZENE | 2X | | 6.1 | | 60 |
| 1663 | NITROPHENOLS (o-,m-,p-) | 2X | | 6.1 | | 60 |
| 1664 | NITROTOLUENES (o-,m-,p-) | 2X | | 6.1 | | 60 |
| 1665 | NITROXYLENES (o-,m-,p-) | 2X | | 6.1 | | 60 |
| 1666 to 1668 | *UN Nos. not used* | | | | | |
| 1669 | PENTACHLOROETHANE | 2Z | | 6.1 | | 60 |
| 1670 | PERCHLOROMETHYL MERCAPTAN | 2XE | B | 6.1 | | 66 |
| 1671 | PHENOL, SOLID | 2X | | 6.1 | | 60 |
| 1672 | PHENYLCARBYLAMINE CHLORIDE | 2XE | B | 6.1 | | 66 |
| 1673 | PHENYLENEDIAMINES (o-,m-,p-) | 2X | | 6.1 | | 60 |
| 1674 | PHENYLMERCURIC ACETATE | 2X | | 6.1 | | 60 |
| 1675 | *UN No. not used* | | | | | |
| 1676 | *UN No. not used* | | | | | |
| 1677 | POTASSIUM ARSENATE | 2X | | 6.1 | | 60 |
| 1678 | POTASSIUM ARSENITE | 2X | | 6.1 | | 60 |
| 1679 | POTASSIUM CUPROCYANIDE | 2X | | 6.1 | | 60 |
| 1680 | POTASSIUM CYANIDE | 2X | | 6.1 | | 66 |
| 1681 | *UN No. not used* | | | | | |
| 1682 | *UN No. not used* | | | | | |
| 1683 | SILVER ARSENITE | 2X | | 6.1 | | 60 |
| 1684 | SILVER CYANIDE | 2X | | 6.1 | | 60 |

| UN | Substance | EAC | APP | Hazards | | ADR |
| | | | | Class | Sub Risks | HIN |
|---|---|---|---|---|---|---|
| 1685 | **SODIUM ARSENATE** | 2X | | 6.1 | | 60 |
| 1686 | **SODIUM ARSENITE, AQUEOUS SOLUTION** | 2X | | 6.1 | | 60 |
| 1687 | **SODIUM AZIDE** | 2X | | 6.1 | | |
| 1688 | **SODIUM CACODYLATE** | 2X | | 6.1 | | 60 |
| 1689 | **SODIUM CYANIDE** | 2X | | 6.1 | | 66 |
| 1690 | **SODIUM FLUORIDE** | 2Z | | 6.1 | | 60 |
| 1691 | **STRONTIUM ARSENITE** | 2X | | 6.1 | | 60 |
| 1692 | **STRYCHNINE** *or* **STRYCHNINE SALTS** | 2X | | 6.1 | | 66 |
| 1693 | **TEAR GAS SUBSTANCE, LIQUID** *or* **SOLID, N.O.S.** | 2XE | B | 6.1 | | 66 |
| 1693 | **TEAR GAS SUBSTANCE, LIQUID** *or* **SOLID, N.O.S.** | 2XE | | 6.1 | | 60 |
| 1694 | **BROMOBENZYL CYANIDES** | 2XE | B | 6.1 | | 66 |
| 1695 | **CHLOROACETONE, STABILIZED** | 2WE | B | 6.1 | 3 8 | 663 |
| 1696 | *UN No. not used* | | | | | |
| 1697 | **CHLOROACETOPHENONE** | 2X | | 6.1 | | 60 |
| 1698 | **DIPHENYLAMINE CHLOROARSINE** | 2XE | | 6.1 | | 66 |
| 1699 | **DIPHENYLCHLOROARSINE** | 2XE | | 6.1 | | 66 |
| 1700 | **TEAR GAS CANDLES** | + | | 6.1 | 4.1 | |
| 1701 | **XYLYL BROMIDE** | 2XE | | 6.1 | | 60 |
| 1702 | **TETRACHLOROETHANE** | 2XE | | 6.1 | | 60 |
| 1703 | *UN No. not used* | | | | | |
| 1704 | **TETRAETHYL DITHIOPYROPHOSPHATE** | 2XE | | 6.1 | | 60 |
| 1705 | *UN No. not used* | | | | | |
| 1706 | *UN No. not used* | | | | | |
| 1707 | **THALLIUM COMPOUNDS, N.O.S.** | 2X | | 6.1 | | 60 |
| 1708 | **TOLUIDINES** | ●3X | | 6.1 | | 60 |

| UN | Substance | EAC | APP | Hazards Class | Sub Risks | ADR HIN |
|---|---|---|---|---|---|---|
| 1709 | 2,4-TOLUYLENEDIAMINE | 2X | | 6.1 | | 60 |
| 1710 | TRICHLOROETHYLENE | 2Z | | 6.1 | | 60 |
| 1711 | XYLIDINES | 3X | | 6.1 | | 60 |
| 1712 | ZINC ARSENATE, ZINC ARSENITE or ZINC ARSENATE AND ZINC ARSENITE MIXTURE | 2Z | | 6.1 | | 60 |
| 1713 | ZINC CYANIDE | 2X | | 6.1 | | 66 |
| 1714 | ZINC PHOSPHIDE | 4W | | 4.3 | 6.1 | |
| 1715 | ACETIC ANHYDRIDE | ●2W | | 8 | 3 | 83 |
| 1716 | ACETYL BROMIDE | 4WE | | 8 | | 80 |
| 1717 | ACETYL CHLORIDE | 4WE | | 3 | 8 | X338 |
| 1718 | BUTYL ACID PHOSPHATE | 2X | | 8 | | 80 |
| 1719 | CAUSTIC ALKALI LIQUID N.O.S. | 2R | | 8 | | 80 |
| 1720 | UN No. not used | | | | | |
| 1721 | UN No. not used | | | | | |
| 1722 | ALLYL CHLOROFORMATE | ●2WE | B | 6.1 | 3 8 | 638 |
| 1723 | ALLYL IODIDE | ●2WE | | 3 | 8 | 338 |
| 1724 | ALLYLTRICHLOROSILANE, STABILIZED | 4WE | | 8 | 3 | X839 |
| 1725 | ALUMINIUM BROMIDE, ANHYDROUS | 4W | | 8 | | 80 |
| 1726 | ALUMINIUM CHLORIDE, ANHYDROUS | 4W | | 8 | | 80 |
| 1727 | AMMONIUM HYDROGEN- DIFLUORIDE, SOLID | 2X | | 8 | | 80 |
| 1728 | AMYLTRICHLOROSILANE | 4W | | 8 | | X80 |
| 1729 | ANISOYL CHLORIDE | 4W | | 8 | | 80 |
| 1730 | ANTIMONY PENTACHLORIDE, LIQUID | 4WE | | 8 | | X80 |
| 1731 | ANTIMONY PENTACHLORIDE, SOLUTION | 4WE | | 8 | | 80 |
| 1732 | ANTIMONY PENTAFLUORIDE | 4WE | | 8 | 6.1 | 86 |
| 1733 | ANTIMONY TRICHLORIDE | 4W | | 8 | | 80 |

| UN | Substance | EAC | APP | Hazards | | ADR |
| | | | | Class | Sub Risks | HIN |
|---|---|---|---|---|---|---|
| 1734 | *UN No. not used* | | | | | |
| 1735 | *UN No. not used* | | | | | |
| 1736 | **BENZOYL CHLORIDE** | 4W | | 8 | | 80 |
| 1737 | **BENZYL BROMIDE** | 2X | | 6.1 | 8 | 68 |
| 1738 | **BENZYL CHLORIDE** | 2W | | 6.1 | 8 | 68 |
| 1739 | **BENZYL CHLOROFORMATE** | 2XE | B | 8 | | 88 |
| 1740 | **HYDROGEN DIFLUORIDES, N.O.S.** | 2X | | 8 | | 80 |
| 1741 | **BORON TRICHLORIDE** | 2WE | B | 2.3 | 8 | |
| 1742 | **BORON TRIFLUORIDE ACETIC ACID COMPLEX** | 2XE | | 8 | | 80 |
| 1743 | **BORON TRIFLUORIDE PROPIONIC ACID COMPLEX** | 2XE | | 8 | | 80 |
| 1744 | **BROMINE** *or* **BROMINE SOLUTION** | 2XE | B | 8 | 6.1 | 886 |
| 1745 | **BROMINE PENTAFLUORIDE** | 4WE | AB | 5.1 | 6.1 8 | 568 |
| 1746 | **BROMINE TRIFLUORIDE** | 4WE | AB | 5.1 | 6.1 8 | 568 |
| 1747 | **BUTYLTRICHLOROSILANE** | 4WE | | 8 | 3 | X83 |
| 1748 | **CALCIUM HYPOCHLORITE, DRY** *or* **CALCIUM HYPOCHLORITE MIXTURE, DRY** *with more than 39% available chlorine (8.8% available oxygen)* | 2WE | | 5.1 | | 50 |
| 1749 | **CHLORINE TRIFLUORIDE** | 2WE | AB | 2.3 | 5.1 8 | 265 |
| 1750 | **CHLOROACETIC ACID SOLUTION** | 2X | | 6.1 | 8 | 68 |
| 1751 | **CHLOROACETIC ACID, SOLID** | 2X | | 6.1 | 8 | 68 |
| 1752 | **CHLOROACETYL CHLORIDE** | 2WE | B | 6.1 | 8 | 668 |
| 1753 | **CHLOROPHENYLTRICHLOROSILANE** | 4W | | 8 | | X80 |
| 1754 | **CHLOROSULPHONIC ACID** *(with or without sulphur trioxide)* | 4WE | B | 8 | | X88 |
| 1755 | **CHROMIC ACID SOLUTION** | 2X | | 8 | | 80 |

| UN | Substance | EAC | APP | Hazards | | ADR |
| --- | --- | --- | --- | --- | --- | --- |
| | | | | Class | Sub Risks | HIN |
| 1756 | **CHROMIC FLUORIDE, SOLID** | 2X | | 8 | | 80 |
| 1757 | **CHROMIC FLUORIDE SOLUTION** | 2X | | 8 | | 80 |
| 1758 | **CHROMIUM OXYCHLORIDE** | 4WE | B | 8 | | X88 |
| 1759 | **CORROSIVE SOLID, N.O.S.** | 2X | | 8 | | 88/ 80 |
| 1760 | **CORROSIVE LIQUID, N.O.S.** | 2X | B | 8 | | 88 |
| 1760 | **CORROSIVE LIQUID, N.O.S.** | 2X | | 8 | | 80 |
| 1761 | **CUPRIETHYLENEDIAMINE SOLUTION** | 2X | | 8 | 6.1 | 86 |
| 1762 | **CYCLOHEXENYLTRICHLOROSILANE** | 4W | | 8 | | X80 |
| 1763 | **CYCLOHEXYLTRICHLOROSILANE** | 4W | | 8 | | X80 |
| 1764 | **DICHLOROACETIC ACID** | 2X | | 8 | | 80 |
| 1765 | **DICHLOROACETYL CHLORIDE** | 4WE | | 8 | | X80 |
| 1766 | **DICHLOROPHENYLTRICHLOROSILANE** | 4W | | 8 | | X80 |
| 1767 | **DIETHYLDICHLOROSILANE** | 4WE | | 8 | 3 | X83 |
| 1768 | **DIFLUOROPHOSPHORIC ACID, ANHYDROUS** | 2XE | | 8 | | 80 |
| 1769 | **DIPHENYLDICHLOROSILANE** | 4W | | 8 | | X80 |
| 1770 | **DIPHENYLMETHYL BROMIDE** | 2X | | 8 | | 80 |
| 1771 | **DODECYLTRICHLOROSILANE** | 4XE | | 8 | | X80 |
| 1772 | *UN No. not used* | | | 8 | | X80 |
| 1773 | **FERRIC CHLORIDE, ANHYDROUS** | 2X | | 8 | | 80 |
| 1774 | **FIRE EXTINGUISHER CHARGES,** *corrosive liquid* | + | | 8 | | |
| 1775 | **FLUOROBORIC ACID** | 2X | | 8 | | 80 |
| 1776 | **FLUOROPHOSPHORIC ACID, ANHYDROUS** | 2XE | | 8 | | 80 |
| 1777 | **FLUOROSULPHONIC ACID** | 4WE | B | 8 | | 88 |
| 1778 | **FLUOROSILICIC ACID** | 2X | | 8 | | 80 |
| 1779 | **FORMIC ACID** | 2X | | 8 | | 80 |

| UN | Substance | EAC | APP | Hazards | | ADR |
|---|---|---|---|---|---|---|
| | | | | Class | Sub Risks | HIN |
| 1780 | FUMARYL CHLORIDE | 4W | | 8 | | 80 |
| 1781 | HEXADECYLTRICHLOROSILANE | 4W | | 8 | | X80 |
| 1782 | HEXAFLUOROPHOSPHORIC ACID | 2XE | | 8 | | 80 |
| 1783 | HEXAMETHYLENEDIAMINE SOLUTION | 2X | | 8 | | 80 |
| 1784 | HEXYLTRICHLOROSILANE | 4W | | 8 | | X80 |
| 1785 | UN No. not used | | | | | |
| 1786 | HYDROFLUORIC ACID AND SULPHURIC ACID MIXTURE | 2WE | B | 8 | 6.1 | 886 |
| 1787 | HYDRIODIC ACID | 2R | | 8 | | 80 |
| 1788 | HYDROBROMIC ACID | 2R | | 8 | | 80 |
| 1789 | HYDROCHLORIC ACID | 2R | | 8 | | 80 |
| 1790 | HYDROFLUORIC ACID with more than 60% | 2XE | B | 8 | 6.1 | 886 |
| 1790 | HYDROFLUORIC ACID with not more than 60% | 2X | | 8 | 6.1 | 86 |
| 1791 | HYPOCHLORITE SOLUTION | 2X | | 8 | | 80 |
| 1792 | IODINE MONOCHLORIDE | 4WE | | 8 | | 80 |
| 1793 | ISOPROPYL ACID PHOSPHATE | 2X | | 8 | | 80 |
| 1794 | LEAD SULPHATE with more than 3% free acid | 2X | | 8 | | 80 |
| 1795 | UN No. not used | | | | | |
| 1796 | NITRATING ACID, MIXTURE, with more than 50% nitric acid | 2WE | B | 8 | 5.1 | 885 |
| 1796 | NITRATING ACID, MIXTURE, with not more than 50% nitric acid | 2WE | | 8 | | 80 |
| 1797 | UN No. not used | | | | | |
| 1798 | NITROHYDROCHLORIC ACID | 2X | | 8 | | |
| 1799 | NONYLTRICHLOROSILANE | 4W | | 8 | | X80 |
| 1880 | OCTADECYLTRICHLOROSILANE | 4W | | 8 | | X80 |
| 1801 | OCTYLTRICHLOROSILANE | 4W | | 8 | | X80 |

| UN | Substance | EAC | APP | Hazards | | ADR |
| | | | | Class | Sub Risks | HIN |
| --- | --- | --- | --- | --- | --- | --- |
| 1802 | **PERCHLORIC ACID** *with not more than 50% acid, by mass* | 2P | | 8 | 5.1 | 85 |
| 1803 | **PHENOLSULPHONIC ACID, LIQUID** | 2X | | 8 | | 80 |
| 1804 | **PHENYLTRICHLOROSILANE** | 4W | | 8 | | X80 |
| 1805 | **PHOSPHORIC ACID** | 2R | | 8 | | 80 |
| 1806 | **PHOSPHORUS PENTACHLORIDE** | 4WE | | 8 | | 80 |
| 1807 | **PHOSPHORUS PENTOXIDE** | 4W | | 8 | | 80 |
| 1808 | **PHOSPHORUS TRIBROMIDE** | 4WE | | 8 | | X80 |
| 1809 | **PHOSPHORUS TRICHLORIDE** | 4WE | B | 6.1 | 8 | 668 |
| 1810 | **PHOSPHORUS OXYCHLORIDE** | 4WE | | 8 | | X80 |
| 1811 | **POTASSIUM HYDROGENDIFLUORIDE** | 2X | | 8 | 6.1 | 86 |
| 1812 | **POTASSIUM FLUORIDE** | 2Z | | 6.1 | | 60 |
| 1813 | **POTASSIUM HYDROXIDE, SOLID** | 2X | | 8 | | 80 |
| 1814 | **POTASSIUM HYDROXIDE SOLUTION** | 2R | | 8 | | 80 |
| 1815 | **PROPIONYL CHLORIDE** | 2WE | | 3 | 8 | 338 |
| 1816 | **PROPYLTRICHLOROSILANE** | 4WE | | 8 | 3 | X83 |
| 1817 | **PYROSULPHURYL CHLORIDE** | 4WE | | 8 | | X80 |
| 1818 | **SILICON TETRACHLORIDE** | 4WE | | 8 | | X80 |
| 1819 | **SODIUM ALUMINATE SOLUTION** | 2X | | 8 | | 80 |
| 1820 to 1822 | *UN Nos. not used* | | | | | |
| 1823 | **SODIUM HYDROXIDE, SOLID** | 2X | | 8 | | 80 |
| 1824 | **SODIUM HYDROXIDE SOLUTION** | 2R | | 8 | | 80 |
| 1824 | **SODIUM HYDROXIDE SOLUTION** *(transported above 100°C)* | 2W | A | 8 | | 80 |
| 1825 | **SODIUM MONOXIDE** | 2X | | 8 | | 80 |

| UN | Substance | EAC | APP | Hazards | | ADR |
| | | | | Class | Sub Risks | HIN |
|---|---|---|---|---|---|---|
| 1826 | **NITRATING ACID MIXTURE, SPENT,** *with more than 50% nitric acid* | 2W | B | 8 | 5.1 | 885 |
| 1826 | **NITRATING ACID MIXTURE, SPENT,** *with not more than 50% nitric acid* | 2W | | 8 | | 80 |
| 1827 | **STANNIC CHLORIDE, ANHYDROUS** | 4WE | | 8 | | X80 |
| 1828 | **SULPHUR CHLORIDES** | 4WE | B | 8 | | X88 |
| 1829 | **SULPHUR TRIOXIDE, INHIBITED** *or* **SULPHUR TRIOXIDE, STABILIZED** | 4WE | B | 8 | | X88 |
| 1830 | **SULPHURIC ACID** *with more than 51% acid* | 2P | | 8 | | 80 |
| 1831 | **SULPHURIC ACID, FUMING** | 4WE | B | 8 | 6.1 | X886 |
| 1832 | **SULPHURIC ACID, SPENT** | 2W | | 8 | | 80 |
| 1833 | **SULPHUROUS ACID** | 2R | | 8 | | 80 |
| 1834 | **SULPHURYL CHLORIDE** | 4WE | B | 8 | | X88 |
| 1835 | **TETRAMETHYLAMMONIUM HYDROXIDE** | 2X | | 8 | | 80 |
| 1836 | **THIONYL CHLORIDE** | 4WE | B | 8 | | X88 |
| 1837 | **THIOPHOSPHORYL CHLORIDE** | 4WE | | 8 | | X80 |
| 1838 | **TITANIUM TETRACHLORIDE** | 4WE | | 8 | | X80 |
| 1839 | **TRICHLOROACETIC ACID** | 2X | | 8 | | 80 |
| 1840 | **ZINC CHLORIDE SOLUTION** | 2X | | 8 | | 80 |
| 1841 | **ACETALDEHYDE AMMONIA** | 2Z | | 9 | | 90 |
| 1842 | *UN No. not used* | | | | | |
| 1843 | **AMMONIUM DINITRO-o-CRESOLATE** | 2W | | 6.1 | | 60 |
| 1844 | *UN No. not used* | | | | | |
| 1845 | *UN No. not used* | | | | | |
| 1846 | **CARBON TETRACHLORIDE** | 2Z | | 6.1 | | 60 |
| 1847 | **POTASSIUM SULPHIDE, HYDRATED** *with not less than 30% water of crystallisation* | 2X | | 8 | | 80 |
| 1848 | **PROPIONIC ACID** | ●2W | | 8 | | 80 |

| UN | Substance | EAC | APP | Hazards | | ADR |
|---|---|---|---|---|---|---|
| | | | | Class | Sub Risks | HIN |
| 1849 | **SODIUM SULPHIDE, HYDRATED** *with not less than 30% water of crystallisation* | 2X | | 8 | | 80 |
| 1850 | *UN No. not used* | | | | | |
| 1851 | **MEDICINE, LIQUID, TOXIC, N.O.S.** | 2X | | 6.1 | | 60 |
| 1852 | *UN No. not used* | | | | | |
| 1853 | *UN No. not used* | | | | | |
| 1854 | **BARIUM ALLOYS, PYROPHORIC** | 4Y | | 4.2 | | |
| 1855 | **CALCIUM, PYROPHORIC** *or* **CALCIUM ALLOYS, PYROPHORIC** | 4Y | | 4.2 | | |
| 1856 | *UN No. not used* | | | | | |
| 1857 | *UN No. not used* | | | | | |
| 1858 | **HEXAFLUOROPROPYLENE (REFRIGERANT GAS R1216)** | 2XE | A | 2.2 | | 20 |
| 1859 | **SILICON TETRAFLUORIDE, COMPRESSED** | 2PE | B | 2.3 | 8 | 268 |
| 1860 | **VINYL FLUORIDE, INHIBITED** | 2WE | A | 2.1 | | 239 |
| 1861 | *UN No. not used* | | | | | |
| 1862 | **ETHYL CROTONATE** | 3YE | | 3 | | 33 |
| 1863 | **FUEL, AVIATION, TURBINE ENGINE,** *flash point less than 23°C* | 3YE | | 3 | | 33 |
| 1863 | **FUEL, AVIATION, TURBINE ENGINE,** *flash point 23°C or above* | 3Y | | 3 | | 30 |
| 1864 | *UN No. not used* | | | | | |
| 1865 | **n-PROPYL NITRATE** | 3YE | | 3 | | |
| 1866 | **RESIN SOLUTION, FLAMMABLE,** *flash point less than 23°C* | ●3YE | | 3 | | 33 |
| 1866 | **RESIN SOLUTION, FLAMMABLE,** *flash point 23°C or above* | ●3Y | | 3 | | 30 |
| 1867 | *UN No. not used* | | | | | |
| 1868 | **DECABORANE** | 2WE | | 4.1 | 6.1 | 46 |

| UN | Substance | EAC | APP | Hazards | | ADR |
| | | | | Class | Sub Risks | HIN |
|---|---|---|---|---|---|---|
| 1869 | **MAGNESIUM** or **MAGNESIUM ALLOYS,** *with more than 50% magnesium in pellets, turnings or ribbons* | 4Y | | 4.1 | | 40 |
| 1870 | **POTASSIUM BOROHYDRIDE** | 4W | | 4.3 | | |
| 1871 | **TITANIUM HYDRIDE** | 4WE | | 4.1 | | 40 |
| 1872 | **LEAD DIOXIDE** | 2Z | | 5.1 | | 56 |
| 1873 | **PERCHLORIC ACID,** *with more than 50% acid and not more than 72% acid, by mass* | 2P | | 5.1 | 8 | 558 |
| 1874 to 1883 | *UN Nos. not used* | | | | | |
| 1884 | **BARIUM OXIDE** | 2Z | | 6.1 | | 60 |
| 1885 | **BENZIDINE** | 2X | | 6.1 | | 60 |
| 1886 | **BENZYLIDINE CHLORIDE** | 2X | | 6.1 | | 60 |
| 1887 | **BROMOCHLOROMETHANE** | 2Z | | 6.1 | | 60 |
| 1888 | **CHLOROFORM** | 2Z | | 6.1 | | 60 |
| 1889 | **CYANOGEN BROMIDE** | 2XE | | 6.1 | 8 | 668 |
| 1890 | *UN No. not used* | | | | | |
| 1891 | **ETHYL BROMIDE** | 3Z | | 6.1 | | 60 |
| 1892 | **ETHYLDICHLOROARSINE** | 2XE | B | 6.1 | | 66 |
| 1893 | *UN No. not used* | | | | | |
| 1894 | **PHENYLMERCURIC HYDROXIDE** | 2X | | 6.1 | | 60 |
| 1895 | **PHENYLMERCURIC NITRATE** | 2X | | 6.1 | | 60 |
| 1896 | *UN No. not used* | | | | | |
| 1897 | **TETRACHLOROETHYLENE** | 2Z | | 6.1 | | 60 |
| 1898 | **ACETYL IODIDE** | 4W | | 8 | | 80 |
| 1899 to 1901 | *UN Nos. not used* | | | | | |
| 1902 | **DIISOOCTYL ACID PHOSPHATE** | 3X | | 8 | | 80 |

| UN | Substance | EAC | APP | Hazards | | ADR |
| | | | | Class | Sub Risks | HIN |
|---|---|---|---|---|---|---|
| 1903 | **DISINFECTANT, LIQUID, CORROSIVE, N.O.S.** | 2X | B | 8 | | 88 |
| 1903 | **DISINFECTANT, LIQUID, CORROSIVE, N.O.S.** | 2X | | 8 | | 80 |
| 1904 | *UN No. not used* | | | | | |
| 1905 | **SELENIC ACID** | 2X | | 8 | | 88 |
| 1906 | **SLUDGE ACID** | 2W | | 8 | | 80 |
| 1907 | **SODA LIME,** *with more than 4% sodium hydroxide* | 2X | | 8 | | 80 |
| 1908 | **CHLORITE SOLUTION** | 2X | | 8 | | 80 |
| 1909 | *UN No. not used* | | | | | |
| 1910 | *UN No. not used* | | | | | |
| 1911 | **DIBORANE, COMPRESSED** | 2PE | B | 2.3 | 2.1 | |
| 1912 | **METHYL CHLORIDE AND METHYLENE CHLORIDE MIXTURE** | 2WE | A | 2.1 | | 23 |
| 1913 | **NEON, REFRIGERATED LIQUID** | 2RE | A | 2.2 | | 22 |
| 1914 | **BUTYL PROPIONATES** | 3Y | | 3 | | 30 |
| 1915 | **CYCLOHEXANONE** | ●3Y | | 3 | | 30 |
| 1916 | **2,2'-DICHLORODIETHYL ETHER** | ●2W | | 6.1 | 3 | 63 |
| 1917 | **ETHYL ACRYLATE, INHIBITED** | ●3WE | | 3 | | 339 |
| 1918 | **ISOPROPYLBENZENE** | 3Y | | 3 | | 30 |
| 1919 | **METHYL ACRYLATE, INHIBITED** | 3WE | | 3 | | 339 |
| 1920 | **NONANES** | 3Y | | 3 | | 30 |
| 1921 | **PROPYLENEIMINE, INHIBITED** | ●2WE | | 3 | 6.1 | 336 |
| 1922 | **PYRROLIDINE** | ●2WE | | 3 | 8 | 338 |
| 1923 | **CALCIUM DITHIONITE** (CALCIUM HYDROSULPHITE) | 1S | | 4.2 | | 40 |
| 1924 to 1927 | *UN Nos. not used* | | | | | |

| UN | Substance | EAC | APP | Hazards | | ADR |
| | | | | Class | Sub Risks | HIN |
|---|---|---|---|---|---|---|
| 1928 | **METHYL MAGNESIUM BROMIDE IN ETHYL ETHER** | 4WE | | 4.3 | 3 | X323 |
| 1929 | **POTASSIUM DITHIONITE** (POTASSIUM HYDROSULPHITE) | 1S | | 4.2 | | 40 |
| 1930 | *UN No. not used* | | | | | |
| 1931 | **ZINC DITHIONITE** (ZINC HYDROSULPHITE) | 2Z | | 9 | | 90 |
| 1932 | **ZIRCONIUM SCRAP** | 4W | | 4.2 | | 40 |
| 1933 | *UN No. not used* | | | | | |
| 1934 | *UN No. not used* | | | | | |
| 1935 | **CYANIDE SOLUTION, N.O.S.** | 2X | B | 6.1 | | 66 |
| 1935 | **CYANIDE SOLUTION, N.O.S.** | 2X | | 6.1 | | 60 |
| 1936 | *UN No. not used* | | | | | |
| 1937 | *UN No. not used* | | | | | |
| 1938 | **BROMOACETIC ACID** | 2X | | 8 | | 80 |
| 1939 | **PHOSPHORUS OXYBROMIDE** | 4W | | 8 | | 80 |
| 1940 | **THIOGLYCOLIC ACID** | 2X | | 8 | | 80 |
| 1941 | **DIBROMODIFLUOROMETHANE** | 2Z | | 9 | | 90 |
| 1942 | **AMMONIUM NITRATE** | 1Y | | 5.1 | | 50 |
| 1943 | *UN No. not used* | | | | | |
| 1944 | **MATCHES, SAFETY** *(book, card or strike on box)* | + | | 4.1 | | |
| 1945 | **MATCHES, WAX "VESTA"** | + | | 4.1 | | |
| 1946 to 1949 | *UN Nos. not used* | | | | | |
| 1950 | **AEROSOLS** | + | | 2 | | |
| 1951 | **ARGON, REFRIGERATED LIQUID** | 2RE | A | 2.2 | | 22 |
| 1952 | **ETHYLENE OXIDE AND CARBON DIOXIDE MIXTURE** *with not more than 9% ethylene oxide* | 2PE | | 2.2 | | 20 |

| UN | Substance | EAC | APP | Hazards | | ADR |
| | | | | Class | Sub Risks | HIN |
|---|---|---|---|---|---|---|
| 1953 | COMPRESSED GAS, TOXIC, FLAMMABLE, N.O.S. | 2PE | B | 2.3 | 2.1 | 263 |
| 1954 | COMPRESSED GAS, FLAMMABLE, N.O.S. | 2SE | | 2.1 | | 23 |
| 1955 | COMPRESSED GAS, TOXIC, N.O.S. | 2RE | B | 2.3 | | 26 |
| 1956 | COMPRESSED GAS, N.O.S. | 2TE | | 2.2 | | 20 |
| 1957 | DEUTERIUM, COMPRESSED | 2SE | | 2.1 | | 23 |
| 1958 | 1,2-DICHLORO-1,1,2,2-TETRAFLUOROETHANE (REFRIGERANT GAS R114) | 2RE | | 2.2 | | 20 |
| 1959 | 1,1-DIFLUOROETHYLENE (REFRIGERANT GAS R1132a) | 2PE | A | 2.1 | | 239 |
| 1960 | *UN No. not used* | | | | | |
| 1961 | ETHANE, REFRIGERATED LIQUID | 2WE | A | 2.1 | | 223 |
| 1962 | ETHYLENE, COMPRESSED | 2PE | | 2.1 | | 23 |
| 1963 | HELIUM , REFRIGERATED LIQUID | 2R | A | 2.2 | | 22 |
| 1964 | HYDROCARBON GAS MIXTURE, COMPRESSED, N.O.S. | 2SE | | 2.1 | | 23 |
| 1965 | HYDROCARBON GAS MIXTURE, LIQUEFIED, N.O.S. | 2WE | | 2.1 | | 23 |
| 1966 | HYDROGEN, REFRIGERATED LIQUID | 2WE | A | 2.1 | | 223 |
| 1967 | INSECTICIDE GAS, TOXIC, N.O.S. | 2XE | AB | 2.3 | | 26 |
| 1968 | INSECTICIDE GAS, N.O.S. | 2XE | A | 2.2 | | 20 |
| 1969 | ISOBUTANE | 2WE | | 2.1 | | 23 |
| 1970 | KRYPTON, REFRIGERATED LIQUID | 2RE | A | 2.2 | | 22 |
| 1971 | METHANE, COMPRESSED *or* NATURAL GAS, COMPRESSED *(with high methane content)* | 2SE | | 2.1 | | 23 |
| 1972 | METHANE, REFRIGERATED LIQUID *or* NATURAL GAS, REFRIGERATED LIQUID *(with high methane content)* | 2WE | A | 2.1 | | 223 |
| 1973 | CHLORODIFLUOROMETHANE AND CHLOROPENTAFLUOROETHANE MIXTURE, *with fixed boiling point with approximately 49% of chlorodifluoromethane* (REFRIGERANT GAS R502) | 2RE | A | 2.2 | | 20 |

| UN | Substance | EAC | APP | Hazards | | ADR |
|---|---|---|---|---|---|---|
| | | | | Class | Sub Risks | HIN |
| 1974 | **CHLORODIFLUOROBROMOMETHANE (REFRIGERANT GAS R12B1)** | 2RE | A | 2.2 | | 20 |
| 1975 | **NITRIC OXIDE AND DINITROGEN TETROXIDE MIXTURE (NITRIC OXIDE AND NITROGEN DIOXIDE MIXTURE)** | 2PE | B | 2.3 | 5.1 8 | |
| 1976 | **OCTAFLUOROCYCLOBUTANE (REFRIGERANT GAS RC318)** | 2RE | | 2.2 | | 20 |
| 1977 | **NITROGEN, REFRIGERATED LIQUID** | 2RE | A | 2.2 | | 22 |
| 1978 | **PROPANE** | 2WE | A | 2.1 | | 23 |
| 1979 | **RARE GASES MIXTURE, COMPRESSED** | 2TE | | 2.2 | | 20 |
| 1980 | **RARE GASES AND OXYGEN MIXTURE, COMPRESSED** | 2SE | | 2.2 | | 20 |
| 1981 | **RARE GASES AND NITROGEN MIXTURE, COMPRESSED** | 2TE | | 2.2 | | 20 |
| 1982 | **TETRAFLUOROMETHANE COMPRESSED, (REFRIGERANT GAS R14, COMPRESSED)** | 2TE | | 2.2 | | 20 |
| 1983 | **1-CHLORO-2,2,2-TRIFLUOROETHANE (REFRIGERANT GAS R133a)** | 2RE | | 2.2 | | 20 |
| 1984 | **TRIFLUOROMETHANE (REFRIGERANT GAS R23)** | 2RE | | 2.2 | | 20 |
| 1985 | *UN No. not used* | | | | | |
| 1986 | **ALCOHOLS, FLAMMABLE, TOXIC, N.O.S.,** *flash point less than 23°C* | ●3WE | | 3 | 6.1 | 336 |
| 1986 | **ALCOHOLS, FLAMMABLE, TOXIC, N.O.S.,** *flash point 23°C or above* | ●3W | | 3 | 6.1 | 36 |
| 1987 | **ALCOHOLS, N.O.S.,** *flash point less than 23°C* | ●3YE | | 3 | | 33 |
| 1987 | **ALCOHOLS, N.O.S.,** *flash point 23°C or above* | ●3Y | | 3 | | 30 |
| 1988 | **ALDEHYDES, FLAMMABLE, TOXIC, N.O.S.,** *flash point less than 23°C* | ●3WE | | 3 | 6.1 | 336 |
| 1988 | **ALDEHYDES, FLAMMABLE, TOXIC, N.O.S.,** *flash point 23°C or above* | ●3W | | 3 | 6.1 | 36 |
| 1989 | **ALDEHYDES, N.O.S.,** *flash point less than 23°C* | ●3YE | | 3 | | 33 |
| 1989 | **ALDEHYDES, N.O.S.,** *flash point 23°C or above* | ●3Y | | 3 | | 30 |

| UN | Substance | EAC | APP | Hazards | | ADR |
| --- | --- | --- | --- | --- | --- | --- |
| | | | | Class | Sub Risks | HIN |
| 1990 | **BENZALDEHYDE** | 3Z | | 9 | | 90 |
| 1991 | **CHLOROPRENE, INHIBITED** | ●3WE | | 3 | 6.1 | 336 |
| 1992 | **FLAMMABLE LIQUID, TOXIC, N.O.S.** | ●3WE | | 3 | 6.1 | 336 |
| 1992 | **FLAMMABLE LIQUID, TOXIC, N.O.S.** | ●3W | | 3 | 6.1 | 36 |
| 1993 | **FLAMMABLE LIQUID, N.O.S.** | ●3YE | | 3 | | 33 |
| 1993 | **FLAMMABLE LIQUID, N.O.S.** | ●3Y | | 3 | | 30 |
| 1994 | **IRON PENTACARBONYL** | 2WE | B | 6.1 | 3 | 663 |
| 1995 to 1998 | *UN Nos. not used* | | | | | |
| 1999 | **TARS, LIQUID,** *including road asphalt and oils, bitumen and cut backs, flash point less than 23°C* | 2WE | | 3 | | 33 |
| 1999 | **TARS, LIQUID,** *including road asphalt and oils, bitumen and cut backs, flash point 23°C or above* | 2W | | 3 | | 30 |
| 2000 | **CELLULOID,** *in blocks, rods, rolls, sheets, tubes, etc., except scrap* | 1Z | | 4.1 | | |
| 2001 | **COBALT NAPTHENATES, POWDER** | 1Z | | 4.1 | | 40 |
| 2002 | **CELLULOID, SCRAP** | 1Y | | 4.2 | | |
| 2003 | **METAL ALKYLS, WATER-REACTIVE, N.O.S.** *or* **METAL ARYLS, WATER-REACTIVE,N.O.S.** | 4WE | | 4.2 | 4.3 | X333 |
| 2004 | **MAGNESIUM DIAMIDE** | 4WE | | 4.2 | | 40 |
| 2005 | **MAGNESIUM DIPHENYL** | 4WE | | 4.2 | | X333 |
| 2006 | **PLASTICS, NITROCELLULOSE-BASED, SELF-HEATING, N.O.S.** | + | | 4.2 | | |
| 2007 | *UN No. not used* | | | | | |
| 2008 | **ZIRCONIUM, POWDER, DRY** | 4Y | | 4.2 | | 40 |
| 2009 | **ZIRCONIUM, DRY,** *finished sheets, strip or coiled wire* | 4Y | | 4.2 | | |
| 2010 | **MAGNESIUM HYDRIDE** | 4W | | 4.3 | | |
| 2011 | **MAGNESIUM PHOSPHIDE** | 4W | | 4.3 | 6.1 | |

| UN | Substance | EAC | APP | Hazards | | ADR |
|----|-----------|-----|-----|---------|---|-----|
| | | | | Class | Sub Risks | HIN |
| 2012 | **POTASSIUM PHOSPHIDE** | 4W | | 4.3 | 6.1 | |
| 2013 | **STRONTIUM PHOSPHIDE** | 4W | | 4.3 | 6.1 | |
| 2014 | **HYDROGEN PEROXIDE, AQUEOUS SOLUTION** *with not less than 20% but not more than 60% hydrogen peroxide (stabilized as necessary)* | 2P | | 5.1 | 8 | 58 |
| 2015 | **HYDROGEN PEROXIDE, STABILIZED** *or* **HYDROGEN PEROXIDE, AQUEOUS SOLUTION, STABILIZED** *with more than 60% hydrogen peroxide* | 2PE | | 5.1 | 8 | 559 |
| 2016 | **AMMUNITION, TOXIC, NON-EXPLOSIVE** | + | | 6.1 | | |
| 2017 | **AMMUNITION, TEAR-PRODUCING, NON-EXPLOSIVE** | + | | 6.1 | | |
| 2018 | **CHLOROANILINES, SOLID** | 2X | | 6.1 | | 60 |
| 2019 | **CHLOROANILINES, LIQUID** | 2X | | 6.1 | | 60 |
| 2020 | **CHLOROPHENOLS, SOLID** | 2X | | 6.1 | | 60 |
| 2021 | **CHLOROPHENOLS, LIQUID** | 2X | | 6.1 | | 60 |
| 2022 | **CRESYLIC ACID** | 2X | | 6.1 | 8 | 68 |
| 2023 | **EPICHLOROHYDRIN** | ●2W | | 6.1 | 3 | 63 |
| 2024 | **MERCURY COMPOUND, LIQUID, N.O.S.** | 2X | B | 6.1 | | 66 |
| 2024 | **MERCURY COMPOUND, LIQUID, N.O.S.** | 2X | | 6.1 | | 60 |
| 2025 | **MERCURY COMPOUND , SOLID, N.O.S.** | 2X | | 6.1 | | 66/ 60 |
| 2026 | **PHENYLMERCURIC COMPOUND, N.O.S.** | 2X | | 6.1 | | 66/ 60 |
| 2027 | **SODIUM ARSENITE, SOLID** | 2X | | 6.1 | | 60 |
| 2028 | **BOMBS, SMOKE, NON-EXPLOSIVE** *with corrosive liquid* | + | | 8 | | |
| 2029 | **HYDRAZINE, ANHYDROUS** | ●2W | B | 8 | 3 6.1 | |
| 2030 | **HYDRAZINE HYDRATE** *or* **HYDRAZINE, AQUEOUS SOLUTION** *with not less than 37% but not more than 64% hydrazine by mass* | 2P | | 8 | 6.1 | 86 |

| UN | Substance | EAC | APP | Hazards | | ADR |
| | | | | Class | Sub Risks | HIN |
|---|---|---|---|---|---|---|
| 2031 | **NITRIC ACID,** *other than red fuming,* *with more than 70% nitric acid* | 2PE | B | 8 | 5.1 | 885 |
| 2031 | **NITRIC ACID,** *other than red fuming,* *with not more than 70% nitric acid* | 2PE | | 8 | | 80 |
| 2032 | **NITRIC ACID, RED FUMING** | 2PE | B | 8 | 5.1 6.1 | 856 |
| 2033 | **POTASSIUM MONOXIDE** | 2W | | 8 | | 80 |
| 2034 | **HYDROGEN AND METHANE MIXTURE, COMPRESSED** | 2SE | | 2.1 | | 23 |
| 2035 | **1,1,1-TRIFLUOROETHANE (REFRIGERANT GAS R143a)** | 2WE | A | 2.1 | | 23 |
| 2036 | **XENON, COMPRESSED** | 2TE | | 2.2 | | 20 |
| 2037 | **RECEPTACLES, SMALL, CONTAINING GAS (GAS CARTRIDGES)** | + | | 2 | | |
| 2038 | **DINITROTOLUENES** | 2W | | 6.1 | | 60 |
| 2039 to 2043 | *UN Nos. not used* | | | | | |
| 2044 | **2,2-DIMETHYLPROPANE** | 2WE | | 2.1 | | 23 |
| 2045 | **ISOBUTYRALDEHYDE (ISOBUTYL ALDEHYDE)** | ●3WE | | 3 | | 33 |
| 2046 | **CYMENES** | 3Y | | 3 | | 30 |
| 2047 | **DICHLOROPROPENES,** *flash point less than 23°C* | 2WE | | 3 | | 33 |
| 2047 | **DICHLOROPROPENES,** *flash point 23°C or above* | 2W | | 3 | | 30 |
| 2048 | **DICYCLOPENTADIENE** | 3Y | | 3 | | 30 |
| 2049 | **DIETHYLBENZENE** | 3Y | | 3 | | 30 |
| 2050 | **DIISOBUTYLENE, ISOMERIC COMPOUNDS** | 3YE | | 3 | | 33 |
| 2051 | **2-DIMETHYLAMINOETHANOL** | ●2W | | 8 | 3 | 83 |
| 2052 | **DIPENTENE** | 3Y | | 3 | | 30 |
| 2053 | **METHYL ISOBUTYL CARBINOL** | ●3Y | | 3 | | 30 |
| 2054 | **MORPHOLINE** | ●2W | | 3 | | 30 |

| UN | Substance | EAC | APP | Hazards | | ADR |
| | | | | Class | Sub Risks | HIN |
|---|---|---|---|---|---|---|
| 2055 | **STYRENE MONOMER, INHIBITED** | 3Y | | 3 | | 39 |
| 2056 | **TETRAHYDROFURAN** | ●2YE | | 3 | | 33 |
| 2057 | **TRIPROPYLENE,** *flash point less than 23°C* | 3YE | | 3 | | 33 |
| 2057 | **TRIPROPYLENE,** *flash point 23°C or above* | 3Y | | 3 | | 30 |
| 2058 | **VALERALDEHYDE** | 3YE | | 3 | | 33 |
| 2059 | **NITROCELLULOSE SOLUTION, FLAMMABLE** *flash point less than 23°C* | ●2YE | | 3 | | 33 |
| 2059 | **NITROCELLULOSE SOLUTION, FLAMMABLE** *flash point 23°C or above* | ●2Y | | 3 | | 30 |
| 2060 to 2066 | *UN Nos. not used* | | | | | |
| 2067 | **AMMONIUM NITRATE FERTILIZERS** | 1Y | | 5.1 | | 50 |
| 2068 | **AMMONIUM NITRATE FERTILIZERS** | 1Y | | 5.1 | | 50 |
| 2069 | **AMMONIUM NITRATE FERTILIZERS** | 1Y | | 5.1 | | 50 |
| 2070 | **AMMONIUM NITRATE FERTILIZERS** | 1Y | | 5.1 | | 50 |
| 2071 | *UN No. not used* | | | | | |
| 2072 | **AMMONIUM NITRATE FERTILIZER, N.O.S.** | 1Y | | 5.1 | | |
| 2073 | **AMMONIA SOLUTION,** *relative density less than 0.880 at 15°C in water, with more than 35% but not more than 50% ammonia* | 2RE | | 2.2 | | 20 |
| 2074 | **ACRYLAMIDE** | 2WE | | 6.1 | | 60 |
| 2075 | **CHLORAL, ANHYDROUS, INHIBITED** | 2X | | 6.1 | | 60 |
| 2076 | **CRESOLS** | ●2X | | 6.1 | 8 | 68 |
| 2077 | **alpha-NAPHTHYLAMINE** | 2X | | 6.1 | | 60 |
| 2078 | **TOLUENE DIISOCYANATE** | 2XE | | 6.1 | | 60 |
| 2079 | **DIETHYLENETRIAMINE** | 2X | | 8 | | 80 |
| 2080 to 2185 | *UN Nos. not used* | | | | | |

| UN | Substance | EAC | APP | Hazards | | ADR |
| | | | | Class | Sub Risks | HIN |
|---|---|---|---|---|---|---|
| 2186 | HYDROGEN CHLORIDE, REFRIGERATED LIQUID | 2RE | AB | 2.3 | 8 | |
| 2187 | CARBON DIOXIDE, REFRIGERATED LIQUID | 2RE | A | 2.2 | | 22 |
| 2188 | ARSINE | 2PE | AB | 2.3 | 2.1 | |
| 2189 | DICHLOROSILANE | 4WE | B | 2.3 | 2.1 8 | 263 |
| 2190 | OXYGEN DIFLUORIDE, COMPRESSED | 2PE | B | 2.3 | 5.1 8 | |
| 2191 | SULPHURYL FLUORIDE | 2XE | AB | 2.3 | | 26 |
| 2192 | GERMANE | 2PE | AB | 2.3 | 2.1 | |
| 2193 | HEXAFLUOROETHANE, COMPRESSED (REFRIGERANT GAS R116, COMPRESSED) | 2RE | | 2.2 | | 20 |
| 2194 | SELENIUM HEXAFLUORIDE | 2RE | AB | 2.3 | 8 | |
| 2195 | TELLURIUM HEXAFLUORIDE | 2RE | AB | 2.3 | 8 | |
| 2196 | TUNGSTEN HEXAFLUORIDE | 2WE | B | 2.3 | 8 | |
| 2197 | HYDROGEN IODIDE, ANHYDROUS | 2RE | AB | 2.3 | 8 | 268 |
| 2198 | PHOSPHORUS PENTAFLUORIDE, COMPRESSED | 2RE | B | 2.3 | 8 | |
| 2199 | PHOSPHINE | 2PE | AB | 2.3 | 2.1 | |
| 2200 | PROPADIENE, INHIBITED | 2WE | A | 2.1 | | 239 |
| 2201 | NITROUS OXIDE, REFRIGERATED LIQUID | 2PE | A | 2.2 | 5.1 | 225 |
| 2202 | HYDROGEN SELENIDE, ANHYDROUS | 2WE | AB | 2.3 | 2.1 | |
| 2203 | SILANE, COMPRESSED | 2SE | | 2.1 | | 23 |
| 2204 | CARBONYL SULPHIDE | 2WE | AB | 2.3 | 2.1 | 263 |
| 2205 | ADIPONITRILE | ●3X | | 6.1 | | 60 |
| 2206 | ISOCYANATES, TOXIC, N.O.S., or ISOCYANATE SOLUTION, TOXIC, N.O.S. | 2X | | 6.1 | | 60 |
| 2207 | UN No. not used | | | | | |
| 2208 | CALCIUM HYPOCHLORITE MIXTURE, DRY with more than 10% but not more than 39% available chlorine | 2X | | 5.1 | | 50 |

| UN | Substance | EAC | APP | Hazards | | ADR |
| | | | | Class | Sub Risks | HIN |
| --- | --- | --- | --- | --- | --- | --- |
| 2209 | **FORMALDEHYDE SOLUTION** *with not less than 25% formaldehyde* | ●2Z | | 8 | | 80 |
| 2210 | **MANEB or MANEB PREPARATION,** *with not less than 60% maneb* | 1Y | | 4.2 | 4.3 | 40 |
| 2211 | **POLYMERIC BEADS, EXPANDABLE,** *evolving flammable vapour* | 3Y | | 9 | | 90 |
| 2212 | **BLUE ASBESTOS** (Crocidolite) *or* **BROWN ASBESTOS** (Amosite, Mysorite) | 2X | | 9 | | 90 |
| 2213 | **PARAFORMALDEHYDE** | 1Z | | 4.1 | | 40 |
| 2214 | **PHTHALIC ANHYDRIDE** *with more than 0.05% maleic anhydride* | 2X | | 8 | | 80 |
| 2215 | **MALEIC ANHYDRIDE** | 2X | | 8 | | 80 |
| 2216 | *UN No. not used* | | | | | |
| 2217 | **SEED CAKE** *with not more than 1.5% oil and not more than 11% moisture* | 1Z | | 4.2 | | 40 |
| 2218 | **ACRYLIC ACID, INHIBITED** | ●2WE | | 8 | 3 | 839 |
| 2219 | **ALLYL GLYCIDYL ETHER** | ●2Y | | 3 | | 30 |
| 2220 | *UN No. not used* | | | | | |
| 2221 | *UN No. not used* | | | | | |
| 2222 | **ANISOLE** | 3Y | | 3 | | 30 |
| 2223 | *UN No. not used* | | | | | |
| 2224 | **BENZONITRILE** | 3X | | 6.1 | | 60 |
| 2225 | **BENZENESULPHONYL CHLORIDE** | 2X | | 8 | | 80 |
| 2226 | **BENZOTRICHLORIDE** | 2X | | 8 | | 80 |
| 2227 | **n-BUTYL METHACRYLATE, INHIBITED** | 3Y | | 3 | | 39 |
| 2228 to 2231 | *UN Nos. not used* | | | | | |
| 2232 | **2-CHLOROETHANAL** | ●2XE | B | 6.1 | . | 66 |
| 2233 | **CHLOROANISIDINES** | 2Z | | 6.1 | | 60 |

| UN | Substance | EAC | APP | Hazards | | ADR |
| --- | --- | --- | --- | --- | --- | --- |
| | | | | Class | Sub Risks | HIN |
| 2234 | CHLOROBENZOTRIFLUORIDES | 2Y | | 3 | | 30 |
| 2235 | CHLOROBENZYL CHLORIDES | 2X | | 6.1 | | 60 |
| 2236 | 3-CHLORO-4-METHYLPHENYL ISOCYANATE | 2X | | 6.1 | | 60 |
| 2237 | CHLORONITROANILINES | 2Z | | 6.1 | | 60 |
| 2238 | CHLOROTOLUENES | 3Y | | 3 | | 30 |
| 2239 | CHLOROTOLUIDINES | 2X | | 6.1 | | 60 |
| 2240 | CHROMOSULPHURIC ACID | 2W | | 8 | | 88 |
| 2241 | CYCLOHEPTANE | 3YE | | 3 | | 33 |
| 2242 | CYCLOHEPTENE | 3YE | | 3 | | 33 |
| 2243 | CYCLOHEXYL ACETATE | 3Y | | 3 | | 30 |
| 2244 | CYCLOPENTANOL | ●3Y | | 3 | | 30 |
| 2245 | CYCLOPENTANONE | ●3Y | | 3 | | 30 |
| 2246 | CYCLOPENTENE | 3YE | | 3 | | 33 |
| 2247 | n-DECANE | 3Y | | 3 | | 30 |
| 2248 | DI-n-BUTYLAMINE | ●3W | | 8 | 3 | 83 |
| 2249 | UN No. not used | | | | | |
| 2250 | DICHLOROPHENYL ISOCYANATES | 2X | | 6.1 | | 60 |
| 2251 | BICYCLO[2,2,1] HEPTA-2, 5-DIENE, INHIBITED (2,5-NORBORNADIENE, INHIBITED) | 3YE | | 3 | | 339 |
| 2252 | 1,2-DIMETHOXYETHANE | ●2YE | | 3 | | 33 |
| 2253 | N,N-DIMETHYLANILINE | 3X | | 6.1 | | 60 |
| 2254 | MATCHES, FUSEE | + | | 4.1 | | |
| 2255 | UN No. not used | | | | | |
| 2256 | CYCLOHEXENE | 3YE | | 3 | | 33 |
| 2257 | POTASSIUM | 4W | | 4.3 | | X423 |
| 2258 | 1,2-PROPYLENEDIAMINE | ●2W | | 8 | 3 | 83 |

| UN | Substance | EAC | APP | Hazards | | ADR |
| | | | | Class | Sub Risks | HIN |
|---|---|---|---|---|---|---|
| 2259 | TRIETHYLENETETRAMINE | 2X | | 8 | | 80 |
| 2260 | TRIPROPYLAMINE | 3W | | 3 | 8 | 38 |
| 2261 | XYLENOLS | 2X | | 6.1 | | 60 |
| 2262 | DIMETHYLCARBAMOYL CHLORIDE | 4W | | 8 | | 80 |
| 2263 | DIMETHYLCYCLOHEXANES | 3YE | | 3 | | 33 |
| 2264 | DIMETHYLCYCLOHEXYLAMINE | ●3W | | 8 | 3 | 83 |
| 2265 | N,N-DIMETHYLFORMAMIDE | ●2W | | 3 | | 30 |
| 2266 | DIMETHYL-N-PROPYLAMINE | 2WE | | 3 | 8 | 338 |
| 2267 | DIMETHYL THIOPHOSPHORYL CHLORIDE | 2X | | 6.1 | 8 | 68 |
| 2268 | *UN No. not used* | | | | | |
| 2269 | 3,3'-IMINODIPROPYLAMINE | 2X | | 8 | | 80 |
| 2270 | ETHYLAMINE, AQUEOUS SOLUTION<br>*with not less than 50% but not more than 70% ethylamine* | ●2PE | | 3 | 8 | 338 |
| 2271 | ETHYL AMYL KETONE | 3Y | | 3 | | 30 |
| 2272 | N-ETHYLANILINE | 3X | | 6.1 | | 60 |
| 2273 | 2-ETHYLANILINE | 3X | | 6.1 | | 60 |
| 2274 | N-ETHYL-N-BENZYLANILINE | 3X | | 6.1 | | 60 |
| 2275 | 2-ETHYLBUTANOL | 3Y | | 3 | | 30 |
| 2276 | 2-ETHYLHEXYLAMINE | ●3W | | 3 | 8 | 38 |
| 2277 | ETHYL METHACRYLATE | 3YE | | 3 | | 339 |
| 2278 | n-HEPTENE | 3YE | | 3 | | 33 |
| 2279 | HEXACHLOROBUTADIENE | 2X | | 6.1 | | 60 |
| 2280 | HEXAMETHYLENEDIAMINE, SOLID | 2X | | 8 | | 80 |
| 2281 | HEXAMETHYLENE DIISOCYANATE | 3X | | 6.1 | | 60 |
| 2282 | HEXANOLS | 3Y | | 3 | | 30 |
| 2283 | ISOBUTYL METHACRYLATE, INHIBITED | 3Y | | 3 | | 39 |

| UN | Substance | EAC | APP | Hazards | | ADR |
| --- | --- | --- | --- | --- | --- | --- |
| | | | | Class | Sub Risks | HIN |
| 2284 | **ISOBUTYRONITRILE** | ●3WE | | 3 | 6.1 | 336 |
| 2285 | **ISOCYANATOBENZOTRIFLUORIDES** | ●2W | | 6.1 | 3 | 63 |
| 2286 | **PENTAMETHYLHEPTANE** | 3Y | | 3 | | 30 |
| 2287 | **ISOHEPTENE** | 3YE | | 3 | | 33 |
| 2288 | **ISOHEXENE** | 3YE | | 3 | | 33 |
| 2289 | **ISOPHORONEDIAMINE** | 2X | | 8 | | 80 |
| 2290 | **ISOPHORONE DIISOCYANATE** | 2X | | 6.1 | | 60 |
| 2291 | **LEAD COMPOUND, SOLUBLE, N.O.S.** | 2Z | | 6.1 | | 60 |
| 2292 | *UN No. not used* | | | | | |
| 2293 | **4-METHOXY-4-METHYLPENTAN-2-ONE** | 3Y | | 3 | | 30 |
| 2294 | **N-METHYLANILINE** | 3X | | 6.1 | | 60 |
| 2295 | **METHYL CHLOROACETATE** | 2W | B | 6.1 | 3 | 663 |
| 2296 | **METHYLCYCLOHEXANE** | 3YE | | 3 | | 33 |
| 2297 | **METHYLCYCLOHEXANONE** | ●3Y | | 3 | | 30 |
| 2298 | **METHYLCYCLOPENTANE** | 3YE | | 3 | | 33 |
| 2299 | **METHYL DICHLOROACETATE** | 2X | | 6.1 | | 60 |
| 2300 | **2-METHYL-5-ETHYLPYRIDINE** | 3X | | 6.1 | | 60 |
| 2301 | **2-METHYLFURAN** | 3YE | | 3 | | 33 |
| 2302 | **5-METHYLHEXAN-2-ONE** | ●3Y | | 3 | | 30 |
| 2303 | **ISOPROPENYLBENZENE** | 3Y | | 3 | | 30 |
| 2304 | **NAPHTHALENE, MOLTEN** | 2X | A | 4.1 | | 44 |
| 2305 | **NITROBENZENESULPHONIC ACID** | 2X | | 8 | | 80 |
| 2306 | **NITROBENZOTRIFLUORIDES** | 2X | | 6.1 | | 60 |
| 2307 | **3-NITRO-4-CHLOROBENZOTRIFLUORIDE** | 2X | | 6.1 | | 60 |
| 2308 | **NITROSYLSULPHURIC ACID** | 4WE | | 8 | | X80 |
| 2309 | **OCTADIENE** | 3YE | | 3 | | 33 |

| UN | Substance | EAC | APP | Hazards | | ADR |
|---|---|---|---|---|---|---|
| | | | | Class | Sub Risks | HIN |
| 2310 | PENTANE-2, 4-DIONE | ●2Y | | 3 | 6.1 | 36 |
| 2311 | PHENETIDINES | 3X | | 6.1 | | 60 |
| 2312 | PHENOL, MOLTEN | ●2X | | 6.1 | | 60 |
| 2313 | PICOLINES | ●2Y | | 3 | | 30 |
| 2314 | UN No. not used | | | | | |
| 2315 | POLYCHLORINATED BIPHENYLS | 2X | | 9 | | 90 |
| 2316 | SODIUM CUPROCYANIDE, SOLID | 2X | | 6.1 | | 66 |
| 2317 | SODIUM CUPROCYANIDE SOLUTION | 2X | B | 6.1 | | 66 |
| 2318 | SODIUM HYDROSULPHIDE with less than 25 % water of crystallization | 2X | | 4.2 | | 40 |
| 2319 | TERPENE HYDROCARBONS, N.O.S. | 3Y | | 3 | | 30 |
| 2320 | TETRAETHYLENEPENTAMINE | 2X | | 8 | | 80 |
| 2321 | TRICHLOROBENZENES, LIQUID | 2Z | | 6.1 | | 60 |
| 2322 | TRICHLOROBUTENE | 2Z | | 6.1 | | 60 |
| 2323 | TRIETHYL PHOSPHITE | 3Y | | 3 | | 30 |
| 2324 | TRIISOBUTYLENE | 3Y | | 3 | | 30 |
| 2325 | 1,3,5-TRIMETHYLBENZENE | 3Y | | 3 | | 30 |
| 2326 | TRIMETHYLCYCLOHEXYLAMINE | 3X | | 8 | | 80 |
| 2327 | TRIMETHYLHEXAMETHYLENEDIAMINES | 2X | | 8 | | 80 |
| 2328 | TRIMETHYLHEXAMETHYLENE DIISOCYANATE | 3X | | 6.1 | | 60 |
| 2329 | TRIMETHYL PHOSPHITE | 3Y | | 3 | | 30 |
| 2330 | UNDECANE | 3Y | | 3 | | 30 |
| 2331 | ZINC CHLORIDE, ANHYDROUS | 2X | | 8 | | 80 |
| 2332 | ACETALDEHYDE OXIME | ●2Y | | 3 | | 30 |
| 2333 | ALLYL ACETATE | ●3WE | | 3 | 6.1 | 336 |
| 2334 | ALLYLAMINE | ●2WE | B | 6.1 | 3 | 663 |

| UN | Substance | EAC | APP | Hazards | | ADR |
| | | | | Class | Sub Risks | HIN |
|---|---|---|---|---|---|---|
| 2335 | **ALLYL ETHYL ETHER** | 3WE | | 3 | 6.1 | 336 |
| 2336 | **ALLYL FORMATE** | 3WE | | 3 | 6.1 | 336 |
| 2337 | **PHENYL MERCAPTAN** | 3WE | B | 6.1 | 3 | 663 |
| 2338 | **BENZOTRIFLUORIDE** | 2YE | | 3 | | 33 |
| 2339 | **2-BROMOBUTANE** | 2YE | | 3 | | 33 |
| 2340 | **2-BROMOETHYL ETHYL ETHER** | ●2YE | | 3 | | 33 |
| 2341 | **1-BROMO-3-METHYLBUTANE** | 2Y | | 3 | | 30 |
| 2342 | **BROMOMETHYLPROPANES** | 2YE | | 3 | | 33 |
| 2343 | **2-BROMOPENTANE** | 2YE | | 3 | | 33 |
| 2344 | **BROMOPROPANES** | 2YE | | 3 | | 33 |
| 2344 | **BROMOPROPANES** | 2Y | | 3 | | 30 |
| 2345 | **3-BROMOPROPYNE** | 2WE | | 3 | | 33 |
| 2346 | **BUTANEDIONE** | ●2YE | | 3 | | 33 |
| 2347 | **BUTYL MERCAPTAN** | ●3WE | | 3 | | 33 |
| 2348 | **BUTYL ACRYLATES, INHIBITED** | 3Y | | 3 | | 39 |
| 2349 | *UN No. not used* | | | | | |
| 2350 | **BUTYL METHYL ETHER** | ●3YE | | 3 | | 33 |
| 2351 | **BUTYL NITRITES**, *flash point less than 23°C* | ●3YE | | 3 | | 33 |
| 2351 | **BUTYL NITRITES**, *flash point 23°C or above* | ●3Y | | 3 | | 30 |
| 2352 | **BUTYL VINYL ETHER, INHIBITED** | ●3YE | | 3 | | 339 |
| 2353 | **BUTYRYL CHLORIDE** | ●2WE | | 3 | 8 | 338 |
| 2354 | **CHLOROMETHYL ETHYL ETHER** | ●3WE | | 3 | 6.1 | 336 |
| 2355 | *UN No. not used* | | | | | |
| 2356 | **2-CHLOROPROPANE** | 3YE | | 3 | | 33 |
| 2357 | **CYCLOHEXYLAMINE** | ●2W | | 8 | 3 | 83 |
| 2358 | **CYCLOOCTATETRAENE** | 3YE | | 3 | | 33 |

| UN | Substance | EAC | APP | Hazards | | ADR |
| | | | | Class | Sub Risks | HIN |
|---|---|---|---|---|---|---|
| 2359 | DIALLYLAMINE | ●2WE | | 3 | 6.1 8 | 338 |
| 2360 | DIALLYL ETHER | ●3WE | | 3 | 6.1 | 336 |
| 2361 | DIISOBUTYLAMINE | 3WE | | 3 | 8 | 38 |
| 2362 | 1,1-DICHLOROETHANE | 2YE | | 3 | | 33 |
| 2363 | ETHYL MERCAPTAN | 3WE | | 3 | | 33 |
| 2364 | n-PROPYLBENZENE | 3Y | | 3 | | 30 |
| 2365 | *UN No. not used* | | | | | |
| 2366 | DIETHYL CARBONATE | 3Y | | 3 | | 30 |
| 2367 | alpha-METHYLVALERALDEHYDE | 3YE | | 3 | | 33 |
| 2368 | alpha-PINENE | 3Y | | 3 | | 30 |
| 2369 | *UN No. not used* | | | | | |
| 2370 | 1-HEXENE | 3YE | | 3 | | 33 |
| 2371 | ISOPENTENES | 3YE | | 3 | | 33 |
| 2372 | 1,2-DI-(DIMETHYLAMINO)ETHANE | ●3WE | | 3 | | 33 |
| 2373 | DIETHOXYMETHANE | ●3YE | | 3 | | 33 |
| 2374 | 3,3-DIETHOXYPROPENE | ●3YE | | 3 | | 33 |
| 2375 | DIETHYL SULPHIDE | 3YE | | 3 | | 33 |
| 2376 | 2,3-DIHYDROPYRAN | ●2YE | | 3 | | 33 |
| 2377 | 1,1-DIMETHOXYETHANE | ●2YE | | 3 | | 33 |
| 2378 | 2-DIMETHYLAMINOACETONITRILE | 2WE | | 3 | 6.1 | 336 |
| 2379 | 1,3-DIMETHYLBUTYLAMINE | 3WE | | 3 | 8 | 338 |
| 2380 | DIMETHYLDIETHOXYSILANE | ●3YE | | 3 | | 33 |
| 2381 | DIMETHYL DISULPHIDE | 3YE | | 3 | | 33 |
| 2382 | DIMETHYLHYDRAZINE, SYMMETRICAL | ●2WE | B | 6.1 | 3 | 663 |
| 2383 | DIPROPYLAMINE | ●2WE | | 3 | 8 | 338 |

| UN | Substance | EAC | APP | Hazards | | ADR |
| | | | | Class | Sub Risks | HIN |
|------|-----------------------------------|-------|---|-----|------------|-----|
| 2384 | DI-n-PROPYL ETHER | 3YE | | 3 | | 33 |
| 2385 | ETHYL ISOBUTYRATE | ●3YE | | 3 | | 33 |
| 2386 | 1-ETHYLPIPERIDINE | 3WE | | 3 | 8 | 338 |
| 2387 | FLUOROBENZENE | 3YE | | 3 | | 33 |
| 2388 | FLUOROTOLUENES | 3YE | | 3 | | 33 |
| 2389 | FURAN | 3WE | | 3 | | 33 |
| 2390 | 2-IODOBUTANE | 2YE | | 3 | | 33 |
| 2391 | IODOMETHYLPROPANES | 2YE | | 3 | | 33 |
| 2392 | IODOPROPANES | 2Y | | 3 | | 30 |
| 2393 | ISOBUTYL FORMATE | ●3YE | | 3 | | 33 |
| 2394 | ISOBUTYL PROPIONATE | 3YE | | 3 | | 33 |
| 2395 | ISOBUTYRYL CHLORIDE | ●2WE | | 3 | 8 | 338 |
| 2396 | METHACRYLALDEHYDE, INHIBITED | ●3WE | | 3 | 6.1 | 336 |
| 2397 | 3-METHYLBUTAN-2-ONE | ●3YE | | 3 | | 33 |
| 2398 | METHYL tert-BUTYL ETHER | ●3YE | | 3 | | 33 |
| 2399 | 1-METHYLPIPERIDINE | ●2WE | | 3 | 8 | 338 |
| 2400 | METHYL ISOVALERATE | ●3YE | | 3 | | 33 |
| 2401 | PIPERIDINE | ●2WE | B | 8 | 3 | 883 |
| 2402 | PROPANETHIOLS | ●3WE | | 3 | | 33 |
| 2403 | ISOPROPENYL ACETATE | ●3YE | | 3 | | 33 |
| 2404 | PROPIONITRILE | ●2WE | | 3 | 6.1 | 336 |
| 2405 | ISOPROPYL BUTYRATE | 3Y | | 3 | | 30 |
| 2406 | ISOPROPYL ISOBUTYRATE | 3YE | | 3 | | 33 |
| 2407 | ISOPROPYL CHLOROFORMATE | ●3WE | B | 6.1 | 3 8 | |
| 2408 | *UN No. not used* | | | | | |

| UN | Substance | EAC | APP | Hazards | | ADR |
| | | | | Class | Sub Risks | HIN |
|---|---|---|---|---|---|---|
| 2409 | **ISOPROPYL PROPIONATE** | 3YE | | 3 | | 33 |
| 2410 | **1,2,3,6-TETRAHYDROPYRIDINE** | ●2WE | | 3 | | 33 |
| 2411 | **BUTYRONITRILE** | ●3WE | | 3 | 6.1 | 336 |
| 2412 | **TETRAHYDROTHIOPHENE** | 3WE | | 3 | | 33 |
| 2413 | **TETRAPROPYL ORTHOTITANATE** | ●2Y | | 3 | | 30 |
| 2414 | **THIOPHENE** | 3WE | | 3 | | 33 |
| 2415 | *UN No. not used* | | | | | |
| 2416 | **TRIMETHYL BORATE** | ●2YE | | 3 | | 33 |
| 2417 | **CARBONYL FLUORIDE, COMPRESSED** | 2PE | B | 2.3 | 8 | 268 |
| 2418 | **SULPHUR TETRAFLUORIDE** | 2PE | B | 2.3 | 8 | |
| 2419 | **BROMOTRIFLUOROETHYLENE** | 2WE | | 2.1 | | 23 |
| 2420 | **HEXAFLUOROACETONE** | 2WE | AB | 2.3 | 8 | 268 |
| 2421 | *UN No. not used* | | | | | |
| 2422 | **OCTAFLUOROBUT-2-ENE** **(REFRIGERANT GAS R1318)** | 2RE | | 2.2 | | 20 |
| 2423 | *UN No. not used* | | | | | |
| 2424 | **OCTAFLUOROPROPANE** **(REFRIGERANT GAS R218)** | 2RE | A | 2.2 | | 20 |
| 2425 | *UN No. not used* | | | | | |
| 2426 | **AMMONIUM NITRATE, LIQUID** *(hot concentrated solution)* | 1W | A | 5.1 | | 59 |
| 2427 | **POTASSIUM CHLORATE, AQUEOUS SOLUTION** | 2S | | 5.1 | | 50 |
| 2428 | **SODIUM CHLORATE, AQUEOUS SOLUTION** | 2S | | 5.1 | | 50 |
| 2429 | **CALCIUM CHLORATE, AQUEOUS SOLUTION** | 2S | | 5.1 | | 50 |
| 2430 | **ALKYL PHENOLS, SOLID, N.O.S.** *(including C2-C12 homologues)* | 2X | | 8 | | 88/ 80 |
| 2431 | **ANISIDINES** | 3X | | 6.1 | | 60 |
| 2432 | **N, N-DIETHYLANILINE** | ●3X | | 6.1 | | 60 |

| UN | Substance | EAC | APP | Hazards | | ADR |
|----|-----------|-----|-----|---------|----|-----|
| | | | | Class | Sub Risks | HIN |
| 2433 | CHLORONITROTOLUENES | 2X | | 6.1 | | 60 |
| 2434 | DIBENZYLDICHLOROSILANE | 4W | | 8 | | X80 |
| 2435 | ETHYLPHENYLDICHLOROSILANE | 4WE | | 8 | | X80 |
| 2436 | THIOACETIC ACID | ●2WE | | 3 | | 33 |
| 2437 | METHYLPHENYLDICHLOROSILANE | 4WE | | 8 | | X80 |
| 2438 | TRIMETHYLACETYL CHLORIDE | ●2WE | B | 6.1 | 3 8 | 663 |
| 2439 | SODIUM HYDROGENDIFLUORIDE | 2X | | 8 | | 80 |
| 2440 | STANNIC CHLORIDE PENTAHYDRATE | 2X | | 8 | | 80 |
| 2441 | TITANIUM TRICHLORIDE, PYROPHORIC *or* TITANIUM TRICHLORIDE MIXTURE, PYROPHORIC | 2W | | 4.2 | 8 | |
| 2442 | TRICHLOROACETYL CHLORIDE | 4W | | 8 | | X80 |
| 2443 | VANADIUM OXYTRICHLORIDE | 4WE | | 8 | | 80 |
| 2444 | VANADIUM TETRACHLORIDE | 4WE | B | 8 | | X88 |
| 2445 | LITHIUM ALKYLS | 4WE | | 4.2 | 4.3 | X333 |
| 2446 | NITROCRESOLS | 2X | | 6.1 | | 60 |
| 2447 | PHOSPHORUS, WHITE, MOLTEN | 2WE | A | 4.2 | 6.1 | 446 |
| 2448 | SULPHUR, MOLTEN | 2X | A | 4.1 | | 44 |
| 2449 | UN No. not used | | | | | |
| 2450 | UN No. not used | | | | | |
| 2451 | NITROGEN TRIFLUORIDE, COMPRESSED | 2PE | | 2.2 | 5.1 | 25 |
| 2452 | ETHYL ACETYLENE, INHIBITED | 2WE | | 2.1 | | 239 |
| 2453 | ETHYL FLUORIDE (REFRIGERANT GAS R161) | 2WE | A | 2.1 | | 23 |
| 2454 | METHYL FLUORIDE (REFRIGERANT GAS R41) | 2WE | A | 2.1 | | 23 |
| 2455 | UN No. not used | | | | | |
| 2456 | 2-CHLOROPROPENE | 3YE | | 3 | | 33 |

| UN | Substance | EAC | APP | Hazards | | ADR |
| | | | | Class | Sub Risks | HIN |
|---|---|---|---|---|---|---|
| 2457 | **2,3-DIMETHYLBUTANE** | 3YE | | 3 | | 33 |
| 2458 | **HEXADIENE** | 3YE | | 3 | | 33 |
| 2459 | **2-METHYL-1-BUTENE** | 3YE | | 3 | | 33 |
| 2460 | **2-METHYL-2-BUTENE** | 3YE | | 3 | | 33 |
| 2461 | **METHYLPENTADIENE** | 3YE | | 3 | | 33 |
| 2462 | *UN No. not used* | | | | | |
| 2463 | **ALUMINIUM HYDRIDE** | 4W | | 4.3 | | |
| 2464 | **BERYLLIUM NITRATE** | 2WE | | 5.1 | 6.1 | 56 |
| 2465 | **DICHLOROISOCYANURIC ACID DRY** *or* **DICHLOROISOCYANURIC ACID SALTS** | 2WE | | 5.1 | | 50 |
| 2466 | **POTASSIUM SUPEROXIDE** | 1W | | 5.1 | | |
| 2467 | *UN No. not used* | | | | | |
| 2468 | **TRICHLOROISOCYANURIC ACID, DRY** | 2WE | | 5.1 | | 50 |
| 2469 | **ZINC BROMATE** | 1YE | | 5.1 | | 50 |
| 2470 | **PHENYLACETONITRILE, LIQUID** | 3X | | 6.1 | | 60 |
| 2471 | **OSMIUM TETROXIDE** | 2X | | 6.1 | | 66 |
| 2472 | *UN No. not used* | | | | | |
| 2473 | **SODIUM ARSANILATE** | 2Z | | 6.1 | | 60 |
| 2474 | **THIOPHOSGENE** | 2XE | | 6.1 | | 60 |
| 2475 | **VANADIUM TRICHLORIDE** | 2X | · | 8 | | 80 |
| 2476 | *UN No. not used* | | | | | |
| 2477 | **METHYL ISOTHIOCYANATE** | ●2WE | B | 6.1 | 3 | 663 |
| 2478 | **ISOCYANATES, FLAMMABLE, TOXIC, N.O.S.** *or* **ISOCYANATE SOLUTION, FLAMMABLE, TOXIC, N.O.S.** | ●3WE | | 3 | 6.1 | 336 |
| 2478 | **ISOCYANATES, FLAMMABLE, TOXIC, N.O.S.** *or* **ISOCYANATE SOLUTION, FLAMMABLE, TOXIC, N.O.S.** | ●3W | | 3 | 6.1 | 36 |

| UN | Substance | EAC | APP | Hazards | | ADR |
|----|-----------|-----|-----|---------|---|-----|
| | | | | Class | Sub Risks | HIN |
| 2479 | *UN No. not used* | | | | | |
| 2480 | **METHYL ISOCYANATE** | ●3WE | B | 6.1 | 3 | |
| 2481 | **ETHYL ISOCYANATE** | ●3WE | | 3 | 6.1 | |
| 2482 | **n-PROPYL ISOCYANATE** | ●3WE | B | 6.1 | 3 | 663 |
| 2483 | **ISOPROPYL ISOCYANATE** | ●3WE | | 3 | 6.1 | 336 |
| 2484 | **tert-BUTYL ISOCYANATE** | ●3WE | B | 6.1 | 3 | 663 |
| 2485 | **n-BUTYL ISOCYANATE** | ●3WE | B | 6.1 | 3 | 663 |
| 2486 | **ISOBUTYL ISOCYANATE** | ●3WE | | 3 | 6.1 | 336 |
| 2487 | **PHENYL ISOCYANATE** | ●3W | B | 6.1 | 3 | 663 |
| 2488 | **CYLOHEXYL ISOCYANATE** | ●3W | B | 6.1 | 3 | 663 |
| 2489 | *UN No. not used* | | | | | |
| 2490 | **DICHLOROISOPROPYL ETHER** | 2Z | | 6.1 | | 60 |
| 2491 | **ETHANOLAMINE** *or* **ETHANOLAMINE SOLUTION** | 2X | | 8 | | 80 |
| 2492 | *UN No. not used* | | | | | |
| 2493 | **HEXAMETHYLENEIMINE** | ●3WE | | 3 | 8 | 338 |
| 2494 | *UN No. not used* | | | | | |
| 2495 | **IODINE PENTAFLUORIDE** | 4WE | AB | 5.1 | 6.1 8 | 568 |
| 2496 | **PROPIONIC ANHYDRIDE** | ●3X | | 8 | | 80 |
| 2497 | *UN No. not used* | | | | | |
| 2498 | **1,2,3,6-TETRAHYDROBENZALDEHYDE** | ●3Y | | 3 | | 30 |
| 2499 | *UN No. not used* | | | | | |
| 2500 | *UN No. not used* | | | | | |
| 2501 | **TRIS(1-AZIRIDINYL) PHOSPHINE OXIDE SOLUTION** | 2X | | 6.1 | | 60 |
| 2502 | **VALERYL CHLORIDE** | 2WE | | 8 | 3 | 83 |
| 2503 | **ZIRCONIUM TETRACHLORIDE** | 4WE | | 8 | | 80 |

| UN | Substance | EAC | APP | Hazards | | ADR |
|---|---|---|---|---|---|---|
| | | | | Class | Sub Risks | HIN |
| 2504 | **TETRABROMOETHANE** | 2Z | | 6.1 | | 60 |
| 2505 | **AMMONIUM FLUORIDE** | 2X | | 6.1 | | 60 |
| 2506 | **AMMONIUM HYDROGEN SULPHATE** | 2X | | 8 | | 80 |
| 2507 | **CHLOROPLATINIC ACID, SOLID** | 2X | | 8 | | 80 |
| 2508 | **MOLYBDENUM PENTACHLORIDE** | 2X | | 8 | | 80 |
| 2509 | **POTASSIUM HYDROGEN SULPHATE** | 2X | | 8 | | 80 |
| 2510 | *UN No. not used* | | | | | |
| 2511 | **2-CHLOROPROPIONIC ACID** | 2X | | 8 | | 80 |
| 2512 | **AMINOPHENOLS (o-,m-,p-)** | 2X | | 6.1 | | 60 |
| 2513 | **BROMOACETYL BROMIDE** | 4WE | | 8 | | X80 |
| 2514 | **BROMOBENZENE** | 2Y | | 3 | | 30 |
| 2515 | **BROMOFORM** | 2X | | 6.1 | | 60 |
| 2516 | **CARBON TETRABROMIDE** | 2Z | | 6.1 | | 60 |
| 2517 | **1-CHLORO-1, 1-DIFLUOROETHANE (REFRIGERANT GAS R142b)** | 2WE | | 2.1 | | 23 |
| 2518 | **1,5,9-CYCLODODECATRIENE** | 3X | | 6.1 | | 60 |
| 2519 | *UN No. not used* | | | | | |
| 2520 | **CYCLOOCTADIENES** | 3Y | | 3 | | 30 |
| 2521 | **DIKETENE, INHIBITED** | ●2W | B | 6.1 | 3 | 663 |
| 2522 | **2-DIMETHYLAMINOETHYL METHACRYLATE** | 2Y | | 6.1 | | 69 |
| 2523 | *UN No. not used* | | | | | |
| 2524 | **ETHYL ORTHOFORMATE** | ●2Y | | 3 | | 30 |
| 2525 | **ETHYL OXALATE** | ●3X | | 6.1 | | 60 |
| 2526 | **FURFURYLAMINE** | ●2W | | 3 | 8 | 38 |
| 2527 | **ISOBUTYL ACRYLATE, INHIBITED** | ●3Y | | 3 | | 39 |
| 2528 | **ISOBUTYL ISOBUTYRATE** | 3Y | | 3 | | 30 |

| UN | Substance | EAC | APP | Hazards | | ADR |
|---|---|---|---|---|---|---|
| | | | | Class | Sub Risks | HIN |
| 2529 | **ISOBUTYRIC ACID** | ●2X | | 3 | 8 | 38 |
| 2530 | **ISOBUTYRIC ANHYDRIDE** | ●2X | | 3 | 8 | 38 |
| 2531 | **METHACRYLIC ACID, INHIBITED** | ●3W | | 8 | | 89 |
| 2532 | *UN No. not used* | | | | | |
| 2533 | **METHYL TRICHLOROACETATE** | 2Z | | 6.1 | | 60 |
| 2534 | **METHYL CHLOROSILANE** | 2WE | B | 2.3 | 2.1 8 | |
| 2535 | **4-METHYLMORPHOLINE (N-METHYLMORPHOLINE)** | ●2WE | | 3 | 8 | 338 |
| 2536 | **METHYLTETRAHYDROFURAN** | ●2YE | | 3 | | 33 |
| 2537 | *UN No. not used* | | | | | |
| 2538 | **NITRONAPHTHALENE** | 1Z | | 4.1 | | 40 |
| 2539 | *UN No. not used* | | | | | |
| 2540 | *UN No. not used* | | | | | |
| 2541 | **TERPINOLENE** | 3Y | | 3 | | 30 |
| 2542 | **TRIBUTYLAMINE** | 3X | | 6.1 | | 60 |
| 2543 | *UN No. not used* | | | | | |
| 2544 | *UN No. not used* | | | | | |
| 2545 | **HAFNIUM POWDER, DRY** | 4Y | | 4.2 | | 40 |
| 2546 | **TITANIUM POWDER, DRY** | 4Y | | 4.2 | | 40 |
| 2547 | **SODIUM SUPEROXIDE** | 1W | | 5.1 | | |
| 2548 | **CHLORINE PENTAFLUORIDE** | 2WE | B | 2.3 | 5.1 8 | |
| 2549 to 2551 | *UN Nos. not used* | | | | | |
| 2552 | **HEXAFLUOROACETONE HYDRATE** | 2X | | 6.1 | | 60 |
| 2553 | *UN No. not used* | | | | | |

| UN | Substance | EAC | APP | Hazards | | ADR |
|---|---|---|---|---|---|---|
| | | | | Class | Sub Risks | HIN |
| 2554 | **METHYLALLYL CHLORIDE** | 3WE | | 3 | | 33 |
| 2555 | **NITROCELLULOSE WITH WATER,** *(not less than 25% water by mass)* | 1Z | | 4.1 | | |
| 2556 | **NITROCELLULOSE WITH ALCOHOL,** *(not less than 25% alcohol by mass and not more than 12.6% nitrogen by dry mass)* | 1Y | | 4.1 | | |
| 2557 | **NITROCELLULOSE,** *with not more than 12.6% nitrogen by dry mass,* **MIXTURE, WITH** *or* **WITHOUT PLASTICIZER, WITH** *or* **WITHOUT PIGMENT** | 1Z | | 4.1 | | |
| 2558 | **EPIBROMOHYDRIN** | ●2W | B | 6.1 | 3 | 663 |
| 2559 | *UN No. not used* | | | | | |
| 2560 | **2-METHYLPENTAN-2-OL** | ●3Y | | 3 | | 30 |
| 2561 | **3-METHYL-1-BUTENE** | ●3YE | | 3 | | 30 |
| 2562 | *UN No. not used* | | | | | |
| 2563 | *UN No. not used* | | | | | |
| 2564 | **TRICHLOROACETIC ACID SOLUTION** | 2X | | 8 | | 80 |
| 2565 | **DICYCLOHEXYLAMINE** | 3X | | 8 | | 80 |
| 2566 | *UN No. not used* | | | | | |
| 2567 | **SODIUM PENTACHLOROPHENATE** | 2X | | 6.1 | | 60 |
| 2568 | *UN No. not used* | | | | | |
| 2569 | *UN No. not used* | | | | | |
| 2570 | **CADMIUM COMPOUND** | 2X | | 6.1 | | 66/ 60 |
| 2571 | **ALKYLSULPHURIC ACIDS** | 2X | | 8 | | 80 |
| 2572 | **PHENYLHYDRAZINE** | ●3X | | 6.1 | | 60 |
| 2573 | **THALLIUM CHLORATE** | 2W | | 5.1 | 6.1 | 56 |
| 2574 | **TRICRESYL PHOSPHATE** *with more than 3% ortho isomer* | 2X | | 6.1 | | 60 |
| 2575 | *UN No. not used* | | | | | |

| UN | Substance | EAC | APP | Hazards | | ADR |
| | | | | Class | Sub Risks | HIN |
|---|---|---|---|---|---|---|
| 2576 | **PHOSPHORUS OXYBROMIDE, MOLTEN** | 2W | | 8 | | 80 |
| 2577 | **PHENYLACETYL CHLORIDE** | 4W | | 8 | | 80 |
| 2578 | **PHOSPHORUS TRIOXIDE** | 2X | | 8 | | 80 |
| 2579 | **PIPERAZINE** | 2X | | 8 | | 80 |
| 2580 | **ALUMINIUM BROMIDE SOLUTION** | 2X | | 8 | | 80 |
| 2581 | **ALUMINIUM CHLORIDE SOLUTION** | 2X | | 8 | | 80 |
| 2582 | **FERRIC CHLORIDE SOLUTION** | 2Z | | 8 | | 80 |
| 2583 | **ALKYLSULPHONIC ACIDS, SOLID** *or* **ARYLSULPHONIC ACIDS, SOLID** *with more than 5% free sulphuric acid* | 2X | | 8 | | 80 |
| 2584 | **ALKYLSULPHONIC ACIDS, LIQUID** *or* **ARYLSULPHONIC ACIDS, LIQUID** *with more than 5% free sulphuric acid* | 2X | | 8 | | 80 |
| 2585 | **ALKYLSULPHONIC ACIDS, SOLID** *or* **ARYLSULPHONIC ACIDS, SOLID** *with not more than 5% free sulphuric acid* | 2X | | 8 | | 80 |
| 2586 | **ALKYLSULPHONIC ACIDS, LIQUID** *or* **ARYLSULPHONIC ACIDS, LIQUID** *with not more than 5% free sulphuric acid* | 2X | | 8 | | 80 |
| 2587 | **BENZOQUINONE** | 2Z | | 6.1 | | 60 |
| 2588 | **PESTICIDE, SOLID, TOXIC, N.O.S.** | 2X | | 6.1 | | 66/ 60 |
| 2589 | **VINYL CHLOROACETATE** | 2WE | | 6.1 | 3 | 63 |
| 2590 | **WHITE ASBESTOS,** *(chrysotile, actinolite, anthophyllite, tremolite)* | 2X | | 9 | | 90 |
| 2591 | **XENON, REFRIGERATED LIQUID** | 2RE | A | 2.2 | | 22 |
| 2592 to 2598 | *UN Nos. not used* | | | | | |
| 2599 | **CHLOROTRIFLUOROMETHANE AND TRIFLUOROMETHANE AZEOTROPIC MIXTURE (REFRIGERANT GAS R503)** *with approximately 60% chlorotrifluoromethane* | 2RE | A | 2.2 | | 20 |

| UN | Substance | EAC | APP | Hazards Class | Sub Risks | ADR HIN |
|---|---|---|---|---|---|---|
| 2600 | **CARBON MONOXIDE AND HYDROGEN MIXTURE, COMPRESSED** | 2SE | | 2.3 | 2.1 | 263 |
| 2601 | **CYCLOBUTANE** | 3WE | | 2.1 | | 23 |
| 2602 | **DICHLORODIFLUOROMETHANE AND DIFLUOROETHANE AZEOTROPIC MIXTURE (REFRIGERANT GAS R500)** *with approximately 74% dichlorodifluoromethane* | 2RE | A | 2.2 | | 20 |
| 2603 | **CYCLOHEPTATRIENE** | 3WE | | 3 | 6.1 | 336 |
| 2604 | **BORON TRIFLUORIDE DIETHYL ETHERATE** | 4WE | B | 8 | 3 | 883 |
| 2605 | **METHOXYMETHYL ISOCYANATE** | 3WE | | 3 | 6.1 | 336 |
| 2606 | **METHYL ORTHOSILICATE** | 3WE | B | 6.1 | 3 | 663 |
| 2607 | **ACROLEIN DIMER, STABILIZED** | ●2Y | | 3 | | 39 |
| 2608 | **NITROPROPANES** | ●2Y | | 3 | | 30 |
| 2609 | **TRIALLYL BORATE** | 2X | | 6.1 | | 60 |
| 2610 | **TRIALLYLAMINE** | ●3Y | | 3 | 8 | 38 |
| 2611 | **PROPYLENE CHLOROHYDRIN** | ●2W | | 6.1 | 3 | 63 |
| 2612 | **METHYL PROPYL ETHER** | ●3YE | | 3 | | 33 |
| 2613 | *UN No. not used* | | | | | |
| 2614 | **METHALLYL ALCOHOL** | ●2W | | 3 | | 30 |
| 2615 | **ETHYL PROPYL ETHER** | ●3YE | | 3 | | 33 |
| 2616 | **TRIISOPROPYL BORATE,** *flash point less than 23°C* | ●2YE | | 3 | | 33 |
| 2616 | **TRIISOPROPYL BORATE,** *flash point 23°C or above* | ●3Y | | 3 | | 30 |
| 2617 | **METHYLCYCLOHEXANOLS,** *flammable* | ●3Y | | 3 | | 30 |
| 2618 | **VINYLTOLUENES INHIBITED** | 3Y | | 3 | | 39 |
| 2619 | **BENZYLDIMETHYLAMINE** | 3W | | 8 | 3 | 83 |
| 2620 | **AMYL BUTYRATES** | ●3Y | | 3 | | 30 |
| 2621 | **ACETYL METHYL CARBINOL** | ●2Y | | 3 | | 30 |
| 2622 | **GLYCIDALDEHYDE** | ●2WE | | 3 | 6.1 | 336 |

| UN | Substance | EAC | APP | Hazards | | ADR |
|---|---|---|---|---|---|---|
| | | | | Class | Sub Risks | HIN |
| 2623 | FIRELIGHTERS, SOLID *with flammable liquid* | + | | 4.1 | | |
| 2624 | MAGNESIUM SILICIDE | 4Y | | 4.3 | | 423 |
| 2625 | *UN No. not used* | | | | | |
| 2626 | CHLORIC ACID, AQUEOUS SOLUTION *with not more than 10% chloric acid* | 2P | | 5.1 | | 50 |
| 2627 | NITRITES, INORGANIC, N.O.S. | 2W | | 5.1 | | 50 |
| 2628 | POTASSIUM FLUOROACETATE | 2X | | 6.1 | | 66 |
| 2629 | SODIUM FLUOROACETATE | 2X | | 6.1 | | 66 |
| 2630 | SELENATES or SELENITES | 2X | | 6.1 | | 66 |
| 2631 to 2641 | *UN Nos. not used* | | | | | |
| 2642 | FLUOROACETIC ACID | 2X | | 6.1 | | 66 |
| 2643 | METHYL BROMOACETATE | 2W | | 6.1 | | 60 |
| 2644 | METHYL IODIDE | 2XE | B | 6.1 | | 66 |
| 2645 | PHENACYL BROMIDE | 2X | | 6.1 | | 60 |
| 2646 | HEXACHLOROCYCLOPENTADIENE | 2X | B | 6.1 | | 66 |
| 2647 | MALONONITRILE | 2X | | 6.1 | | 60 |
| 2648 | 1,2-DIBROMOBUTAN-3-ONE | 2XE | | 6.1 | | 60 |
| 2649 | 1,3-DICHLOROACETONE | 2WE | | 6.1 | | 60 |
| 2650 | 1-1-DICHLORO-1-NITROETHANE | 2X | | 6.1 | | 60 |
| 2651 | 4,4'-DIAMINODIPHENYLMETHANE | 2Z | | 6.1 | | 60 |
| 2652 | *UN No. not used* | | | | | |
| 2653 | BENZYL IODIDE | 2X | | 6.1 | | 60 |
| 2654 | *UN No. not used* | | | | | |
| 2655 | POTASSIUM FLUOROSILICATE | 2Z | | 6.1 | | 60 |
| 2656 | QUINOLINE | ●3Z | | 6.1 | | 60 |

| UN | Substance | EAC | APP | Hazards | | ADR |
| | | | | Class | Sub Risks | HIN |
|---|---|---|---|---|---|---|
| 2657 | **SELENIUM DISULPHIDE** | 2Z | | 6.1 | | 60 |
| 2658 | *UN No. not used* | | | | | |
| 2659 | **SODIUM CHLOROACETATE** | 2X | | 6.1 | | 60 |
| 2660 | **NITROTOLUIDINES (mono)** | 2Z | | 6.1 | | 60 |
| 2661 | **HEXACHLOROACETONE** | 2X | | 6.1 | | 60 |
| 2662 | **HYDROQUINONE** | 2Z | | 6.1 | | 60 |
| 2663 | *UN No. not used* | | | | | |
| 2664 | **DIBROMOMETHANE** | 2Z | | 6.1 | | 60 |
| 2665 | *UN No. not used* | | | | | |
| 2666 | *UN No. not used* | | | | | |
| 2667 | **BUTYLTOLUENES** | 3Z | | 6.1 | | 60 |
| 2668 | **CHLOROACETONITRILE** | 2W | | 6.1 | 3 | 63 |
| 2669 | **CHLOROCRESOLS** | 2X | | 6.1 | | 60 |
| 2670 | **CYANURIC CHLORIDE** | 2X | | 8 | | 80 |
| 2671 | **AMINOPYRIDINES (o-,m-,p-)** | 2X | | 6.1 | | 60 |
| 2672 | **AMMONIA SOLUTION,** *relative density between 0.880 and 0.957 at 15°C in water with more than 10% but not more than 35% ammonia* | 2R | | 8 | | 80 |
| 2673 | **2-AMINO-4-CHLOROPHENOL** | 2X | | 6.1 | | 60 |
| 2674 | **SODIUM FLUOROSILICATE** | 2Z | | 6.1 | | 60 |
| 2675 | *UN No. not used* | | | | | |
| 2676 | **STIBINE** | 2 PE | B | 2.3 | 2.1 | |
| 2677 | **RUBIDIUM HYDROXIDE SOLUTION** | 2R | | 8 | | 80 |
| 2678 | **RUBIDIUM HYDROXIDE** | 2X | | 8 | | 80 |
| 2679 | **LITHIUM HYDROXIDE SOLUTION** | 2R | | 8 | | 80 |
| 2680 | **LITHIUM HYDROXIDE MONOHYDRATE** | 2X | | 8 | | 80 |
| 2681 | **CAESIUM HYDROXIDE SOLUTION** | 2R | | 8 | | 80 |

| UN | Substance | EAC | APP | Hazards Class | Sub Risks | ADR HIN |
|---|---|---|---|---|---|---|
| 2682 | CAESIUM HYDROXIDE | 2X | | 8 | | 80 |
| 2683 | AMMONIUM SULPHIDE SOLUTION | ●2X | | 8 | 6.1 3 | 86 |
| 2684 | DIETHYLAMINOPROPYLAMINE | ●2W | | 3 | 8 | 38 |
| 2685 | N,N-DIETHYLETHYLENEDIAMINE | ●2W | | 8 | 3 | 83 |
| 2686 | 2-DIETHYLAMINOETHANOL | ●2W | | 8 | 3 | 83 |
| 2687 | DICYCLOHEXYLAMMONIUM NITRITE | 1Z | | 4.1 | | 40 |
| 2688 | 1-BROMO-3-CHLOROPROPANE | 2Z | | 6.1 | | 60 |
| 2689 | GLYCEROL alpha-MONOCHLOROHYDRIN | 2X | | 6.1 | | 60 |
| 2690 | N,n-BUTYLIMIDAZOLE | 2X | | 6.1 | | 60 |
| 2691 | PHOSPHORUS PENTABROMIDE | 4W | | 8 | | 80 |
| 2692 | BORON TRIBROMIDE | 4WE | B | 8 | | X88 |
| 2693 | BISULPHITES, AQUEOUS SOLUTION, N.O.S. | 2X | | 8 | | 80 |
| 2694 to 2697 | UN Nos. not used | | | | | |
| 2698 | TETRAHYDROPHTHALIC ANHYDRIDES with more than 0.05% of malic anhydride | 2Z | | 8 | | 80 |
| 2699 | TRIFLUOROACETIC ACID | 2X | B | 8 | | 88 |
| 2700 to 2704 | UN Nos. not used | | | | | |
| 2705 | 1-PENTOL | 3X | | 8 | | 80 |
| 2706 | UN No. not used | | | | | |
| 2707 | DIMETHYLDIOXANES, flash point less than 23°C | ●3YE | | 3 | | 33 |
| 2707 | DIMETHYLDIOXANES, flash point 23°C or above | ●3Y | | 3 | | 30 |
| 2708 | UN No. not used | | | | | |
| 2709 | BUTYLBENZENES | 3Y | | 3 | | 30 |
| 2710 | DIPROPYL KETONE | 3Y | | 3 | | 30 |

| UN | Substance | EAC | APP | Hazards Class | Sub Risks | ADR HIN |
|---|---|---|---|---|---|---|
| 2711 | *UN No. not used* | | | | | |
| 2712 | *UN No. not used* | | | | | |
| 2713 | **ACRIDINE** | 2X | | 6.1 | | 60 |
| 2714 | **ZINC RESINATE** | 1Z | | 4.1 | | 40 |
| 2715 | **ALUMINIUM RESINATE** | 1Z | | 4.1 | | 40 |
| 2716 | **1,4-BUTYNEDIOL** | 2W | | 6.1 | | 60 |
| 2717 | **CAMPHOR,** *synthetic* | 1Z | | 4.1 | | 40 |
| 2718 | *UN No. not used* | | | | | |
| 2719 | **BARIUM BROMATE** | 2YE | | 5.1 | 6.1 | 56 |
| 2720 | **CHROMIUM NITRATE** | 1Y | | 5.1 | | 50 |
| 2721 | **COPPER CHLORATE** | 1YE | | 5.1 | | 50 |
| 2722 | **LITHIUM NITRATE** | 1Y | | 5.1 | | 50 |
| 2723 | **MAGNESIUM CHLORATE** | 1YE | | 5.1 | | 50 |
| 2724 | **MANGANESE NITRATE** | 1Y | | 5.1 | | 50 |
| 2725 | **NICKEL NITRATE** | 1Y | | 5.1 | | 50 |
| 2726 | **NICKEL NITRITE** | 1Y | | 5.1 | | 50 |
| 2727 | **THALLIUM NITRATE** | 2W | | 6.1 | 5.1 | 65 |
| 2728 | **ZIRCONIUM NITRATE** | 1Y | | 5.1 | | 50 |
| 2729 | **HEXACHLOROBENZENE** | 2Z | | 6.1 | | 60 |
| 2730 | **NITROANISOLE** | 2Z | | 6.1 | | 60 |
| 2731 | *UN No. not used* | | | | | |
| 2732 | **NITROBROMOBENZENE** | 2X | | 6.1 | | 60 |
| 2733 | **AMINES, FLAMMABLE, CORROSIVE, N.O.S** *or* **POLYAMINES, FLAMMABLE CORROSIVE, N.O.S.,** *flash point less than 23°C* | ●3WE | | 3 | 8 | 338 |
| 2733 | **AMINES, FLAMMABLE, CORROSIVE, N.O.S** *or* **POLYAMINES, FLAMMABLE CORROSIVE, N.O.S.,** *flash point 23°C or above* | ●3W | | 3 | 8 | 38 |

| UN | Substance | EAC | APP | Hazards | | ADR |
|---|---|---|---|---|---|---|
| | | | | Class | Sub Risks | HIN |
| 2734 | AMINES, LIQUID, CORROSIVE, FLAMMABLE, N.O.S. *or* POLYAMINES, LIQUID, CORROSIVE, FLAMMABLE, N.O.S. | ●3W | B | 8 | 3 | 883 |
| 2734 | AMINES, LIQUID, CORROSIVE, FLAMMABLE, N.O.S. *or* POLYAMINES, LIQUID, CORROSIVE, FLAMMABLE, N.O.S. | ●3W | | 8 | 3 | 83 |
| 2735 | AMINES, LIQUID, CORROSIVE, N.O.S. *or* POLYAMINES, LIQUID, CORROSIVE, N.O.S. | 3X | B | 8 | | 88 |
| 2735 | AMINES, LIQUID, CORROSIVE, N.O.S. *or* POLYAMINES, LIQUID, CORROSIVE, N.O.S. | 3X | | 8 | | 80 |
| 2736 | *UN No. not used* | | | | | |
| 2737 | *UN No. not used* | | | | | |
| 2738 | N-BUTYLANILINE | 3X | | 6.1 | | 60 |
| 2739 | BUTYRIC ANHYDRIDE | 2X | | 8 | | 80 |
| 2740 | n-PROPYL CHLOROFORMATE | ●3WE | B | 6.1 | 3 8 | 668 |
| 2741 | BARIUM HYPOCHLORITE *with more than 22% available chlorine* | 2WE | | 5.1 | 6.1 | 56 |
| 2742 | CHLOROFORMATES, TOXIC, CORROSIVE, FLAMMABLE, N.O.S. | ●3W | | 6.1 | 3 8 | 638 |
| 2743 | n-BUTYL CHLOROFORMATE | ●3W | | 6.1 | 3 8 | 638 |
| 2744 | CYCLOBUTYL CHLOROFORMATE | ●3W | | 6.1 | 3 8 | 638 |
| 2745 | CHLOROMETHYL CHLOROFORMATE | 2WE | | 6.1 | 8 | 68 |
| 2746 | PHENYL CHLOROFORMATE | 2W | | 6.1 | 8 | 68 |
| 2747 | tert-BUTYLCYCLOHEXYL CHLOROFORMATE | 3W | | 6.1 | | 60 |
| 2748 | 2-ETHYLHEXYL CHLOROFORMATE | 3W | | 6.1 | 8 | 68 |
| 2749 | TETRAMETHYSILANE | 3WE | | 3 | | 33 |
| 2750 | 1,3-DICHLOROPROPANOL-2 | 2X | | 6.1 | | 60 |
| 2751 | DIETHYLTHIOPHOSPHORYL CHLORIDE | 4W | | 8 | | 80 |

| UN | Substance | EAC | APP | Hazards | | ADR |
| | | | | Class | Sub Risks | HIN |
|---|---|---|---|---|---|---|
| 2752 | 1,2-EPOXY-3-ETHOXYPROPANE | 3W | | 3 | | 30 |
| 2753 | N-ETHYLBENZYLTOLUIDINES | 3X | | 6.1 | | 60 |
| 2754 | N-ETHYLTOLUIDINES | 3X | | 6.1 | | 60 |
| 2755 | *UN No. not used* | | | | | |
| 2756 | *UN No. not used* | | | | | |
| 2757 | CARBAMATE PESTICIDE, SOLID, TOXIC | 2X | | 6.1 | | 66/ 60 |
| 2758 | CARBAMATE PESTICIDE, LIQUID, FLAMMABLE, TOXIC *flash point less than 23°C* | ●3WE | | 3 | 6.1 | 336 |
| 2759 | ARSENICAL PESTICIDE, SOLID, TOXIC | 2X | | 6.1 | | 66/ 60 |
| 2760 | ARSENICAL PESTICIDE, LIQUID, FLAMMABLE, TOXIC *flash point less than 23°C* | ●3WE | | 3 | 6.1 | 336 |
| 2761 | ORGANOCHLORINE PESTICIDE, SOLID, TOXIC | 2X | | 6.1 | | 66/ 60 |
| 2762 | ORGANOCHLORINE PESTICIDE, LIQUID, FLAMMABLE, TOXIC *flash point less than 23°C* | ●3WE | | 3 | 6.1 | 336 |
| 2763 | TRIAZINE PESTICIDE, SOLID, TOXIC | 2X | | 6.1 | | 66/ 60 |
| 2764 | TRIAZINE PESTICIDE, LIQUID, FLAMMABLE, TOXIC *flash point less than 23°C* | ●3WE | | 3 | 6.1 | 336 |
| 2765 to 2770 | *UN No. not used* | | | | | |
| 2771 | THIOCARBAMATE PESTICIDE, SOLID, TOXIC | 2X | | 6.1 | | 66/ 60 |
| 2772 | THIOCARBAMATE PESTICIDE, LIQUID, FLAMMABLE, TOXIC, *flash point less than 23°C* | ●3WE | | 3 | 6.1 | 336 |
| 2773 | *UN No. not used* | | | | | |
| 2774 | *UN No. not used* | | | | | |
| 2775 | COPPER BASED PESTICIDE, SOLID, TOXIC | 2X | | 6.1 | | 66/ 60 |

| UN | Substance | EAC | APP | Hazards | | ADR |
|---|---|---|---|---|---|---|
| | | | | Class | Sub Risks | HIN |
| 2776 | **COPPER BASED PESTICIDE, LIQUID, FLAMMABLE, TOXIC,** *flash point less than 23ºC* | ●3WE | | 3 | 6.1 | 336 |
| 2777 | **MERCURY BASED PESTICIDE, SOLID, TOXIC** | 2X | | 6.1 | | 66/60 |
| 2778 | **MERCURY BASED PESTICIDE, LIQUID, FLAMMABLE, TOXIC** *flash point less than 23ºC* | ●3WE | | 3 | 6.1 | 336 |
| 2779 | **SUBSTITUTED NITROPHENOL PESTICIDE, SOLID, TOXIC** | 2X | | 6.1 | | 66/60 |
| 2780 | **SUBSTITUTED NITROPHENOL PESTICIDE, LIQUID, FLAMMABLE, TOXIC** *flash point less than 23ºC* | ●3WE | | 3 | 6.1 | 336 |
| 2781 | **BIPYRIDILIUM PESTICIDE, SOLID, TOXIC** | 2X | | 6.1 | | 66/60 |
| 2782 | **BIPYRIDILIUM PESTICIDE, LIQUID, FLAMMABLE, TOXIC,** *flash point less than 23ºC* | ●3WE | | 3 | 6.1 | 336 |
| 2783 | **ORGANOPHOSPHORUS PESTICIDE, SOLID, TOXIC** | 2X | | 6.1 | | 66/60 |
| 2784 | **ORGANOPHOSPHORUS PESTICIDE, LIQUID, FLAMMABLE, TOXIC** *flash point less than 23ºC* | ●3WE | | 3 | 6.1 | 336 |
| 2785 | **4-THIAPENTANAL** | 2X | | 6.1 | | 60 |
| 2786 | **ORGANOTIN PESTICIDE, SOLID, TOXIC** | 2X | | 6.1 | | 66/60 |
| 2787 | **ORGANOTIN PESTICIDE, LIQUID, FLAMMABLE, TOXIC** *flash point less than 23ºC* | ●3WE | | 3 | 6.1 | 336 |
| 2788 | **ORGANOTIN COMPOUND, LIQUID, N.O.S.** | 2X | B | 6.1 | | 66 |
| 2788 | **ORGANOTIN COMPOUND, LIQUID, N.O.S.** | 2X | | 6.1 | | 60 |
| 2789 | **ACETIC ACID, GLACIAL or ACETIC ACID SOLUTION,** *more than 80% acid, by mass* | ●2P | | 8 | 3 | 83 |
| 2790 | **ACETIC ACID SOLUTION** *more than 10% but not more than 80% acid, by mass* | ●2R | | 8 | | 80 |
| 2791 | *UN No. not used* | | | | | |
| 2792 | *UN No. not used* | | | | | |

| UN | Substance | EAC | APP | Hazards | | ADR |
| | | | | Class | Sub Risks | HIN |
|---|---|---|---|---|---|---|
| 2793 | **FERROUS METAL BORINGS, SHAVINGS, TURNINGS or CUTTINGS,** *in a form liable to self-heating* | 4Y | | 4.2 | | 40 |
| 2794 | **BATTERIES, WET, FILLED WITH ACID,** *electric storage* | 2R | | 8 | | 80 |
| 2795 | **BATTERIES, WET, FILLED WITH ALKALI,** *electric, storage* | 2R | | 8 | | 80 |
| 2796 | **SULPHURIC ACID** *with not more than 51% acid or* **BATTERY FLUID, ACID** | 2R | | 8 | | 80 |
| 2797 | **BATTERY FLUID, ALKALI** | 2R | | 8 | | 80 |
| 2798 | **PHENYLPHOSPHORUS DICHLORIDE** | 2X | | 8 | | 80 |
| 2799 | **PHENYLPHOSPHORUS THIODICHLORIDE** | 2X | | 8 | | 80 |
| 2800 | **BATTERIES, WET, NON-SPILLABLE,** *electric, storage* | 2X | | 8 | | 80 |
| 2801 | **DYE, LIQUID, CORROSIVE, N.O.S.,** *or* **DYE INTERMEDIATE, LIQUID, CORROSIVE, N.O.S.** | 2X | B | 8 | | 88 |
| 2801 | **DYE, LIQUID, CORROSIVE, N.O.S.,** *or* **DYE INTERMEDIATE, LIQUID, CORROSIVE, N.O.S.** | 2X | | 8 | | 80 |
| 2802 | **COPPER CHLORIDE** | 2Z | | 8 | | 80 |
| 2803 | **GALLIUM** | 2Z | | 8 | | 80 |
| 2804 | *UN No. not used* | | | | | |
| 2805 | **LITHIUM HYDRIDE, FUSED SOLID** | 4W | | 4.3 | | 423 |
| 2806 | **LITHIUM NITRIDE** | 4Y | | 4.3 | | |
| 2807 | *UN No. not used* | | | | | |
| 2808 | *UN No. not used* | | | | | |
| 2809 | **MERCURY** | 2Z | | 8 | | 80 |
| 2810 | **TOXIC LIQUID, ORGANIC, N.O.S.** | 2XE | B | 6.1 | | 66 |
| 2810 | **TOXIC LIQUID, ORGANIC, N.O.S.** | 2X | | 6.1 | | 60 |
| 2811 | **TOXIC SOLID, ORGANIC, N.O.S.** | 2XE | | 6.1 | | 66/ 60 |
| 2812 | **SODIUM ALUMINATE, SOLID** | 2X | | 8 | | |

| UN | Substance | EAC | APP | Hazards | | ADR |
| | | | | Class | Sub Risks | HIN |
|---|---|---|---|---|---|---|
| 2813 | WATER-REACTIVE SOLID, N.O.S. | 4W | | 4.3 | | 423 |
| 2814 | INFECTIOUS SUBSTANCE, AFFECTING HUMANS | 2X | | 6.2 | | 606 |
| 2815 | N-AMINOETHYLPIPERAZINE | ●2X | | 8 | | 80 |
| 2816 | *UN No. not used* | | | | | |
| 2817 | AMMONIUM HYDROGEN - DIFLUORIDE SOLUTION | 2X | | 8 | 6.1 | 86 |
| 2818 | AMMONIUM POLYSULPHIDE SOLUTION | 2X | | 8 | 6.1 | 86 |
| 2819 | AMYL ACID PHOSPHATE | 3X | | 8 | | 80 |
| 2820 | BUTYRIC ACID | ●2X | | 8 | | 80 |
| 2821 | PHENOL SOLUTION | 2X | | 6.1 | | 60 |
| 2822 | 2-CHLOROPYRIDINE | 2X | | 6.1 | | 60 |
| 2823 | CROTONIC ACID | ·2X | | 8 | | 80 |
| 2824 | *UN No. not used* | | | | | |
| 2825 | *UN No. not used* | | | | | |
| 2826 | ETHYL CHLOROTHIOFORMATE | 2W | | 8 | 3 | 80 |
| 2827 | *UN No. not used* | | | | | |
| 2828 | *UN No. not used* | | | | | |
| 2829 | CAPROIC ACID | 3Z | | 8 | | 80 |
| 2830 | LITHIUM FERROSILICON | 4W | | 4.3 | | 423 |
| 2831 | 1,1,1-TRICHLOROETHANE | 2Z | | 6.1 | | 60 |
| 2832 | *UN No. not used* | | | | | |
| 2833 | *UN No. not used* | | | | | |
| 2834 | PHOSPHOROUS ACID | 2R | | 8 | | 80 |
| 2835 | SODIUM ALUMINIUM HYDRIDE | 4W | | 4.3 | | 423 |
| 2836 | *UN No. not used* | | | | | |
| 2837 | BISULPHATES, AQUEOUS SOLUTION | 2R | | 8 | | 80 |

| UN | Substance | EAC | APP | Hazards | | ADR |
|---|---|---|---|---|---|---|
| | | | | Class | Sub Risks | HIN |
| 2838 | **VINYL BUTYRATE, INHIBITED** | ●3YE | | 3 | | 339 |
| 2839 | **ALDOL** | ●2X | | 6.1 | | 60 |
| 2840 | **BUTYRALDOXIME** | ●3Y | | 3 | | 30 |
| 2841 | **DI-n-AMYLAMINE** | ●3W | | 3 | 6.1 | 36 |
| 2842 | **NITROETHANE** | ●2Y | | 3 | | 30 |
| 2843 | *UN No. not used* | | | | | |
| 2844 | **CALCIUM MANGANESE SILICON** | 4Y | | 4.3 | | 423 |
| 2845 | **PYROPHORIC LIQUID, ORGANIC, N.O.S.** | ●3WE | | 4.2 | | 333 |
| 2846 | **PYROPHORIC SOLID, ORGANIC, N.O.S.** | 4Y | | 4.2 | | |
| 2847 | *UN No. not used* | | | | | |
| 2848 | *UN No. not used* | | | | | |
| 2849 | **3-CHLOROPROPANOL-1** | ●2Z | | 6.1 | | 60 |
| 2850 | **PROPYLENE TETRAMER** | 3Y | | 3 | | 30 |
| 2851 | **BORON TRIFLUORIDE DIHYDRATE** | 4W | | 8 | | 80 |
| 2852 | **DIPICRYL SULPHIDE, WETTED** *with not less than 10% water, by mass* | 1W | | 4.1 | | |
| 2853 | **MAGNESIUM FLUOROSILICATE** | 2Z | | 6.1 | | 60 |
| 2854 | **AMMONIUM FLUOROSILICATE** | 2Z | | 6.1 | | 60 |
| 2855 | **ZINC FLUOROSILICATE** | 2Z | | 6.1 | | 60 |
| 2856 | **FLUOROSILICATES, N.O.S.** | 2X | | 6.1 | | 60 |
| 2857 | **REFRIGERATING MACHINES,** *containing non-flammable, non-toxic, liquefied gas or ammonia solutions (UN 2672)* | + | | 2.2 | | |
| 2858 | **ZIRCONIUM, DRY,** *coiled wire, finished metal sheets, strip* | 4Z | | 4.1 | | 40 |
| 2859 | **AMMONIUM METAVANADATE** | 2Z | | 6.1 | | 60 |
| 2860 | *UN No. not used* | | | | | |
| 2861 | **AMMONIUM POLYVANADATE** | 2Z | | 6.1 | | 60 |

| UN | Substance | EAC | APP | Hazards | | ADR |
| | | | | Class | Sub Risks | HIN |
|---|---|---|---|---|---|---|
| 2862 | VANADIUM PENTOXIDE, *non-fused form* | 2Z | | 6.1 | | 60 |
| 2863 | SODIUM AMMONIUM VANADATE | 2Z | | 6.1 | | 60 |
| 2864 | POTASSIUM METAVANADATE | 2Z | | 6.1 | | 60 |
| 2865 | HYDROXYLAMINE SULPHATE | 2X | | 8 | | 80 |
| 2866 to 2868 | *UN Nos. not used* | | | | | |
| 2869 | TITANIUM TRICHLORIDE, MIXTURE | 4W | | 8 | | 80 |
| 2870 | ALUMINIUM BOROHYDRIDE *or* ALUMINIUM BOROHYDRIDE IN DEVICES | 4WE | | 4.2 | 4.3 | X333 |
| 2871 | ANTIMONY POWDER | 2Z | | 6.1 | | 60 |
| 2872 | DIBROMOCHLOROPROPANES | 2X | | 6.1 | | 60 |
| 2873 | DIBUTYLAMINOETHANOL | 3Z | | 6.1 | | 60 |
| 2874 | FURFURYL ALCOHOL | ●2X | | 6.1 | | 60 |
| 2875 | HEXACHLOROPHENE | 2X | | 6.1 | | 60 |
| 2876 | RESORCINOL | 2X | | 6.1 | | 60 |
| 2877 | *UN No. not used* | | | | | |
| 2878 | TITANIUM SPONGE GRANULES *or* TITANIUM SPONGE POWDERS | 4Y | | 4.1 | | 40 |
| 2879 | SELENIUM OXYCHLORIDE | 4WE | B | 8 | 6.1 | X886 |
| 2880 | CALCIUM HYPOCHLORITE, HYDRATED, *or* CALCIUM HYPOCHLORITE, HYDRATED MIXTURE *with not less than 5.5% but not more than 10% water* | 2W | | 5.1 | | 50 |
| 2881 | METAL CATALYST, DRY | 4Y | | 4.2 | | 40 |
| 2882 to 2899 | *UN Nos. not used* | | | | | |
| 2900 | INFECTIOUS SUBSTANCE, AFFECTING ANIMALS *only* | 2X | | 6.2 | | 606 |
| 2901 | BROMINE CHLORIDE | 2WE | B | 2.3 | 5.1 8 | 265 |

| UN | Substance | EAC | APP | Hazards | | ADR |
|---|---|---|---|---|---|---|
| | | | | Class | Sub Risks | HIN |
| 2902 | **PESTICIDE, LIQUID, TOXIC, N.O.S.** | 2X | B | 6.1 | | 66 |
| 2902 | **PESTICIDE, LIQUID, TOXIC, N.O.S.** | 2X | | 6.1 | | 60 |
| 2903 | **PESTICIDE, LIQUID, TOXIC, FLAMMABLE, N.O.S.,** *flash point 23°C or above* | ●3W | B | 6.1 | 3 | 663 |
| 2903 | **PESTICIDE, LIQUID, TOXIC, FLAMMABLE, N.O.S.,** *flash point 23°C or above* | ●3W | | 6.1 | 3 | 63 |
| 2904 | **CHLOROPHENOLATES, LIQUID** *or* **PHENOLATES, LIQUID** | 2X | | 8 | | 80 |
| 2905 | **CHLOROPHENOLATES, SOLID** *or* **PHENOLATES, SOLID** | 2X | | 8 | | 80 |
| 2906 | *UN No. not used* | | | | | |
| 2907 | **ISOSORBIDE DINITRATE MIXTURE** *with not less than 60% lactose, mannose, starch, or calcium hydrogen phosphate* | *1Z* | | 4.1 | | |
| 2908 | *UN No. not used* | | | | | |
| 2909 | *UN No. not used* | | | | | |
| 2910 | **RADIOACTIVE MATERIAL, EXCEPTED PACKAGE - INSTRUMENTS** *or* **ARTICLES, - LIMITED QUANTITY OF MATERIAL – ARTICLES MANUFACTURED FROM NATURAL URANIUM** *or* **DEPLETED URANIUM** *or* **NATURAL THORIUM, - EMPTY PACKAGING** | + | | 7 | | |
| 2911 | *UN No. not used* | | | | | |
| 2912 | **RADIOACTIVE MATERIAL, LOW SPECIFIC ACTIVITY (LSA), N.O.S.** | + | | 7 | | 70/ 72/ 73/ 74/ 75/ 76/ 78/ 723 |
| 2913 | **RADIOACTIVE MATERIAL, SURFACE CONTAMINATED OBJECTS (SCO)** | + | | 7 | | |
| 2914 to 2917 | *UN Nos. not used* | | | | | |
| 2918 | **RADIOACTIVE MATERIAL, FISSILE, N.O.S.** | + | | 7 | | |

| UN | Substance | EAC | APP | Hazards | | ADR |
| | | | | Class | Sub Risks | HIN |
|------|-----------|-----|-----|-------|-----------|-----|
| 2919 | *UN No. not used* | | | | | |
| 2920 | **CORROSIVE LIQUID, FLAMMABLE, N.O.S.** | ●2W | B | 8 | 3 | 883 |
| 2920 | **CORROSIVE LIQUID, FLAMMABLE, N.O.S.** | ●2W | | 8 | 3 | 83 |
| 2921 | **CORROSIVE SOLID, FLAMMABLE, N.O.S.** | 2W | | 8 | 4.1 | 884/ 84 |
| 2922 | **CORROSIVE LIQUID, TOXIC, N.O.S.** | 2XE | B | 8 | 6.1 | 886 |
| 2922 | **CORROSIVE LIQUID, TOXIC, N.O.S.** | 2XE | | 8 | 6.1 | 86 |
| 2923 | **CORROSIVE SOLID, TOXIC, N.O.S.** | 2X | | 8 | 6.1 | 886/ 86 |
| 2924 | **FLAMMABLE LIQUID, CORROSIVE, N.O.S.** | ●3WE | | 3 | 8 | 338 |
| 2924 | **FLAMMABLE LIQUID, CORROSIVE, N.O.S.** | ●3W | | 3 | 8 | 38 |
| 2925 | **FLAMMABLE, SOLID, CORROSIVE ORGANIC, N.O.S.** | 1W | | 4.1 | 8 | 48 |
| 2926 | **FLAMMABLE, SOLID, TOXIC ORGANIC, N.O.S.** | 2W | | 4.1 | 6.1 | 46 |
| 2927 | **TOXIC LIQUID, CORROSIVE, ORGANIC, N.O.S.** | 2XE | B | 6.1 | 8 | 668 |
| 2927 | **TOXIC LIQUID, CORROSIVE, ORGANIC, N.O.S.** | 2XE | | 6.1 | 8 | 68 |
| 2928 | **TOXIC SOLID, CORROSIVE, ORGANIC, N.O.S.** | 2XE | | 6.1 | 8 | 668/ 68 |
| 2929 | **TOXIC LIQUID, FLAMMABLE, ORGANIC, N.O.S.** | ●3WE | B | 6.1 | 3 | 663 |
| 2929 | **TOXIC LIQUID, FLAMMABLE, ORGANIC, N.O.S.** | ●3WE | | 6.1 | 3 | 63 |
| 2930 | **TOXIC SOLID, FLAMMABLE, ORGANIC, N.O.S.** | 2W | | 6.1 | 4.1 | 664/ 64 |
| 2931 | **VANADYL SULPHATE** | 2Z | | 6.1 | | 60 |
| 2932 | *UN No. not used* | | | | | |
| 2933 | **METHYL 2-CHLOROPROPIONATE** | ●2Y | | 3 | | 30 |
| 2934 | **ISOPROPYL 2-CHLOROPROPIONATE** | 3Y | | 3 | | 30 |
| 2935 | **ETHYL 2-CHLOROPROPIONATE** | 3Y | | 3 | | 30 |
| 2936 | **THIOLACTIC ACID** | 2X | | 6.1 | | 60 |

| UN | Substance | EAC | APP | Hazards | | ADR |
| | | | | Class | Sub Risks | HIN |
|---|---|---|---|---|---|---|
| 2937 | alpha-METHYLBENZYL ALCOHOL | 3Z | | 6.1 | | 60 |
| 2938 | *UN No. not used* | | | | | |
| 2939 | *UN No. not used* | | | | | |
| 2940 | 9-PHOSPHABICYCLONONANES (CYCLOOCTADIENE PHOSPHINES) | 2WE | | 4.2 | | 40 |
| 2941 | FLUOROANILINES | 2W | | 6.1 | | 60 |
| 2942 | 2-TRIFLUOROMETHYLANILINE | 2X | | 6.1 | | 60 |
| 2943 | TETRAHYDROFURFURYLAMINE | ●2W | | 3 | | 30 |
| 2944 | *UN No. not used* | | | | | |
| 2945 | N-METHYLBUTYLAMINE | ●2WE | | 3 | 8 | 338 |
| 2946 | 2-AMINO-5-DIETHYLAMINOPENTANE | 2X | | 6.1 | | 60 |
| 2947 | ISOPROPYL CHLOROACETATE | 3Y | | 3 | | 30 |
| 2948 | 3-TRIFLUOROMETHYLANILINE | 2X | | 6.1 | | 60 |
| 2949 | SODIUM HYDROSULPHIDE *with not less than 25% water of crystallization* | 2X | | 8 | | 80 |
| 2950 | MAGNESIUM GRANULES, COATED | 4Y | | 4.3 | | 423 |
| 2951 to 2955 | *UN Nos. not used* | | | | | |
| 2956 | 5-tert-BUTYL-2,4,6-TRINITRO-m-XYLENE, (MUSK XYLENE) | 1Y | | 4.1 | | |
| 2957 to 2964 | *UN Nos. not used* | | | | | |
| 2965 | BORON TRIFLUORIDE DIMETHYL ETHERATE | 4WE | | 4.3 | 3 8 | 382 |
| 2966 | THIOGLYCOL | 2X | | 6.1 | | 60 |
| 2967 | SULPHAMIC ACID | 2Z | | 8 | | 80 |
| 2968 | MANEB, STABILIZED *or* MANEB PREPARATION, STABILIZED *against self-heating* | 4WE | | 4.3 | | 423 |

| UN | Substance | EAC | APP | Hazards | | ADR |
|---|---|---|---|---|---|---|
| | | | | Class | Sub Risks | HIN |
| 2969 | **CASTOR BEANS** *or* **CASTOR MEAL** *or* **CASTOR POMACE** *or* **CASTOR FLAKE** | 2Z | | 9 | | 90 |
| 2970 to 2973 | *UN Nos. not used* | | | | | |
| 2974 | **RADIOACTIVE MATERIAL, SPECIAL FORM, N.O.S.** | + | | 7 | | |
| 2975 | **THORIUM METAL, PYROPHORIC** | + | | 7 | 4.2 | |
| 2976 | **THORIUM NITRATE, SOLID** | + | | 7 | 5.1 | |
| 2977 | **URANIUM HEXAFLUORIDE, FISSILE,** *containing more than 1.0 % Uranium-235* | + | | 7 | 8 | |
| 2978 | **URANIUM HEXAFLUORIDE,** *fissile excepted or non-fissile* | + | | 7 | 8 | |
| 2979 | **URANIUM METAL, PYROPHORIC** | + | | 7 | 4.2 | |
| 2980 | **URANYL NITRATE HEXAHYDRATE SOLUTION** | + | | 7 | 8 | 78 |
| 2981 | **URANYL NITRATE, SOLID** | + | | 7 | 5.1 | |
| 2982 | **RADIOACTIVE MATERIAL, N.O.S.** | + | | 7 | | 70/ 72/ 73/ 74/ 75/ 76/ 78/ 723 |
| 2983 | **ETHYLENE OXIDE AND PROPYLENE OXIDE MIXTURE** *not more than 30% ethylene oxide* | ●2PE | | 3 | 6.1 | 336 |
| 2984 | **HYDROGEN PEROXIDE, AQUEOUS SOLUTION,** *with not less than 8% but less than 20% hydrogen peroxide (stabilized as necessary)* | 2P | | 5.1 | | 50 |
| 2985 | **CHLOROSILANES, FLAMMABLE, CORROSIVE, N.O.S.** | 4WE | | 3 | 8 | 338 |
| 2986 | **CHLOROSILANES, CORROSIVE, FLAMMABLE, N.O.S.** | 4WE | | 8 | 3 | X83 |
| 2987 | **CHLOROSILANES, CORROSIVE, N.O.S.** | 4WE | | 8 | | 80 |
| 2988 | **CHILOROSILANES, WATER-REACTIVE, FLAMMABLE, CORROSIVE, N.O.S.** | 4WE | | 4.3 | 3 8 | X338 |

| UN | Substance | EAC | APP | Hazards | | ADR |
| --- | --- | --- | --- | --- | --- | --- |
| | | | | Class | Sub Risks | HIN |
| 2989 | **LEAD PHOSPHITE DIBASIC** | 1Z | | 4.1 | | 40 |
| 2990 | **LIFE-SAVING APPLIANCES, SELF-INFLATING** | + | | 9 | | |
| 2991 | **CARBAMATE PESTICIDE, LIQUID, TOXIC, FLAMMABLE,** *flash point 23°C or above* | ●3W | B | 6.1 | 3 | 663 |
| 2991 | **CARBAMATE PESTICIDE, LIQUID, TOXIC, FLAMMABLE,** *flash point 23°C or above* | ●3W | | 6.1 | 3 | 63 |
| 2992 | **CARBAMATE PESTICIDE, LIQUID, TOXIC** | 2X | B | 6.1 | | 66 |
| 2992 | **CARBAMATE PESTICIDE, LIQUID, TOXIC** | 2X | | 6.1 | | 60 |
| 2993 | **ARSENICAL PESTICIDE, LIQUID, TOXIC, FLAMMABLE,** *flash point 23°C or above* | ●3W | B | 6.1 | 3 | 663 |
| 2993 | **ARSENICAL PESTICIDE, LIQUID, TOXIC, FLAMMABLE,** *flash point 23°C or above* | ●3W | | 6.1 | 3 | 63 |
| 2994 | **ARSENICAL PESTICIDE, LIQUID, TOXIC** | 2X | B | 6.1 | | 66 |
| 2994 | **ARSENICAL PESTICIDE, LIQUID, TOXIC** | 2X | | 6.1 | | 60 |
| 2995 | **ORGANOCHLORINE PESTICIDE, LIQUID, TOXIC, FLAMMABLE,** *flash point 23°C or above* | ●3W | B | 6.1 | 3 | 663 |
| 2995 | **ORGANOCHLORINE PESTICIDE, LIQUID, TOXIC, FLAMMABLE,** *flash point 23°C or above* | ●3W | | 6.1 | 3 | 63 |
| 2996 | **ORGANOCHLORINE PESTICIDE, LIQUID, TOXIC** | 2X | B | 6.1 | | 66 |
| 2996 | **ORGANOCHLORINE PESTICIDE, LIQUID, TOXIC** | 2X | | 6.1 | | 60 |
| 2997 | **TRIAZINE PESTICIDE, LIQUID, TOXIC, FLAMMABLE,** *flash point 23°C or above* | ●3W | B | 6.1 | 3 | 663 |
| 2997 | **TRIAZINE PESTICIDE, LIQUID, TOXIC, FLAMMABLE,** *flash point 23°C or above* | ●3W | | 6.1 | 3 | 63 |
| 2998 | **TRIAZINE PESTICIDE, LIQUID, TOXIC** | 2X | B | 6.1 | | 66 |
| 2998 | **TRIAZINE PESTICIDE, LIQUID, TOXIC** | 2X | | 6.1 | | 60 |
| 2999 to 3004 | *UN Nos. not used* | | | | | |
| 3005 | **THIOCARBAMATE PESTICIDE, LIQUID, TOXIC, FLAMMABLE,** *flash point 23°C or above* | ●3W | B | 6.1 | 3 | 663 |

| UN | Substance | EAC | APP | Hazards | | ADR |
|---|---|---|---|---|---|---|
| | | | | Class | Sub Risks | HIN |
| 3005 | THIOCARBAMATE PESTICIDE, LIQUID, TOXIC, FLAMMABLE, *flash point 23°C or above* | ●3W | | 6.1 | 3 | 63 |
| 3006 | THIOCARBAMATE PESTICIDE, LIQUID, TOXIC | 2X | B | 6.1 | | 66 |
| 3006 | THIOCARBAMATE PESTICIDE, LIQUID, TOXIC | 2X | | 6.1 | | 60 |
| 3007 | *UN No. not used* | | | | | |
| 3008 | *UN No. not used* | | | | | |
| 3009 | COPPER BASED PESTICIDE, LIQUID, TOXIC, FLAMMABLE, *flash point 23°C or above* | ●3W | B | 6.1 | 3 | 663 |
| 3009 | COPPER BASED PESTICIDE, LIQUID, TOXIC, FLAMMABLE, *flash point 23°C or above* | ●3W | | 6.1 | 3 | 63 |
| 3010 | COPPER BASED PESTICIDE, LIQUID, TOXIC | 2X | B | 6.1 | | 66 |
| 3010 | COPPER BASED PESTICIDE, LIQUID, TOXIC | 2X | | 6.1 | | 60 |
| 3011 | MERCURY BASED PESTICIDE, LIQUID, TOXIC, FLAMMABLE, *flash point 23°C or above* | ●3W | B | 6.1 | 3 | 663 |
| 3011 | MERCURY BASED PESTICIDE, LIQUID, TOXIC, FLAMMABLE, *flash point 23°C or above* | ●3W | | 6.1 | 3 | 63 |
| 3012 | MERCURY BASED PESTICIDE, LIQUID, TOXIC | 2X | B | 6.1 | | 66 |
| 3012 | MERCURY BASED PESTICIDE, LIQUID, TOXIC | 2X | | 6.1 | | 60 |
| 3013 | SUBSTITUTED NITROPHENOL PESTICIDE, LIQUID, TOXIC, FLAMMABLE, *flash point 23°C or above* | ●3W | B | 6.1 | 3 | 663 |
| 3013 | SUBSTITUTED NITROPHENOL PESTICIDE, LIQUID, TOXIC, FLAMMABLE, *flash point 23°C or above* | ●3W | | 6.1 | 3 | 63 |
| 3014 | SUBSTITUTED NITROPHENOL PESTICIDE, LIQUID, TOXIC | 2X | B | 6.1 | | 66 |
| 3014 | SUBSTITUTED NITROPHENOL PESTICIDE, LIQUID, TOXIC | 2X | | 6.1 | | 60 |
| 3015 | BIPYRIDILIUM PESTICIDE, LIQUID, TOXIC, FLAMMABLE, *flash point 23°C or above* | ●3W | B | 6.1 | 3 | 663 |
| 3015 | BIPYRIDILIUM PESTICIDE, LIQUID, TOXIC, FLAMMABLE, *flash point 23°C or above* | ●3W | | 6.1 | 3 | 63 |

| UN | Substance | EAC | APP | Hazards | | ADR |
|----|-----------|-----|-----|---------|---|-----|
| | | | | Class | Sub Risks | HIN |
| 3016 | **BIPYRIDILIUM PESTICIDE, LIQUID, TOXIC** | 2X | B | 6.1 | | 66 |
| 3016 | **BIPYRIDILIUM PESTICIDE, LIQUID, TOXIC** | 2X | | 6.1 | | 60 |
| 3017 | **ORGANOPHOSPHORUS PESTICIDE, LIQUID, TOXIC, FLAMMABLE,** *flash point 23°C or above* | ●3W | B | 6.1 | 3 | 663 |
| 3017 | **ORGANOPHOSPHORUS PESTICIDE, LIQUID, TOXIC, FLAMMABLE,** *flash point 23°C or above* | ●3W | | 6.1 | 3 | 63 |
| 3018 | **ORGANOPHOSPHORUS PESTICIDE, LIQUID, TOXIC** | 2X | B | 6.1 | | 66 |
| 3018 | **ORGANOPHOSPHORUS PESTICIDE, LIQUID, TOXIC** | 2X | | 6.1 | | 60 |
| 3019 | **ORGANOTIN PESTICIDE, LIQUID, TOXIC, FLAMMABLE,** *flash point 23°C or above* | ●3W | B | 6.1 | 3 | 663 |
| 3019 | **ORGANOTIN PESTICIDE, LIQUID, TOXIC, FLAMMABLE,** *flash point 23°C or above* | ●3W | | 6.1 | 3 | 63 |
| 3020 | **ORGANOTIN PESTICIDE, LIQUID, TOXIC** | 2X | B | 6.1 | | 66 |
| 3020 | **ORGANOTIN PESTICIDE, LIQUID, TOXIC** | 2X | | 6.1 | | 60 |
| 3021 | **PESTICIDE, LIQUID, FLAMMABLE, TOXIC, N.O.S.** *flash point less than 23°C* | ●3WE | | 3 | 6.1 | 336 |
| 3022 | **1,2-BUTYLENE OXIDE, STABILIZED** | ●3YE | | 3 | | 339 |
| 3023 | **2-METHYL-2-HEPTANETHIOL** | 3WE | B | 6.1 | 3 | 663 |
| 3024 | **COUMARIN DERIVATIVE PESTICIDE, LIQUID, FLAMMABLE, TOXIC,** *flash point less than 23°C* | ●3WE | | 3 | 6.1 | 336 |
| 3025 | **COUMARIN DERIVATIVE PESTICIDE, LIQUID, TOXIC, FLAMMABLE,** *flash point 23°C or above* | ●3W | B | 6.1 | 3 | 663 |
| 3025 | **COUMARIN DERIVATIVE PESTICIDE, LIQUID, TOXIC, FLAMMABLE,** *flash point 23°C or above* | ●3W | | 6.1 | 3 | 63 |
| 3026 | **COUMARIN DERIVATIVE PESTICIDE, LIQUID, TOXIC** | 2X | B | 6.1 | | 66 |
| 3026 | **COUMARIN DERIVATIVE PESTICIDE, LIQUID, TOXIC** | 2X | | 6.1 | | 60 |
| 3027 | **COUMARIN, DERIVATIVE PESTICIDE, SOLID, TOXIC** | 2X | | 6.1 | | 66/ 60 |

| UN | Substance | EAC | APP | Hazards | | ADR |
|----|-----------|-----|-----|---------|---|-----|
| | | | | Class | Sub Risks | HIN |
| 3028 | **BATTERIES, DRY, CONTAINING POTASSIUM HYDROXIDE SOLID,** *electric, storage* | 2X | | 8 | | 80 |
| 3029 to 3047 | *UN Nos. not used* | | | | | |
| 3048 | **ALUMINIUM PHOSPHIDE PESTICIDES** | 2W | | 6.1 | | 642 |
| 3049 | **METAL ALKYL HALIDES, WATER REACTIVE, N.O.S.** *or* **METAL ARYL HALIDES, WATER REACTIVE, N.O.S.** | 4WE | | 4.2 | 4.3 | X333 |
| 3050 | **METAL ALKYL HYDRIDES, WATER REACTIVE, N.O.S.** *or* **METAL ARYL HYDRIDES, WATER REACTIVE, N.O.S.** | 4WE | | 4.2 | 4.3 | X333 |
| 3051 | **ALUMINIUM ALKYLS** | 4WE | | 4.2 | 4.3 | X333 |
| 3052 | **ALUMINIUM ALKYL HALIDES** | 4WE | | 4.2 | 4.3 | X333 |
| 3053 | **MAGNESIUM ALKYLS** | 4WE | | 4.2 | 4.3 | X333 |
| 3054 | **CYCLOHEXYL MERCAPTAN** | 3WE | | 3 | | 30 |
| 3055 | **2-(2-AMINOETHOXY)ETHANOL** | 2X | | 8 | | 80 |
| 3056 | **n-HEPTALDEHYDE** | ●3Y | | 3 | | 30 |
| 3057 | **TRIFLUOROACETYL CHLORIDE** | 2XE | AB | 2.3 | 8 | 268 |
| 3058 to 3063 | *UN Nos. not used* | | | | | |
| 3064 | **NITROGLYCERIN, SOLUTION IN ALCOHOL,** *with more than 1% but not more than 5% nitroglycerin* | + | | 3 | | |
| 3065 | **ALCOHOLIC BEVERAGES,** *with more than 70% alcohol by volume* | ●2YE | | 3 | | 33 |
| 3065 | **ALCOHOLIC BEVERAGES,** *with more than 24% and not more than 70% alcohol by volume* | ●2Y | | 3 | | 30 |
| 3066 | **PAINT** (*including paint, lacquer, enamel, stain, shellac, varnish, polish, liquid filler and liquid lacquer base) or,* **PAINT RELATED MATERIAL** (*including paint-thinning or reducing compound*) | ●3X | | 8 | | 80 |
| 3067 to 3069 | *UN Nos. not used* | | | | | |

| UN | Substance | EAC | APP | Hazards | | ADR |
|----|-----------|-----|-----|---------|---|-----|
| | | | | Class | Sub Risks | HIN |
| 3070 | **ETHYLENE OXIDE AND DICHLORODIFLUOROMETHANE MIXTURE** *with not more than 12.5% ethylene oxide* | 2RE | A | 2.2 | | 20 |
| 3071 | **MERCAPTANS, LIQUID, TOXIC, FLAMMABLE, N.O.S.** *or* **MERCAPTAN MIXTURE, LIQUID, TOXIC, FLAMMABLE, N.O.S.** | ●3WE | | 6.1 | 3 | 63 |
| 3072 | **LIFE SAVING APPLIANCES NOT SELF INFLATING,** *containing dangerous goods as equipment* | + | | 9 | | |
| 3073 | **VINYLPYRIDINES, INHIBITED** | ●3W | | 6.1 | 3 8 | 639 |
| 3074 | *UN No. not used* | | | | | |
| 3075 | *UN No. not used* | | | | | |
| 3076 | **ALUMINIUM ALKYL HYDRIDES** | 4WE | | 4.2 | 4.3 | X333 |
| 3077 | **ENVIRONMENTALLY HAZARDOUS SUBSTANCE, SOLID, N.O.S.** | 2X | | 9 | | 90 |
| 3078 | **CERIUM,** *turnings or gritty powder* | 4Y | | 4.3 | | 423 |
| 3079 | **METHACRYLONITRILE, INHIBITED** | ●3WE | | 3 | 6.1 | 336 |
| 3080 | **ISOCYANATES, TOXIC, FLAMMABLE, N.O.S.** *or* **ISOCYANATE SOLUTION, TOXIC, FLAMMABLE, N.O.S.** | ●2W | | 6.1 | 3 | 63 |
| 3081 | *UN No. not used* | | | | | |
| 3082 | **ENVIRONMENTALLY HAZARDOUS SUBSTANCE, LIQUID, N.O.S.** | 2X | | 9 | | 90 |
| 3083 | **PERCHLORYL FLUORIDE** | 2XE | AB | 2.3 | 5.1 | 265 |
| 3084 | **CORROSIVE SOLID, OXIDISING, N.O.S.** | 2W | | 8 | 5.1 | 885/ 85 |
| 3085 | **OXIDISING SOLID, CORROSIVE, N.O.S.** | 2W | | 5.1 | 8 | 58 |
| 3086 | **TOXIC SOLID, OXIDISING, N.O.S.** | 2W | | 6.1 | 5.1 | 665/ 65 |
| 3087 | **OXIDISING SOLID, TOXIC, N.O.S.** | 2W | | 5.1 | 6.1 | 56 |
| 3088 | **SELF-HEATING SOLID, ORGANIC, N.O.S.** | 1Y | | 4.2 | | 40 |
| 3089 | **METAL POWDER, FLAMMABLE, N.O.S.** | 4Z | | 4.1 | | 40 |

| UN | Substance | EAC | APP | Hazards | | ADR |
| --- | --- | --- | --- | --- | --- | --- |
| | | | | Class | Sub Risks | HIN |
| 3090 | **LITHIUM BATTERIES** | + | | 9 | | |
| 3091 | **LITHIUM BATTERIES CONTAINED IN EQUIPMENT** *or* **LITHIUM BATTERIES PACKED WITH EQUIPMENT** | + | | 9 | | |
| 3092 | **1-METHOXY-2-PROPANOL** | ●2Y | | 3 | | 30 |
| 3093 | **CORROSIVE LIQUID, OXIDISING, N.O.S.** | 2W | B | 8 | 5.1 | 885 |
| 3093 | **CORROSIVE LIQUID, OXIDISING, N.O.S.** | 2W | | 8 | 5.1 | 85 |
| 3094 | **CORROSIVE LIQUID, WATER-REACTIVE, N.O.S.** | 4W | | 8 | 4.3 | 823 |
| 3095 | **CORROSIVE SOLID, SELF-HEATING, N.O.S.** | 2W | | 8 | 4.2 | 884/ 84 |
| 3096 | **CORROSIVE SOLID, WATER-REACTIVE, N.O.S.** | 4W | | 8 | 4.3 | 842 |
| 3097 | **FLAMMABLE SOLID, OXIDISING, N.O.S.** | + | | 4.1 | 5.1 | |
| 3098 | **OXIDISING LIQUID, CORROSIVE, N.O.S.** | 2W | | 5.1 | 8 | |
| 3099 | **OXIDISING LIQUID, TOXIC, N.O.S.** | 2W | | 5.1 | 6.1 | |
| 3100 | *UN No. not used* | | | | | |
| 3101 | **ORGANIC PEROXIDE TYPE B, LIQUID** | 2WE | | 5.2 | | |
| 3102 | **ORGANIC PEROXIDE TYPE B, SOLID** | 1WE | | 5.2 | | |
| 3103 | **ORGANIC PEROXIDE TYPE C, LIQUID** | 2WE | | 5.2 | | |
| 3104 | **ORGANIC PEROXIDE TYPE C, SOLID** | 1WE | | 5.2 | | |
| 3105 | **ORGANIC PEROXIDE TYPE D, LIQUID** | 2WE | | 5.2 | | |
| 3106 | **ORGANIC PEROXIDE TYPE D, SOLID** | 1WE | | 5.2 | | |
| 3107 | **ORGANIC PEROXIDE TYPE E, LIQUID** | 2W | | 5.2 | | |
| 3108 | **ORGANIC PEROXIDE TYPE E, SOLID** | 1W | | 5.2 | | |
| 3109 | **ORGANIC PEROXIDE TYPE F, LIQUID** | 2W | | 5.2 | | 539 |
| 3109 | **ORGANIC PEROXIDE TYPE F, LIQUID** | 2W | | 5.2 | 8 | 539 |
| 3110 | **ORGANIC PEROXIDE TYPE F, SOLID** | 2W | | 5.2 | | 539 |
| 3111 | **ORGANIC PEROXIDE TYPE B, LIQUID, TEMPERATURE CONTROLLED** | 2WE | | 5.2 | | |

| UN | Substance | EAC | APP | Hazards | | ADR |
| | | | | Class | Sub Risks | HIN |
|---|---|---|---|---|---|---|
| 3112 | ORGANIC PEROXIDE TYPE B, SOLID, TEMPERATURE CONTROLLED | 1WE | | 5.2 | | |
| 3113 | ORGANIC PEROXIDE TYPE C, LIQUID, TEMPERATURE CONTROLLED | 2WE | | 5.2 | | |
| 3114 | ORGANIC PEROXIDE TYPE C, SOLID, TEMPERATURE CONTROLLED | 1WE | | 5.2 | | |
| 3115 | ORGANIC PEROXIDE TYPE D, LIQUID, TEMPERATURE CONTROLLED | 2WE | | 5.2 | | |
| 3116 | ORGANIC PEROXIDE TYPE D, SOLID, TEMPERATURE CONTROLLED | 1WE | | 5.2 | | |
| 3117 | ORGANIC PEROXIDE TYPE E, LIQUID, TEMPERATURE CONTROLLED | 2W | | 5.2 | | |
| 3118 | ORGANIC PEROXIDE TYPE E, SOLID, TEMPERATURE CONTROLLED | 1W | | 5.2 | | |
| 3119 | ORGANIC PEROXIDE TYPE F, LIQUID, TEMPERATURE CONTROLLED | 2W | | 5.2 | | 539 |
| 3120 | ORGANIC PEROXIDE TYPE F, SOLID, TEMPERATURE CONTROLLED | 1W | | 5.2 | | |
| 3121 | UN No. not used | | | | | |
| 3122 | TOXIC LIQUID, OXIDISING, N.O.S. | 2W | B | 6.1 | 5.1 | 665 |
| 3122 | TOXIC LIQUID, OXIDISING, N.O.S. | 2W | | 6.1 | 5.1 | 65 |
| 3123 | TOXIC LIQUID, WATER-REACTIVE, N.O.S. | 4W | | 6.1 | 4.3 | 623 |
| 3124 | TOXIC SOLID, SELF-HEATING, N.O.S. | 2W | | 6.1 | 4.2 | 664/ 64 |
| 3125 | TOXIC SOLID, WATER-REACTIVE, N.O.S. | 4W | | 6.1 | 4.3 | 642 |
| 3126 | SELF-HEATING SOLID, ORGANIC, CORROSIVE, N.O.S | 2W | | 4.2 | 8 | 48 |
| 3127 | UN No. not used | | | | | |
| 3128 | SELF-HEATING SOLID, ORGANIC, TOXIC, N.O.S. | 2W | | 4.2 | 6.1 | 46 |
| 3129 | WATER-REACTIVE LIQUID, CORROSIVE, N.O.S. | 4W | | 4.3 | 8 | X382/ 382 |
| 3130 | WATER-REACTIVE LIQUID, TOXIC, N.O.S. | 4W | | 4.3 | 6.1 | X362/ 362 |

| UN | Substance | EAC | APP | Hazards | | ADR |
| | | | | Class | Sub Risks | HIN |
|---|---|---|---|---|---|---|
| 3131 | WATER-REACTIVE SOLID, CORROSIVE, N.O.S. | 4W | | 4.3 | 8 | 482 |
| 3132 | WATER-REACTIVE SOLID, FLAMMABLE, N.O.S. | 4Y | | 4.3 | 4.1 | |
| 3133 | *UN No. not used* | | | | | |
| 3134 | WATER-REACTIVE SOLID, TOXIC, N.O.S. | 4W | | 4.3 | 6.1 | 462 |
| 3135 | WATER-REACTIVE SOLID, SELF-HEATING, N.O.S. | 4Y | | 4.3 | 4.2 | |
| 3136 | TRIFLUOROMETHANE, REFRIGERATED LIQUID | 2RE | A | 2.2 | | 22 |
| 3137 | *UN No. not used* | | | | | |
| 3138 | ETHYLENE, ACETYLENE AND PROPYLENE MIXTURE, REFRIGERATED LIQUID, *containing at least 71.5% ethylene with not more than 22.5% acetylene and not more than 6% propylene* | 2WE | A | 2.1 | | 223 |
| 3139 | OXIDISING LIQUID, N.O.S. | 2Y | | 5.1 | | |
| 3140 | ALKALOIDS, LIQUID, N.O.S. *or* ALKALOID SALTS, LIQUID, N.O.S. | 2X | B | 6.1 | | 66 |
| 3140 | ALKALOIDS, LIQUID, N.O.S. *or* ALKALOID SALTS, LIQUID, N.O.S. | 2X | | 6.1 | | 60 |
| 3141 | ANTIMONY COMPOUND, INORGANIC, LIQUID, N.O.S. | 2X | | 6.1 | | 60 |
| 3142 | DISINFECTANT, LIQUID, TOXIC, N.O.S. | 2XE | B | 6.1 | | 66 |
| 3142 | DISINFECTANT, LIQUID, TOXIC, N.O.S. | 2X | | 6.1 | | 60 |
| 3143 | DYE, SOLID, TOXIC, N.O.S. *or* DYE INTERMEDIATE, SOLID, TOXIC, N.O.S. | 2X | | 6.1 | | 66/ 60 |
| 3144 | NICOTINE COMPOUND, LIQUID, N.O.S. *or* NICOTINE PREPARATION, LIQUID, N.O.S. | 2X | B | 6.1 | | 66 |
| 3144 | NICOTINE COMPOUND, LIQUID, N.O.S *or* NICOTINE PREPARATION, LIQUID, N.O.S. | 2X | | 6.1 | | 60 |
| 3145 | ALKYLPHENOLS, LIQUID, N.O.S. *(including C2-C12 homologues)* | 2X | B | 8 | | 88 |
| 3145 | ALKLPHENOLS, LIQUID, N.O.S. *(including C2-C12 homologues)* | 2X | | 8 | | 80 |
| 3146 | ORGANOTIN COMPOUND, SOLID, N.O.S. | 2X | | 6.1 | | 66/ 60 |

| UN | Substance | EAC | APP | Hazards | | ADR |
| | | | | Class | Sub Risks | HIN |
|---|---|---|---|---|---|---|
| 3147 | DYE, SOLID, CORROSIVE, N.O.S. *or* DYE INTERMEDIATE, SOLID, CORROSIVE, N.O.S. | 2X | | 8 | | 88/ 80 |
| 3148 | WATER-REACTIVE LIQUID, N.O.S. | 4W | | 4.3 | | X323/ 323 |
| 3149 | HYDROGEN PEROXIDE AND PEROXYACETIC ACID MIXTURE, STABILIZED, *with acid(s), water and not more than 5% peroxyacetic acid* | 2W | | 5.1 | 8 | 58 |
| 3150 | DEVICES, SMALL, HYDROCARBON GAS POWERED *or* HYDROCARBON GAS REFILLS FOR SMALL DEVICES, *with release device* | + | | 2.1 | | |
| 3151 | POLYHALOGENATED BIPHENYLS, LIQUID *or* POLYHALOGENATED TERPHENYLS, LIQUID | 2X | | 9 | | 90 |
| 3152 | POLYHALOGENATED BIPHENYLS, SOLID *or* POLYHALOGENATED TERPHENYLS, SOLID | 2X | | 9 | | 90 |
| 3153 | PERFLUORO (METHYL VINYL ETHER) | 2WE | A | 2.1 | | 23 |
| 3154 | PERFLUORO (ETHYL VINYL ETHER) | 2WE | | 2.1 | | 23 |
| 3155 | PENTACHLOROPHENOL | 2X | | 6.1 | | 60 |
| 3156 | COMPRESSED GAS, OXIDISING, N.O.S. | 2S | | 2.2 | 5.1 | 25 |
| 3157 | LIQUEFIED GAS, OXIDISING, N.O.S. | 2P | A | 2.2 | 5.1 | 25 |
| 3158 | GAS, REFRIGERATED LIQUID, N.O.S. | 2RE | A | 2.2 | | 22 |
| 3159 | 1,1,1,2-TETRAFLUOROETHANE (REFRIGERANT GAS R134a) | 2RE | A | 2.2 | | 20 |
| 3160 | LIQUEFIED GAS, TOXIC, FLAMMABLE, N.O.S. | 2WE | AB | 2.3 | 2.1 | 263 |
| 3161 | LIQUEFIED GAS, FLAMMABLE, N.O.S. | 2WE | A | 2.1 | | 23 |
| 3162 | LIQUEFIED GAS, TOXIC, N.O.S. | 2XE | AB | 2.3 | | 26 |
| 3163 | LIQUEFIED GAS, N.O.S. | 2RE | A | 2.2 | | 20 |
| 3164 | ARTICLES, PRESSURIZED PNEUMATIC *or* HYDRAULIC *(containing non-flammable gas)* | + | | 2.2 | | |
| 3165 | AIRCRAFT HYDRAULIC POWER UNIT FUEL TANK *(containing a mixture of anhydrous hydrazine and methylhydrazine) (M86 fuel)* | + | | 3 | 6.1 8 | |
| 3166 | *UN No. not used* | | | | | |

| UN | Substance | EAC | APP | Hazards | | ADR |
|---|---|---|---|---|---|---|
| | | | | Class | Sub Risks | HIN |
| 3167 | **GAS SAMPLE, NON-PRESSURIZED, FLAMMABLE, N.O.S.** *not refrigerated liquid* | + | | 2.1 | | |
| 3168 | **GAS SAMPLE, NON-PRESSURIZED, TOXIC, FLAMMABLE, N.O.S.,** *not refrigerated liquid* | + | | 2.3 | 2.1 | |
| 3169 | **GAS SAMPLE, NON-PRESSURIZED, TOXIC, N.O.S.,** *not refrigerated liquid* | + | | 2.3 | | |
| 3170 | **ALUMINIUM SMELTING BY-PRODUCTS** *or* **ALUMINIUM REMELTING BY-PRODUCTS** | 4W | | 4.3 | | 42.3 |
| 3171 | *UN No. not used* | | | | | |
| 3172 | **TOXINS, EXTRACTED FROM LIVING SOURCES, TOXIC, N.O.S.** | 2X | B | 6.1 | | 66 |
| 3172 | **TOXINS, EXTRACTED FROM LIVING SOURCES, TOXIC, N.O.S.** | 2X | | 6.1 | | 60 |
| 3173 | *UN No. not used* | | | | | |
| 3174 | **TITANIUM DISULPHIDE** | 4W | | 4.2 | | 40 |
| 3175 | **SOLIDS CONTAINING FLAMMABLE LIQUID, N.O.S.** | 2Y | | 4.1 | | 40 |
| 3176 | **FLAMMABLE SOLID, ORGANIC, MOLTEN, N.O.S.** | 2W | A | 4.1 | | 44 |
| 3177 | *UN No. not used* | | | | | |
| 3178 | **FLAMMABLE SOLID, INORGANIC, N.O.S.** | 1Z | | 4.1 | | 40 |
| 3179 | **FLAMMABLE SOLID, TOXIC, INORGANIC, N.O.S.** | 2X | | 4.1 | 6.1 | 46 |
| 3180 | **FLAMMABLE SOLID, CORROSIVE, INORGANIC, N.O.S.** | 2X | | 4.1 | 8 | 48 |
| 3181 | **METAL SALTS OF ORGANIC COMPOUNDS, FLAMMABLE, N.O.S.** | 1Z | | 4.1 | | 40 |
| 3182 | **METAL HYDRIDES, FLAMMABLE, N.O.S.** | 1Z | | 4.1 | | 40 |
| 3183 | **SELF-HEATING LIQUID, ORGANIC, N.O.S.** | ●2Y | | 4.2 | | 30 |
| 3184 | **SELF-HEATING LIQUID, TOXIC ORGANIC, N.O.S.** | ●2W | | 4.2 | 6.1 | 36 |
| 3185 | **SELF-HEATING LIQUID, CORROSIVE ORGANIC, N.O.S.** | ●2W | | 4.2 | 8 | 38 |
| 3186 | **SELF-HEATING LIQUID, INORGANIC, N.O.S.** | ●2Y | | 4.2 | | 30 |

| UN | Substance | EAC | APP | Hazards | | ADR |
| | | | | Class | Sub Risks | HIN |
|---|---|---|---|---|---|---|
| 3187 | SELF-HEATING LIQUID, TOXIC, INORGANIC, N.O.S. | ●2W | | 4.2 | 6.1 | 36 |
| 3188 | SELF-HEATING LIQUID, CORROSIVE, INORGANIC, N.O.S. | ●2W | | 4.2 | 8 | 38 |
| 3189 | METAL POWDER, SELF-HEATING, N.O.S. | 4Y | | 4.2 | | 40 |
| 3190 | SELF-HEATING SOLID, INORGANIC, N.O.S. | 1Y | | 4.2 | | 40 |
| 3191 | SELF-HEATING SOLID, TOXIC, INORGANIC, N.O.S. | 2W | | 4.2 | 6.1 | 46 |
| 3192 | SELF HEATING SOLID, CORROSIVE, INORGANIC, N.O.S. | 2W | | 4.2 | 8 | 48 |
| 3193 | *UN No. not used* | | | | | |
| 3194 | PYROPHORIC LIQUID, INORGANIC, N.O.S. | 2WE | | 4.2 | | 333 |
| 3195 to 3199 | *UN Nos. not used* | | | | | |
| 3200 | PYROPHORIC SOLID, INORGANIC, N.O.S. | 4W | | 4.2 | | |
| 3201 | *UN No. not used* | | | | | |
| 3202 | *UN No. not used* | | | | | |
| 3203 | PYROPHORIC ORGANOMETALLIC COMPOUND, WATER REACTIVE, N.O.S. | 4WE | | 4.2 | 4.3 | X333 |
| 3204 | *UN No. not used* | | | | | |
| 3205 | ALKALINE EARTH METAL ALCOHOLATES, N.O.S. | 1Y | | 4.2 | | 40 |
| 3206 | ALKALI METAL ALCOHOLATES, SELF-HEATING, CORROSIVE, N.O.S. | 2W | | 4.2 | 8 | 48 |
| 3207 | ORGANOMETALLIC COMPOUND, SOLUTION, *or* COMPOUND DISPERSION, WATER-REACTIVE, FLAMMABLE, N.O.S. | 4WE | | 4.3 | 3 | X323/ 323 |
| 3208 | METALLIC SUBSTANCE, WATER-REACTIVE, N.O.S. | 4W | | 4.3 | | 423 |
| 3209 | METALLIC SUBSTANCE, WATER-REACTIVE, SELF-HEATING, N.O.S. | 4W | | 4.3 | 4.2 | 423 |
| 3210 | CHLORATES, INORGANIC, AQUEOUS SOLUTION, N.O.S. | 2X | | 5.1 | | 50 |

| UN | Substance | EAC | APP | Hazards | | ADR |
| | | | | Class | Sub Risks | HIN |
|---|---|---|---|---|---|---|
| 3211 | PERCHLORATES, INORGANIC, AQUEOUS SOLUTION, N.O.S. | 2X | | 5.1 | | 50 |
| 3212 | HYPOCHLORITES, INORGANIC, N.O.S | 2WE | | 5.1 | | 50 |
| 3213 | BROMATES, INORGANIC, AQUEOUS, SOLUTION, N.O.S. | 2X | | 5.1 | | 50 |
| 3214 | PERMANGANATES, INORGANIC, AQUEOUS SOLUTION, N.O.S. | 2X | | 5.1 | | 50 |
| 3215 | PERSULPHATES, INORGANIC, N.O.S. | 2W | | 5.1 | | 50 |
| 3216 | PERSULPHATES, INORGANIC, AQUEOUS SOLUTION, N.O.S. | 2X | | 5.1 | | 50 |
| 3217 | *UN No. not used* | | | | | |
| 3218 | NITRATES, INORGANIC, AQUEOUS SOLUTION, N.O.S. | 2Z | | 5.1 | | 50 |
| 3219 | NITRITES, INORGANIC, AQUEOUS SOLUTION, N.O.S. | 2X | | 5.1 | | 50 |
| 3220 | PENTAFLUOROETHANE (REFRIGERANT GAS R125) | 2RE | A | 2.2 | | 20 |
| 3221 | SELF-REACTIVE LIQUID TYPE B | + | | 4.1 | | |
| 3222 | SELF-REACTIVE SOLID TYPE B | + | | 4.1 | | |
| 3223 | SELF-REACTIVE LIQUID TYPE C | + | | 4.1 | | |
| 3224 | SELF-REACTIVE SOLID TYPE C | + | | 4.1 | | |
| 3225 | SELF-REACTIVE LIQUID TYPE D | + | | 4.1 | | |
| 3226 | SELF-REACTIVE SOLID TYPE D | + | | 4.1 | | |
| 3227 | SELF-REACTIVE LIQUID TYPE E | + | | 4.1 | | |
| 3228 | SELF-REACTIVE SOLID TYPE E | + | | 4.1 | | |
| 3229 | SELF-REACTIVE LIQUID TYPE F | + | | 4.1 | | |
| 3230 | SELF-REACTIVE SOLID TYPE F | + | | 4.1 | | |
| 3231 | SELF-REACTIVE LIQUID TYPE B, TEMPERATURE CONTROLLED | + | | 4.1 | | |

| UN | Substance | EAC | APP | Hazards | | ADR |
| | | | | Class | Sub Risks | HIN |
| --- | --- | --- | --- | --- | --- | --- |
| 3232 | SELF-REACTIVE SOLID TYPE B, TEMPERATURE CONTROLLED | + | | 4.1 | | |
| 3233 | SELF-REACTIVE LIQUID TYPE C, TEMPERATURE CONTROLLED | + | | 4.1 | | |
| 3234 | SELF-REACTIVE SOLID TYPE C, TEMPERATURE CONTROLLED | + | | 4.1 | | |
| 3235 | SELF-REACTIVE LIQUID TYPE D, TEMPERATURE CONTROLLED | + | | 4.1 | | |
| 3236 | SELF-REACTIVE SOLID TYPE D, TEMPERATURE CONTROLLED | + | | 4.1 | | |
| 3237 | SELF-REACTIVE LIQUID TYPE E, TEMPERATURE CONTROLLED | + | | 4.1 | | |
| 3238 | SELF-REACTIVE SOLID TYPE E, TEMPERATURE CONTROLLED | + | | 4.1 | | |
| 3239 | SELF-REACTIVE LIQUID TYPE F, TEMPERATURE CONTROLLED | + | | 4.1 | | |
| 3240 | SELF-REACTIVE SOLID TYPE F, TEMPERATURE CONTROLLED | + | | 4.1 | | |
| 3241 | 2-BROMO-2-NITROPROPANE-1,3-DIOL | 1Y | | 4.1 | | 40 |
| 3242 | AZODICARBONAMIDE | 1Y | | 4.1 | | |
| 3243 | SOLIDS CONTAINING TOXIC LIQUID, N.O.S. | 2X | | 6.1 | | 60 |
| 3244 | SOLIDS CONTAINING CORROSIVE LIQUID, N.O.S. | 2X | | 8 | | 80 |
| 3245 | GENETICALLY MODIFIED MICRO-ORGANISMS | 2X | | 9 | | |
| 3246 | METHANESULPHONYL CHLORIDE | 2XE | B | 6.1 | 8 | 668 |
| 3247 | SODIUM PEROXOBORATE, ANHYDROUS | 1Y | | 5.1 | | 50 |
| 3248 | MEDICINE, LIQUID, FLAMMABLE, TOXIC, N.O.S., *flash point less than 23°C* | 3WE | | 3 | 6.1 | 336 |
| 3248 | MEDICINE, LIQUID, FLAMMABLE, TOXIC, N.O.S., *flash point 23°C or above* | 3W | | 3 | 6.1 | 36 |
| 3249 | MEDICINE, SOLID, TOXIC, N.O.S. | 2X | | 6.1 | | 60 |
| 3250 | CHLOROACETIC ACID, MOLTEN | 2X | | 6.1 | 8 | 68 |

| UN | Substance | EAC | APP | Hazards | | ADR |
| | | | | Class | Sub Risks | HIN |
|---|---|---|---|---|---|---|
| 3251 | ISOSORBIDE-5-MONONITRATE | 1Y | | 4.1 | | |
| 3252 | DIFLUOROMETHANE (REFRIGERANT GAS R32) | 2WE | A | 2.1 | | 23 |
| 3253 | DISODIUM TRIOXOSILICATE | 2X | | 8 | | 80 |
| 3254 | TRIBUTYLPHOSPHANE | 3W | | 4.2 | | |
| 3255 | *UN No. not used* | | | | | |
| 3256 | ELEVATED TEMPERATURE LIQUID, FLAMMABLE, N.O.S., *with flash point above 60.5°C, at or above its flash point* | 2W | A | 3 | | 30 |
| 3257 | ELEVATED TEMPERATURE LIQUID, N.O.S., *at or above 100°C and below its flash point (including molten metals, molten salts etc)* | 2W | A | 9 | | 99 |
| 3258 | ELEVATED TEMPERATURE SOLID, N.O.S., *at or above 240°C* | 2W | A | 9 | | 99 |
| 3259 | AMINES, SOLID, CORROSIVE, N.O.S. *or* POLYAMINES, SOLID, CORROSIVE, N.O.S. | 2X | | 8 | | 88/80 |
| 3260 | CORROSIVE SOLID, ACIDIC, INORGANIC, N.O.S. | 2X | | 8 | | 88/80 |
| 3261 | CORROSIVE SOLID, ACIDIC, ORGANIC, N.O.S. | 2X | | 8 | | 88/80 |
| 3262 | CORROSIVE SOLID, BASIC, INORGANIC, N.O.S. | 2X | | 8 | | 88/80 |
| 3263 | CORROSIVE SOLID, BASIC, ORGANIC, N.O.S. | 2X | | 8 | | 88/80 |
| 3264 | CORROSIVE LIQUID, ACIDIC, INORGANIC, N.O.S. | 2X | B | 8 | | 88 |
| 3264 | CORROSIVE LIQUID, ACIDIC, INORGANIC, N.O.S. | 2X | | 8 | | 80 |
| 3265 | CORROSIVE LIQUID, ACIDIC, ORGANIC, N.O.S. | 2X | B | 8 | | 88 |
| 3265 | CORROSIVE LIQUID, ACIDIC, ORGANIC, N.O.S. | 2X | | 8 | | 80 |
| 3266 | CORROSIVE LIQUID, BASIC, INORGANIC, N.O.S. | 2X | B | 8 | | 88 |
| 3266 | CORROSIVE LIQUID, BASIC, INORGANIC, N.O.S. | 2X | | 8 | | 80 |
| 3267 | CORROSIVE LIQUID, BASIC, ORGANIC, N.O.S. | 2X | B | 8 | | 88 |
| 3267 | CORROSIVE LIQUID, BASIC, ORGANIC, N.O.S. | 2X | | 8 | | 80 |

| UN | Substance | EAC | APP | Hazards | | ADR |
| | | | | Class | Sub Risks | HIN |
|---|---|---|---|---|---|---|
| 3268 | AIR BAG INFLATORS pyrotechnic *or* AIR BAG MODULES, pyrotechnic *or* SEAT-BELT PRETENSIONERS, pyrotechnic | + | | 9 | | |
| 3269 | POLYESTER RESIN KIT | + | | 3 | | |
| 3270 | NITROCELLULOSE MEMBRANE FILTERS | 1Z | | 4.1 | | |
| 3271 | ETHERS, N.O.S. *flash point less than 23°C* | 3YE | | 3 | | 33 |
| 3271 | ETHERS, N.O.S. *flash point 23°C or above* | 3Y | | 3 | | 30 |
| 3272 | ESTERS, N.O.S. *flash point less than 23°C* | ●3YE | | 3 | | 33 |
| 3272 | ESTERS, N.O.S. *flash point 23°C or above* | ●3Y | | 3 | | 30 |
| 3273 | NITRILES, FLAMMABLE, TOXIC, N.O.S. | 3WE | | 3 | 6.1 | 336 |
| 3274 | ALCOHOLATES SOLUTION, N.O.S., *in alcohol* | ●3WE | | 3 | 8 | 338 |
| 3275 | NITRILES, TOXIC, FLAMMABLE, N.O.S. | 3W | B | 6.1 | 3 | 663 |
| 3275 | NITRILES, TOXIC, FLAMMABLE, N.O.S. | 3W | | 6.1 | 3 | 63 |
| 3276 | NITRILES, TOXIC, N.O.S. | 3X | B | 6.1 | | 66 |
| 3276 | NITRILES, TOXIC, N.O.S. | 3X | | 6.1 | | 60 |
| 3277 | CHLOROFORMATES, TOXIC, CORROSIVE, N.O.S. | 2X | | 6.1 | 8 | 68 |
| 3278 | ORGANOPHOSPHORUS COMPOUND, TOXIC, N.O.S. | 2X | B | 6.1 | | 66 |
| 3278 | ORGANOPHOSPHORUS COMPOUND, TOXIC, N.O.S. | 2X | | 6.1 | | 60 |
| 3279 | ORGANOPHOSPHORUS COMPOUND, TOXIC, FLAMMABLE, N.O.S. | ●3W | B | 6.1 | 3 | 663 |
| 3279 | ORGANOPHOSPHORUS COMPOUND, TOXIC, FLAMMABLE, N.O.S. | ●3W | | 6.1 | 3 | 63 |
| 3280 | ORGANOARSENIC COMPOUND, N.O.S. | 2X | B | 6.1 | | 66 |
| 3280 | ORGANOARSENIC COMPOUNDS, N.O.S. | 2X | | 6.1 | | 60 |
| 3281 | METAL CARBONYLS, N.O.S. | 2X | B | 6.1 | | 66 |
| 3281 | METAL CARBONYLS, N.O.S. | 2X | | 6.1 | | 60 |
| 3282 | ORGANOMETALLIC COMPOUND, TOXIC, N.O.S. | 2X | B | 6.1 | | 66 |

| UN | Substance | EAC | APP | Hazards | | ADR |
| --- | --- | --- | --- | --- | --- | --- |
| | | | | Class | Sub Risks | HIN |
| 3282 | ORGANOMETALLIC COMPOUND, TOXIC, N.O.S. | 2X | | 6.1 | | 60 |
| 3283 | SELENIUM COMPOUND, N.O.S. | 2X | B | 6.1 | | 66 |
| 3283 | SELENIUM COMPOUND, N.O.S. | 2X | | 6.1 | | 60 |
| 3284 | TELLURIUM COMPOUND, N.O.S. | 2X | | 6.1 | | 60 |
| 3285 | VANADIUM COMPOUND, N.O.S. | 2X | | 6.1 | | 60 |
| 3286 | FLAMMABLE LIQUID, TOXIC, CORROSIVE, N.O.S. | ●3WE | | 3 | 6.1 8 | 368 |
| 3287 | TOXIC LIQUID, INORGANIC, N.O.S. | 2X | B | 6.1 | | 66 |
| 3287 | TOXIC LIQUID, INORGANIC, N.O.S. | 2X | | 6.1 | | 60 |
| 3288 | TOXIC SOLID, INORGANIC, N.O.S. | 2X | | 6.1 | | 66/ 60 |
| 3289 | TOXIC LIQUID, CORROSIVE, INORGANIC, N.O.S. | 2X | B | 6.1 | 8 | 668 |
| 3289 | TOXIC LIQUID, CORROSIVE, INORGANIC, N.O.S. | 2X | | 6.1 | 8 | 68 |
| 3290 | TOXIC SOLID, CORROSIVE, INORGANIC, N.O.S. | 2X | | 6.1 | 8 | 668/ 68 |
| 3291 | CLINICAL WASTE, UNSPECIFIED, N.O.S. *or* (BIO) MEDICAL WASTE, N.O.S. *or* REGULATED MEDICAL WASTE, N.O.S. | 2X | | 6.2 | | 606 |
| 3292 | BATTERIES, CONTAINING SODIUM *or* CELLS, CONTAINING SODIUM | + | | 4.3 | | |
| 3293 | HYDRAZINE, AQUEOUS SOLUTION *with not more than 37% hydrazine, by mass* | 2X | | 6.1 | | 60 |
| 3294 | HYDROGEN CYANIDE, SOLUTION IN ALCOHOL *with not more than 45% hydrogen cyanide* | ●2WE | B | 6.1 | 3 | 663 |
| 3295 | HYDROCARBONS, LIQUID, N.O.S. *flash point less than 23°C* | 3WE | | 3 | | 33 |
| 3295 | HYDROCARBONS, LIQUID, N.O.S. *flash point 23°C or above* | 3W | | 3 | | 30 |
| 3296 | HEPTAFLUOROPROPANE (REFRIGERANT GAS R227) | 2RE | A | 2.2 | | 20 |
| 3297 | ETHYLENE OXIDE AND CHLOROTETRAFLUOROETHANE MIXTURE, *with not more than 8.8% ethylene oxide* | 2RE | A | 2.2 | | 20 |

| UN | Substance | EAC | APP | Hazards | | ADR |
|---|---|---|---|---|---|---|
| | | | | Class | Sub Risks | HIN |
| 3298 | ETHYLENE OXIDE AND PENTAFLUOROETHANE MIXTURE, *with not more than 7.9% ethylene oxide* | 2RE | A | 2.2 | | 20 |
| 3299 | ETHYLENE OXIDE AND TETRAFLUOROETHANE MIXTURE, *with not more than 5.6% ethylene oxide* | 2RE | A | 2.2 | | 20 |
| 3300 | ETHYLENE OXIDE AND CARBON DIOXIDE MIXTURE, *with more than 87% ethylene oxide* | 2PE | B | 2.3 | 2.1 | 263 |
| 3301 | CORROSIVE LIQUID, SELF-HEATING, N.O.S. | 2X | B | 8 | 4.2 | 884 |
| 3301 | CORROSIVE LIQUID, SELF-HEATING, N.O.S. | 2X | | 8 | 4.2 | 84 |
| 3302 | 2-DIMETHYLAMINOETHYL ACRYLATE | 2Y | | 6.1 | | 60 |
| 3303 | COMPRESSED GAS, TOXIC, OXIDISING, N.O.S. | 2PE | B | 2.3 | 5.1 | 265 |
| 3304 | COMPRESSED GAS, TOXIC, CORROSIVE, N.O.S. | 2RE | B | 2.3 | 8 | 268 |
| 3305 | COMPRESSED GAS, TOXIC, FLAMMABLE, CORROSIVE, N.O.S. | 2PE | B | 2.3 | 2.1 8 | 263 |
| 3306 | COMPRESSED GAS, TOXIC, OXIDISING, CORROSIVE, N.O.S. | 2PE | B | 2.3 | 5.1 8 | 265 |
| 3307 | LIQUEFIED GAS, TOXIC, OXIDISING, N.O.S. | 2WE | AB | 2.3 | 5.1 | 265 |
| 3308 | LIQUEFIED GAS, TOXIC, CORROSIVE, N.O.S. | 2XE | AB | 2.3 | 8 | 268 |
| 3309 | LIQUEFIED GAS, TOXIC, FLAMMABLE, CORROSIVE, N.O.S. | 2WE | AB | 2.3 | 2.1 8 | 263 |
| 3310 | LIQUEFIED GAS, TOXIC, OXIDISING, CORROSIVE, N.O.S. | 2WE | AB | 2.3 | 5.1 8 | 265 |
| 3311 | GAS, REFRIGERATED LIQUID, OXIDISING, N.O.S. | 2PE | A | 2.2 | 5.1 | 225 |
| 3312 | GAS, REFRIGERATED LIQUID, FLAMMABLE, N.O.S. | 2WE | A | 2.1 | | 223 |
| 3313 | ORGANIC PIGMENTS SELF-HEATING | 1Y | | 4.2 | | 40 |
| 3314 | PLASTICS MOULDING COMPOUND *in dough, sheet or extruded rope form evolving flammable vapour* | 3Y | | 9 | | 90 |
| 3315 | CHEMICAL SAMPLE, TOXIC, *liquid or solid* | + | | 6.1 | | |
| 3316 | CHEMICAL KIT *or* FIRST AID KIT | + | | 9 | | |
| 3317 | 2-AMINO-4,6-DINITROPHENOL, WETTED *with not less than 20% water by mass* | + | | 4.1 | | |

| UN | Substance | EAC | APP | Hazards | | ADR |
|----|-----------|-----|-----|---------|---|-----|
| | | | | **Class** | **Sub Risks** | **HIN** |
| 3318 | **AMMONIA SOLUTION,** *relative density less than 0.880 at 15°C in water, with more than 50% ammonia* | 2RE | B | 2.3 | 8 | 268 |
| 3319 | **NITROGLYCERIN MIXTURE DESENSITIZED, SOLID, N.O.S.** *with more than 2% but not more than 10% nitroglycerin, by mass* | + | | 4.1 | | |
| 3320 | **SODIUM BOROHYDRIDE AND SODIUM HYDROXIDE SOLUTION,** *with not more than 12% sodium borohydride and not more than 40% sodium hydroxide, by mass* | 2X | | 8 | | 80 |
| 3321 | **RADIOACTIVE MATERIAL, LOW SPECIFIC ACTIVITY (LSA-II),** *non fissile or fissile-excepted* | | | 7 | | |
| 3322 | **RADIOACTIVE MATERIAL, LOW SPECIFIC ACTIVITY (LSA-III),** *non fissile or fissile-excepted* | | | 7 | | |
| 3323 | **RADIOACTIVE MATERIAL, TYPE C PACKAGE,** *non fissile or fissile-excepted* | | | 7 | | |
| 3324 | **RADIOACTIVE MATERIAL, LOW SPECIFIC ACTIVITY (LSA-II),** *FISSILE* | | | 7 | | |
| 3325 | **RADIOACTIVE MATERIAL, LOW SPECIFIC ACTIVITY (LSA-III),** *FISSILE* | | | 7 | | |
| 3326 | **RADIOACTIVE MATERIAL, SURFACE CONTAMINATED OBJECTS (SCO-I or SCO-II),** *FISSILE* | | | 7 | | |
| 3327 | **RADIOACTIVE MATERIAL, TYPE A PACKAGE,** *FISSILE, non special form* | | | 7 | | |
| 3328 | **RADIOACTIVE MATERIAL, TYPE B (U) PACKAGE,** *FISSILE* | | | 7 | | |
| 3329 | **RADIOACTIVE MATERIAL, TYPE B (M) PACKAGE,** *FISSILE* | | | 7 | | |
| 3330 | **RADIOACTIVE MATERIAL, TYPE C PACKAGE,** *FISSILE* | | | 7 | | |
| 3331 | **RADIOACTIVE MATERIAL, TRANSPORTED UNDER SPECIAL ARRANGEMENTS,** *FISSILE* | | | 7 | | |
| 3332 | **RADIOACTIVE MATERIAL, TYPE A PACKAGE, SPECIAL FORM,** *non-fissile or fissile excepted* | | | 7 | | |
| 3333 | **RADIOACTIVE MATERIAL, TYPE A PACKAGE, SPECIAL FORM,** *FISSILE* | | | 7 | | |

| UN | Substance | EAC | APP | Hazards | | ADR |
| | | | | Class | Sub Risks | HIN |
|---|---|---|---|---|---|---|
| 3334 | AVIATION REGULATED LIQUID, N.O.S. | 2Z | | 9 | | |
| 3335 | AVIATION REGULATED SOLID, N.O.S. | 2Z | | 9 | | |
| 3336 | MERCAPTANS, LIQUID, FLAMMABLE, N.O.S. *or* MERCAPTANS MIXTURE, LIQUID, FLAMMABLE, N.O.S. | 3WE | | 3 | | 33/ 30 |
| 3337 | REFRIGERANT GAS R404A | 2RE | A | 2.2 | | 20 |
| 3338 | REFRIGERANT GAS R407A | 2RE | A | 2.2 | | 20 |
| 3339 | REFRIGERANT GAS R407B | 2RE | A | 2.2 | | 20 |
| 3340 | REFRIGERANT GAS R407C | 2RE | A | 2.2 | | 20 |
| 3341 | THIOUREA DIOXIDE | 1Y | | 4.2 | | 40 |
| 3342 | XANTHATES | 4W | | 4.2 | | 40 |
| 3343 | NITROGLYCERIN MIXTURE, DESENSITIZED, LIQUID, FLAMMABLE, N.O.S. *with not more than 30% nitroglycerin by mass* | ●2Y | | 3 | | |
| 3344 | PENTAERYTHRITE TETRANITRATE MIXTURE, DESENSITIZED, SOLID, N.O.S. *with more than 10% but not more than 20% PETN by mass* | 1Y | | 4.1 | | |
| 3345 | PHENOXYACETIC ACID DERIVATIVE PESTICIDE, SOLID, TOXIC | 2X | | 6.1 | | 66/ 60 |
| 3346 | PHENOXYACETIC ACID DERIVATIVE PESTICIDE, LIQUID, FLAMMABLE, TOXIC, *flash point less than 23°C* | 2WE | | 3 | 6.1 | 336 |
| 3347 | PHENOXYACETIC ACID DERIVATIVE PESTICIDE, LIQUID, TOXIC, FLAMMABLE, *flash point 23°C or more* | 2W | B | 6.1 | 3 | 663 |
| 3347 | PHENOXYACETIC ACID DERIVATIVE PESTICIDE, LIQUID, TOXIC, FLAMMABLE, *flash point 23°C or more* | 2W | | 6.1 | 3 | 63 |
| 3348 | PHENOXYACETIC ACID DERIVATIVE PESTICIDE, LIQUID, TOXIC | 2X | B | 6.1 | | 66 |
| 3348 | PHENOXYACETIC ACID DERIVATIVE PESTICIDE, LIQUID, TOXIC | 2X | | 6.1 | | 60 |
| 3349 | PYRETHROID PESTICIDE, SOLID, TOXIC | 2X | | 6.1 | | 66/ 60 |

| UN | Substance | EAC | APP | Hazards | | ADR |
|----|-----------|-----|-----|---------|---|-----|
| | | | | Class | Sub Risks | HIN |
| 3350 | **PYRETHROID PESTICIDE, LIQUID, FLAMMABLE TOXIC,** *flash point less than 23°C* | 2WE | | 3 | 6.1 | 336 |
| 3351 | **PYRETHROID PESTICIDE, LIQUID, TOXIC FLAMMABLE,** *flash point 23°C or more* | 2W | B | 6.1 | 3 | 663 |
| 3351 | **PYRETHROID PESTICIDE, LIQUID, TOXIC FLAMMABLE,** *flash point 23°C or more* | 2W | | 6.1 | 3 | 63 |
| 3352 | **PYRETHROID PESTICIDE, LIQUID, TOXIC** | 2X | B | 6.1 | | 66 |
| 3352 | **PYRETHROID PESTICIDE, LIQUID, TOXIC** | 2X | | 6.1 | | 60 |
| 3353 | **AIR BAG INFLATORS, COMPRESSED GAS** *or* **AIR MODULES, COMPRESSED GAS** *or* **SEAT BELT PRETENSIONERS, COMPRESSED GAS** | 2T | | 2.2 | | |
| 3354 | **INSECTICIDE GAS, FLAMMABLE, N.O.S.** | 2WE | A | 2.1 | | 23 |
| 3355 | **INSECTICIDE GAS, TOXIC, FLAMMABLE, N.O.S.** | 2WE | AB | 2.3 | 2.1 | 263 |
| 3356 | **OXYGEN GENERATOR, CHEMICAL** | 1Y | | 5.1 | | |

# ALPHABETICAL LIST OF

# DANGEROUS SUBSTANCES

| Substance | UN Number | Substance | UN Number |
|---|---|---|---|
| *Accumulators, electric, see* | 2794 | *Acid mixtures, spent, nitrating acid, see* | 1826 |
|  | 2795 |  |  |
|  | 2800 | *Acraldehyde, inhibited, see* | 1092 |
|  | 3028 |  |  |
|  |  | **ACRIDINE** | 2713 |
| **ACETAL** | 1088 |  |  |
|  |  | **ACROLEIN DIMER, STABILISED** | 2607 |
| **ACETALDEHYDE** | 1089 |  |  |
|  |  | **ACROLEIN, INHIBITED** | 1092 |
| **ACETALDEHYDE AMMONIA** | 1841 |  |  |
|  |  | **ACRYLAMIDE** | 2074 |
| **ACETALDEHYDE OXIME** | 2332 |  |  |
|  |  | **ACRYLIC ACID, INHIBITED** | 2218 |
| **ACETIC ACID, GLACIAL** *or* |  |  |  |
| **ACETIC ACID SOLUTION,** |  | **ACRYLONITRILE, INHIBITED** | 1093 |
| *more than 80 per cent acid, by mass* | 2789 |  |  |
|  |  | *Actinolite, see* | 2590 |
| **ACETIC ACID SOLUTION,** |  |  |  |
| *more than 10 per cent but not* |  | *Activated carbon, see* | 1362 |
| *more than 80 per cent acid, by mass* | 2790 |  |  |
|  |  | *Activated charcoal, see* | 1362 |
| **ACETIC ANHYDRIDE** | 1715 |  |  |
|  |  | **ADHESIVES,** *containing flammable* |  |
| *Acetoin, see* | 2621 | *liquid* | 1133 |
|  |  |  |  |
| **ACETONE** | 1090 | **ADIPONITRILE** | 2205 |
|  |  |  |  |
| **ACETONE CYANOHYDRIN,** |  | **AEROSOLS** | 1950 |
| **STABILISED** | 1541 |  |  |
|  |  | **AIR BAG INFLATORS** | 3268 |
| **ACETONE OILS** | 1091 |  | 3353 |
|  |  |  |  |
| **ACETONITRILE** | 1648 | **AIR BAG MODULES** | 3268 |
|  |  |  | 3353 |
| **ACETYL BROMIDE** | 1716 |  |  |
|  |  | **AIR, COMPRESSED** | 1002 |
| **ACETYL CHLORIDE** | 1717 |  |  |
|  |  | **AIRCRAFT EVACUATION SLIDES** | 2990 |
| **ACETYLENE, DISSOLVED** | 1001 |  |  |
|  |  | **AIRCRAFT HYDRAULIC POWER** |  |
| *Acetylene tetrabromide, see* | 2504 | **UNIT FUEL TANK** *(containing a* |  |
|  |  | *mixture of anhydrous hydrazine and* |  |
| *Acetylene tetrachloride, see* | 1702 | *methylhydrazine) (M85 fuel)* | 3165 |
|  |  |  |  |
| **ACETYL IODIDE** | 1898 | **AIRCRAFT SURVIVAL KITS** | 2990 |
|  |  |  |  |
| **ACETYL METHYL CARBINOL** | 2621 | **AIR, REFRIGERATED LIQUID** | 1003 |
|  |  |  |  |
| *Acid butyl phosphate, see* | 1718 | **ALCOHOLATES SOLUTIONS,** |  |
|  |  | **N.O.S.,** *in alcohol* | 3274 |
| *Acid mixtures, hydrofluoric* |  |  |  |
| *and sulphuric, see* | 1786 | *Alcohol, denatured, see* | 1986 |
|  |  |  | 1987 |
| *Acid mixtures, nitrating acid, see* | 1796 |  |  |
|  |  | **ALCOHOLIC BEVERAGES** | 3065 |

| Substance | UN Number | Substance | UN Number |
|---|---|---|---|
| *Alcohol, industrial, see* | 1986 1987 | ALKYLPHENOLS, LIQUID, N.O.S., *(including $C_2$-$C_{12}$ homologues)* | 3145 |
| ALCOHOLS, N.O.S. | 1987 | ALKYLPHENOLS, SOLID, N.O.S., *(including $C_2$-$C_{12}$ homologues)* | 2430 |
| ALCOHOLS, FLAMMABLE, TOXIC, N.O.S. | 1986 | ALKYL SULPHONIC ACIDS, LIQUID, *or* ARYL SULPHONIC ACIDS, LIQUID, *with more than 5 per cent free sulphuric acid* | 2584 |
| *Aldehyde, see* | 1089 | | |
| ALDEHYDES, N.O.S 2584 | 1989 | ALKYL SULPHONIC ACIDS, LIQUID, *or* ARYL SULPHONIC ACIDS, LIQUID, *with not more than 5 per cent free sulphuric acid* | 2586 |
| ALDEHYDES, FLAMMABLE, TOXIC, N.O.S. | 1988 | ALKYL SULPHONIC ACIDS, SOLID *or* ARYL SULPHONIC ACIDS, SOLID *with more than 5 per cent free sulphuric acid* | 2583 |
| ALDOL | 2839 | | |
| ALKALI METAL ALCOHOLATES, SELF-HEATING, CORROSIVE, N.O.S. | 3206 | ALKYL SULPHONIC ACIDS, SOLID *or* ARYL SULPHONIC ACIDS, SOLID *with not more than 5 per cent sulphuric acid* | 2585 |
| ALKALI METAL ALLOY, LIQUID, N.O.S. | 1421 | ALKYL SULPHURIC ACIDS | 2571 |
| ALKALI METAL AMALGAM | 1389 | *Allene, see* | 2200 |
| ALKALI METAL AMIDES | 1390 | ALLYL ACETATE | 2333 |
| ALKALI METAL DISPERSION | 1391 | ALLYL ALCOHOL | 1098 |
| *Alkaline corrosive battery fluid, see* | 2797 | ALLYLAMINE | 2334 |
| ALKALINE EARTH METAL ALCOHOLATES, N.O.S. | 3205 | ALLYL BROMIDE | 1099 |
| ALKALINE EARTH METAL ALLOY, N.O.S. | 1393 | ALLYL CHLORIDE | 1100 |
| ALKALINE EARTH METAL AMALGAM | 1392 | *Allyl chlorocarbonate, see* | 1722 |
| ALKALINE EARTH METAL DISPERSION | 1391 | ALLYL CHLOROFORMATE | 1722 |
| | | ALLYL ETHYL ETHER | 2335 |
| ALKALOIDS, LIQUID, N.O.S. | 3140 | ALLYL FORMATE | 2236 |
| ALKALOIDS, SOLID, N.O.S. | 1544 | ALLYL GLYCIDYL ETHER | 2219 |
| ALKALOID SALTS, LIQUID, N.O.S. | 1544 | ALLYL IODIDE | 1723 |
| ALKALOID SALTS, SOLID, N.O.S. | 3140 | ALLYL ISOTHIOCYANATE, INHIBITED | 1545 |
| *Alkyl aluminium halides, see* | 3052 | | |

| Substance | UN Number | Substance | UN Number |
|---|---|---|---|
| ALLYLTRICHLOROSILANE, STABILISED | 1724 | AMINES, FLAMMABLE, CORROSIVE, N.O.S. | 2733 |
| ALUMINIUM ALKYL HALIDES | 3052 | AMINES, LIQUID, CORROSIVE, N.O.S. | 2735 |
| ALUMINIUM ALKYL HYDRIDES | 3076 | AMINES, LIQUID, CORROSIVE, FLAMMABLE, N.O.S. | 2734 |
| ALUMINIUM ALKYLS | 3051 | AMINES, SOLID, CORROSIVE, N.O.S. | 3259 |
| ALUMINIUM BOROHYDRIDE *or* ALUMINIUM BOROHYDRIDE IN DEVICES | 2870 | *Aminobenzene, see* | 1547 |
| ALUMINIUM BROMIDE, ANHYDROUS | 1725 | *2-Aminobenzotrifluoride, see* | 2942 |
| ALUMINIUM BROMIDE SOLUTION | 2580 | *3-Aminobenzotrifluoride, see* | 2948 |
| ALUMINIUM CARBIDE | 1394 | *Aminobutane, see* | 1125 |
| ALUMINIUM CHLORIDE, ANHYDROUS | 1726 | 2-AMINO-4-CHLOROPHENOL | 2673 |
| ALUMINIUM CHLORIDE SOLUTION | 2581 | 2-AMINO-4,6-DINITROPHENOL, WETTED with not less than 20% water by mass | 3317 |
| ALUMINIUM FERROSILICON POWDER | 1395 | 2-AMINO-5-DIETHYLAMINO-PENTANE | 2946 |
| ALUMINIUM HYDRIDE | 2463 | 2-(2-AMINOETHOXY) ETHANOL | 3055 |
| ALUMINIUM NITRATE | 1438 | N-AMINOETHYLPIPERAZINE | 2815 |
| ALUMINIUM PHOSPHIDE | 1397 | *1-Amino-2-nitrobenzene, see* | 1661 |
| ALUMINIUM PHOSPHIDE PESTICIDES | 3048 | *1-Amino-3-nitrobenzene, see* | 1661 |
| ALUMINIUM POWDER, COATED | 1309 | *1-Amino-4-nitrobenzene, see* | 1661 |
| ALUMINIUM POWDER, UNCOATED | 1396 | AMINOPHENOLS *(o-,m-,p-)* | 2512 |
| ALUMINIUM PROCESSING BY-PRODUCTS | 3170 | AMINOPYRIDINES *(o-,m-,p-)* | 2671 |
| ALUMINIUM RE-MELTING BY-PRODUCTS | 3170 | AMMONIA, ANHYDROUS | 1005 |
| ALUMINIUM RESINATE | 2715 | AMMONIA SOLUTION, *relative density (specific gravity) between 0.880 and 0.957 at 15°C in water with more than 10 per cent and not more than 35 per cent ammonia* | 2672 |
| ALUMINIUM SILICON POWDER, UNCOATED | 1398 | | |
| ALUMINIUM SMELTING BY-PRODUCTS | 3170 | | |

| Substance | UN Number |
|---|---|
| AMMONIA SOLUTION, *relative density (specific gravity) less than 0.880 at 15°C in water with more than 35 per cent and not more than 50 per cent ammonia* | 2073 |
| AMMONIA SOLUTION, *relative density (specific gravity) less than 0.880 at 15°C in water, with more than 50 per cent ammonia* | 3318 |
| AMMONIUM ARSENATE | 1546 |
| *Ammonium bichromate, see* | 1439 |
| *Ammonium bifluoride solid, see* | 1727 |
| *Ammonium bifluoride solution, see* | 2817 |
| *Ammonium bisulphate, see* | 2506 |
| AMMONIUM DICHROMATE | 1439 |
| AMMONIUM DINITRO-o-CRESOLATE | 1843 |
| AMMONIUM FLUORIDE | 2505 |
| AMMONIUM FLUOROSILICATE | 2854 |
| AMMONIUM HYDROGEN DIFLUORIDE, SOLID | 1727 |
| AMMONIUM HYDROGEN DIFLUORIDE SOLUTION | 2817 |
| AMMONIUM HYDROGEN SULPHATE | 2506 |
| *Ammonium hydrosulphide, this may be treated as for ammonium sulphide, see* | 2683 |
| AMMONIUM METAVANDATE | 2859 |
| AMMONIUM NITRATE *with not more than 0.2 per cent of combustible substances, including any organic substance calculated as carbon, to the exclusion of any other added substance* | 1942 |

| Substance | UN Number |
|---|---|
| AMMONIUM NITRATE FERTILISERS: *uniform non-segregating mixtures of ammonium nitrate with added matter which is inorganic and chemically inert towards ammonium nitrate, containing less than 90 per cent ammonium nitrate and not more than 0.2 per cent of combustible material (including organic material calculated as carbon), or containing more than 70 per cent but less than 90 per cent of ammonium nitrate and not more than 0.4 per cent of total combustible material* | 2067 |
| AMMONIUM NITRATE FERTILISERS: *uniform non-segregating mixtures of ammonium nitrate/ammonium sulphate, with more than 45 per cent but not more than 70 per cent of ammonium nitrate and not more than 0.4 per cent total combustible material* | 2069 |
| AMMONIUM NITRATE FERTILISERS: *uniform non-segregating mixtures of ammonium nitrate with calcium carbonate and/or dolomite, with more than 80 per cent but less than 90 per cent of ammonium nitrate and not more than 0.4 per cent total combustible material* | 2068 |
| AMMONIUM NITRATE FERTILISERS: *uniform non-segregating mixtures of nitrogen/phosphate or nitrogen/potash types or complete fertilizers of nitrogen/phosphate/potash type, with more than 70 per cent but less than 90 per cent of ammonium nitrate and not more than 0.4 per cent combustible material* | 2070 |
| AMMONIUM NITRATE FERTILISER, N.O.S. | 2072 |
| AMMONIUM NITRATE LIQUID *(hot concentrated solution)* | 2426 |
| AMMONIUM PERCHLORATE | 1442 |
| *Ammonium permanganate, see* | 1482 |
| AMMONIUM PERSULPHATE | 1444 |

| Substance | UN Number | Substance | UN Number |
|---|---|---|---|
| **AMMONIUM PICRATE, WETTED** *with not less than 10 per cent water, by weight* | 1310 | *Anhydrous ammonia, see* | 1005 |
| | | **ANILINE** | 1547 |
| **AMMONIUM POLYSULPHIDE SOLUTION** | 2818 | *Aniline chloride, see* | 1548 |
| | | **ANILINE HYDROCHLORIDE** | 1548 |
| **AMMONIUM POLYVANADATE** | 2861 | *Aniline oil, see* | 1547 |
| *Ammonium silicofluoride, see* | 2854 | *Aniline salt, see* | 1548 |
| **AMMONIUM SULPHIDE SOLUTION** | 2683 | **ANISIDINES** | 2431 |
| *Ammunition, lachrymatory, see* | 2017 | **ANISOLE** | 2222 |
| **AMMUNITION, TEAR-PRODUCING, NON-EXPLOSIVE** *without burster or expelling charge, non-fused* | 2017 | **ANISOYL CHLORIDE** | 1729 |
| | | *Anthophyllite, see* | 2590 |
| **AMMUNITION, TOXIC, NON-EXPLOSIVE** *without burster or expelling charge, non-fused* | 2016 | **ANTI-KNOCK MIXTURE, MOTOR FUEL** | 1649 |
| | | *Antimonous chloride, see* | 1733 |
| *Amosite, see* | 2212 | **ANTIMONY COMPOUND, INORGANIC, LIQUID, N.O.S.** | 3141 |
| **AMYL ACETATES** | 1104 | **ANTIMONY COMPOUND, INORGANIC, SOLID, N.O.S.** | 1549 |
| **AMYL ACID PHOSPHATE** | 2819 | | |
| *Amyl Alcohols, see* | 1105 | *Antimony hydride, see* | 2676 |
| *Amyl aldehyde, see* | 2058 | **ANTIMONY LACTATE** | 1550 |
| **AMYLAMINE** | 1106 | **ANTIMONY PENTACHLORIDE, LIQUID** | 1730 |
| **AMYL BUTYRATES** | 2620 | | |
| **AMYL CHLORIDE** | 1107 | **ANTIMONY PENTACHLORIDE, SOLUTION** | 1731 |
| *n-Amylene, see* | 1108 | **ANTIMONY PENTAFLUORIDE** | 1732 |
| **AMYL FORMATES** | 1109 | *Antimony perchloride, liquid, see* | 1730 |
| **AMYL MERCAPTAN** | 1111 | **ANTIMONY POTASSIUM TARTRATE** | 1551 |
| **n-AMYL METHYL KETONE** | 1110 | | |
| **AMYL NITRATE** | 1112 | **ANTIMONY POWDER** | 2871 |
| **AMYL NITRITE** | 1113 | **ANTIMONY TRICHLORIDE** | 1733 |
| **AMYLTRICHLOROSILANE** | 1728 | *Antu, see* | 1651 |
| *Anaesthetic ether, see* | 1155 | **ARGON, COMPRESSED** | 1006 |

| Substance | UN Number | Substance | UN Number |
|---|---|---|---|
| **ARGON, REFRIGERATED LIQUID** | 1951 | *Arsenites, n.o.s., liquid, see* | 1556 |
| *Arsenates, n.o.s. liquid, see* | 1556 | *Arsenites, n.o.s., solid, see* | 1557 |
| *Arsenates, n.o.s., solid, see* | 1557 | *Arsenous chloride, see* | 1560 |
| **ARSENIC** | 1558 | **ARSINE** | 2188 |
| **ARSENIC ACID, LIQUID** | 1553 | **ARTICLES PRESSURISED PNEUMATIC** *or* **HYDRAULIC** *(containing non-flammable gas)* | 3164 |
| **ARSENIC ACID, SOLID** | 1554 | | |
| **ARSENICAL DUST** | 1562 | **ARYL SULPHONIC ACID** | 2583 2584 2585 2586 |
| *Arsenical flue dust, see* | 1562 | | |
| **ARSENICAL PESTICIDE, LIQUID, FLAMMABLE, TOXIC,** *flash point less than 23°C* | 2760 | *Asbestos, blue or brown, see* | 2212 |
| | | *Asbestos, white, see* | 2590 |
| **ARSENICAL PESTICIDE, LIQUID, TOXIC, FLAMMABLE,** *flash point 23°C or above* | 2993 | *Asphalt, see* | 1999 |
| | | *Aviation fuel, see* | 1863 |
| **ARSENICAL PESTICIDE, LIQUID, TOXIC** | 2994 | **AZODICARBONAMIDE** | 3242 |
| **ARSENICAL PESTICIDE, SOLID, TOXIC** | 2759 | **BARIUM** | 1400 |
| | | **BARIUM ALLOYS, PYROPHORIC** | 1854 |
| **ARSENIC BROMIDE** | 1555 | **BARIUM AZIDE, WETTED** *with not less than 50 per cent water, by mass* | 1571 |
| *Arsenic chloride, see* | 1560 | | |
| **ARSENIC COMPOUND, LIQUID, INORGANIC, TOXIC, N.O.S.,** *including: Arsenates, n.o.s.; Arsenites, n.o.s.; Arsenic sulphides, n.o.s.* | 1556 | *Barium binoxide, see* | 1449 |
| | | **BARIUM BROMATE** | 2719 |
| | | **BARIUM CHLORATE** | 1445 |
| **ARSENIC COMPOUND SOLID, INORGANIC, TOXIC, N.O.S.,** *inlcuding Arsenates, n.o.s.; Arsenites, n.o.s.; Arsenic sulphides, n.o.s.* | 1557 | **BARIUM COMPOUND, TOXIC, N.O.S.** | 1564 |
| | | **BARIUM CYANIDE** | 1565 |
| **ARSENIC PENTOXIDE** | 1559 | *Barium dioxide, see* | 1449 |
| **ARSENIC TRICHLORIDE** | 1560 | **BARIUM HYPOCHLORITE** *with more than 22 per cent available chlorine* | 2741 |
| *Arsenic sulphides, n.o.s. see* | 1556 1557 | | |
| | | **BARIUM NITRATE** | 1446 |
| **ARSENIC TRIOXIDE** | 1561 | **BARIUM OXIDE** | 1884 |
| *Arsenious chloride, see* | 1560 | | |

| Substance | UN Number | Substance | UN Number |
|---|---|---|---|
| **BARIUM PERCHLORATE** | 1447 | **BENZOTRIFLUORIDE** | 2338 |
| **BARIUM PERMANGANATE** | 1448 | **BENZOYL CHLORIDE** | 1736 |
| **BARIUM PEROXIDE** | 1449 | **BENZYL BROMIDE** | 1737 |
| *Barium selenate, see* | 2630 | **BENZYL CHLORIDE** | 1738 |
| *Barium selenite, see* | 2630 | *Benzyl chlorocarbonate, see* | 1739 |
| *Barium superoxide, see* | 1449 | **BENZYL CHLOROFORMATE** | 1739 |
| **BATTERIES, CONTAINING SODIUM** | 3292 | *Benzyl cyanide, see* | 2470 |
| **BATTERIES, DRY, CONTAINING POTASSIUM HYDROXIDE SOLID,** *electric, storage* | 3028 | **BENZYL DIMETHYLAMINE** | 2619 |
| | | **BENZYLIDENE CHLORIDE** | 1886 |
| **BATTERIES, WET, FILLED WITH ACID,** *electric, storage* | 2794 | **BENZYL IODIDE** | 2653 |
| **BATTERIES, WET, FILLED WITH ALKALI,** *electric, storage* | 2795 | **BERYLLIUM COMPOUND, TOXIC, N.O.S.** | 1566 |
| | | **BERYLLIUM POWDER** | 1567 |
| **BATTERIES, WET, NON-SPILLABLE,** *electric, storage* | 2800 | **BERYLLIUM NITRATE** | 2464 |
| **BATTERY FLUID, ACID** | 2796 | **BICYCLO[2,2,1]HEPTA-2,5-DIENE, INHIBITED** | 2251 |
| **BATTERY FLUID, ALKALI** | 2797 | *Biflourides, n.o.s., see* | 1740 |
| **BENZALDEHYDE** | 1990 | **(BIO) MEDICAL WASTE, N.O.S.** | 3291 |
| **BENZENE** | 1114 | **BIPYRIDILIUM PESTICIDE, LIQUID, FLAMMABLE, TOXIC,** *flash point less than 23°C* | 2782 |
| *1, 4-Benzendiol, see* | 2662 | |
| **BENZENESULPHONYL CHLORIDE** | 2225 | **BIPYRIDILIUM PESTICIDE, LIQUID, TOXIC, FLAMMABLE,** *flash point 23°C or above* | 3015 |
| *Benzenethiol, see* | 2337 | |
| **BENZIDINE** | 1885 | **BIPYRIDILIUM PESTICIDE, LIQUID, TOXIC** | 3016 |
| *Benzolene, see* | 1271 | |
| *Benzol, see* | 1114 | **BIPYRIDILIUM PESTICIDE, SOLID, TOXIC** | 2781 |
| **BENZONITRILE** | 2224 | |
| **BENZOQUINONE** | 2587 | **BISULPHATES, AQUEOUS SOLUTION** | 2837 |
| *Benzosulphochloride, see* | 2225 | **BISULPHITES, AQUEOUS SOLUTION, N.O.S.** | 2693 |
| **BENZOTRICHLORIDE** | 2226 | |

| Substance | UN Number | Substance | UN Number |
|---|---|---|---|
| Bitumen, see | 1999 | BROMOACETONE | 1969 |
| Blau gas, see | 2600 | omega-Bromoacetophenone, see | 2645 |
| Bleaching powder, see | 2208 | BROMOACETYL BROMIDE | 2513 |
| BLUE ASBESTOS (crocidolite) | 2212 | BROMOBENZENE | 2514 |
| BOMBS, SMOKE, NON-EXPLOSIVE, with corrosive liquid, without initiating device | 2028 | BROMOBENZYL CYANIDES | 1694 |
| | | 1-BROMOBUTANE | 1126 |
| Borate and chlorate mixtures, see | 1458 | 2-BROMOBUTANE | 2339 |
| BORNEOL | 1312 | BROMOCHLOROMETHANE | 1887 |
| BORON TRIBROMIDE | 2692 | 1-BROMO-3-CHLOROPROPANE | 2688 |
| BORON TRICHLORIDE | 1741 | 1-Bromo-2,3-epoxypropane, see | 2558 |
| BORON TRIFLUORIDE, COMPRESSED | 1008 | Bromoethane, see | 1891 |
| BORON TRIFLUORIDE ACETIC ACID COMPLEX | 1742 | 2-BROMOETHYL ETHYL ETHER | 2340 |
| | | BROMOFORM | 2515 |
| BORON TRIFLUORIDE DIETHYL ETHERATE | 2604 | Bromomethane, see | 1062 |
| BORON TRIFLUORIDE DIMETHYL ETHERATE | 2965 | 1-BROMO-3-METHYLBUTANE | 2341 |
| | | BROMOMETHYLPROPANES | 2342 |
| BORON TRIFLUORIDE DIHYDRATE | 2851 | 2-BROMO-2-NITROPROPANE-1, 3-DIOL | 3241 |
| BORON TRIFLUORIDE PROPIONIC ACID COMPLEX | 1743 | 2-BROMOPENTANE | 2343 |
| BROMATES, INORGANIC, N.O.S. | 1450 | BROMOPROPANES | 2344 |
| BROMATES, INORGANIC, AQUEOUS SOLUTION, N.O.S. | 3213 | 3-BROMOPROPYNE | 2345 |
| | | BROMOTRIFLUOROETHYLENE | 2419 |
| BROMINE | 1744 | BROMOTRIFLUOROMETHANE | 1009 |
| BROMINE CHLORIDE | 2901 | BROWN ASBESTOS (amosite, mysorite) | 2212 |
| BROMINE PENTAFLUORIDE | 1745 | | |
| BROMINE SOLUTION | 1744 | BRUCINE | 1570 |
| BROMINE TRIFLUORIDE | 1746 | BUTADIENES, INHIBITED | 1010 |
| BROMOACETIC ACID | 1938 | BUTANE | 1011 |
| | | BUTANEDIONE | 2346 |

| Substance | UN Number | Substance | UN Number |
|---|---|---|---|
| *Butane-1-thiol, see* | 2347 | **n-BUTYL CHLOROFORMATE** | 2743 |
| *Butan-2-ol, see* | 1120 | **tert-BUTYLCYCLOHEXYL CHLOROFORMATE** | 2747 |
| **n-BUTANOL** | 1120 | **BUTYLENE** | 1012 |
| **sec-BUTANOL** | 1120 | | |
| **tert-BUTANOL** | 1120 | **1.2-BUTYLENE OXIDE, STABILISED** | 3022 |
| *1-Butanol, see* | 1120 | *Butyl ethers, see* | 1149 |
| *Butanol, secondary, see* | 1120 | *Butyl ethyl ether, see* | 1179 |
| *Butanol, tertiary, see* | 1120 | **n-BUTYL FORMATE** | 1128 |
| *Butanone, see* | 1193 | **N,n-BUTYLIMIDAZOLE** | 2690 |
| *2-Butenal, see* | 1143 | *N,n-Butyl iminazole, see* | 2690 |
| *Butene, see* | 1012 | **n-BUTYL ISOCYANATE** | 2485 |
| *But-1-ene-3-one, see* | 1251 | **tert-BUTYL ISOCYANATE** | 2484 |
| *1, 2-Buteneoxide, see* | 3022 | *Butyl lithium, see* | 2445 |
| *2-Buten-1-ol, see* | 2614 | **BUTYL MERCAPTAN** | 2347 |
| **BUTYL ACETATES** | 1123 | **n-BUTYL METHACRYLATE, INHIBITED** | 2227 |
| *Butyl acetate, secondary, see* | 1123 | **BUTYL METHYL ETHER** | 2350 |
| **BUTYL ACID PHOSPHATE** | 1718 | **BUTYL NITRITES** | 2351 |
| **BUTYL ACRYLATES, INHIBITED** | 2348 | **BUTYL PROPIONATES** | 1914 |
| *Butyl alcohol, normal, see* | 1120 | *p-tert-Butyltoluene, see* | 2667 |
| *Butyl alcohol, secondary, see* | 1120 | **BUTYL TOLUENES** | 2667 |
| *Butyl alcohol, tertiary, see* | 1120 | **BUTYL TRICHLOROSILANE** | 1747 |
| *Butyl alcohols, see* | 1120 | **5-tert-BUTYL-2,4,6-TRINITRO -m-XYLENE** | 2956 |
| **n-BUTYLAMINE** | 1125 | | |
| **N-BUTYLANILINE** | 2738 | **BUTYL VINYL ETHER, INHIBITED** | 2352 |
| **BUTYLBENZENES** | 2709 | *But-1-yne, see* | 2452 |
| *sec-Butyl benzene, see* | 2709 | **1,4-BUTYNEDIOL** | 2716 |
| *n-Butyl bromide, see* | 1126 | *2-Butyne-1, 4-diol, see* | 2716 |
| *n-Butyl chloride, see* | 1127 | **BUTYRALDEHYDE** | 1129 |

| Substance | UN Number | Substance | UN Number |
|-----------|-----------|-----------|-----------|
| **BUTYRALDOXIME** | 2840 | **CALCIUM DITHIONITE** | 1923 |
| **BUTYRIC ACID** | 2820 | **CALCIUM HYDRIDE** | 1404 |
| **BUTYRIC ANHYDRIDE** | 2739 | *Calcium hydrosulphite, see* | 1923 |
| *Butyrone, see* | 2710 | **CALCIUM HYPOCHLORITE, DRY** *or* **CALCIUM HYPOCHLORITE MIXTURE, DRY** *with more than 39 per cent available chlorine (8.8 per cent available oxygen)* | 1748 |
| **BUTYRONITRILE** | 2411 | | |
| *Butyroyl chloride, see* | 2353 | | |
| **BUTYRYL CHLORIDE** | 2353 | | |
| **CACODYLIC ACID** | 1572 | **CALCIUM HYPOCHLORITE, HYDRATED** *or* **CALCIUM HYPOCHLORITE, HYDRATED MIXTURE,** *with not less than 5.5 per cent but not more than 10 per cent water* | 2880 |
| **CADMIUM COMPOUND** | 2570 | | |
| **CAESIUM** | 1407 | | |
| **CAESIUM HYDROXIDE** | 2682 | **CALCIUM HYPOCHLORITE MIXTURE, DRY** *with more than 10 per cent but not more than 39 per cent available chlorine* | 2208 |
| **CAESIUM HYDROXIDE SOLUTION** | 2681 | | |
| **CAESIUM NITRATE** | 1451 | | |
| *Caffeine, see* | 1544 | **CALCIUM MANGANESE SILICON** | 2844 |
| *Cajeputene, see* | 2052 | **CALCIUM, PYROPHORIC** | 1855 |
| **CALCIUM** | 1401 | **CALCIUM NITRATE** | 1454 |
| **CALCIUM ALLOYS, PYROPHORIC** | 1855 | **CALCIUM PERMANGANATE** | 1456 |
| **CALCIUM ARSENATE** | 1573 | **CALCIUM PEROXIDE** | 1457 |
| **CALCIUM ARSENATE AND CALCIUM** | 1574 | **CALCIUM PHOSPHIDE** | 1360 |
| | | **CALCIUM RESINATE** | 1313 |
| *Calcium bisulphite solutions, see* | 2693 | **CALCIUM RESINATE, FUSED** | 1314 |
| **CALCIUM CARBIDE** | 1402 | *Calcium selenate, see* | 2630 |
| **CALCIUM CHLORATE** | 1452 | **CALCIUM SILICIDE** | 1405 |
| **CALCIUM CHLORATE, AQUEOUS SOLUTION** | 2429 | *Calcium superoxide, see* | 1457 |
| | | *Camphanone, see* | 2717 |
| **CALCIUM CHLORITE** | 1453 | **CAMPHOR OIL** | 1130 |
| **CALCIUM CYANAMIDE** *with more than 0.1 per cent calcium carbide* | 1403 | **CAMPHOR, synethetic** | 2717 |
| | | **CAPROIC ACID** | 2829 |
| **CALCIUM CYANIDE** | 1575 | | |

| Substance | UN Number | Substance | UN Number |
|---|---|---|---|
| **CARBAMATE PESTICIDE, LIQUID, FLAMMABLE, TOXIC,** *flash point less than 23°C* | 2758 | **CARBON TETRABROMIDE** | 2516 |
| | | **CARBON TETRACHLORIDE** | 1846 |
| **CARBAMATE PESTICIDE, LIQUID, TOXIC, FLAMMABLE,** *flash point 23°C or above* | 2991 | *Carbonyl chloride, see* | 1076 |
| | | **CARBONYL FLUORIDE, COMPRESSED** | 2417 |
| **CARBAMATE PESTICIDE, LIQUID, TOXIC** | 2992 | **CARBONYL SULPHIDE** | 2204 |
| **CARBAMATE PESTICIDE, SOLID, TOXIC** | 2757 | **CASTOR BEANS** *or* **CASTOR MEAL** *or* **CASTOR POMACE** *or* **CASTOR LAKE** | 2969 |
| *Carbolic acid, see* | 1671 2312 2821 | **CAUSTIC ALKALI LIQUID, N.O.S.** | 1719 |
| **CARBON ACTIVATED** | 1362 | *Caustic potash, see* | 1814 |
| **CARBON,** *animal or vegetable origin* | 1361 | *Caustic soda, see* | 1824 |
| *Carbon bisulphide, see* | 1131 | *Caustic soda liquor, see* | 1824 |
| *Carbon black, animal or vegetable origin, see* | 1361 | **CELLS, CONTAINING SODIUM** | 3292 |
| **CARBON DIOXIDE** | 1013 | **CELLULOID,** *in blocks, rods, rolls, sheets, tubes, etc., except scrap* | 2000 |
| *Carbon dioxide and ethylene oxide mixtures, see* | 1041 1952 | *Cement, see* | 1133 |
| | | **CERIUM,** *slabs, ingots, or rods* | 1333 |
| **CARBON DIOXIDE AND NITROUS OXIDE MIXTURE** | 1015 | **CERIUM,** *turnings or gritty powder* | 3078 |
| **CARBON DIOXIDE AND OXYGEN MIXTURE, COMPRESSED** | 1014 | **CAESIUM** | 1407 |
| | | *Charcoal, activated, see* | 1362 |
| **CARBON DIOXIDE, REFRIGERATED LIQUID** | 2187 | *Charcoal, non-activated, see* | 1361 |
| **CARBON DISULPHIDE** | 1131 | **CHEMICAL KIT** | 3316 |
| *Carbonic anhydride, see* | 1013 2187 | **CHEMICAL SAMPLE, TOXIC,** *liquid or solid* | 3315 |
| | | *Chile saltpetre, see* | 1498 |
| **CARBON MONOXIDE, COMPRESSED** | 1016 | **CHLORAL, ANHYDROUS, INHIBITED** | 2075 |
| **CARBON MONOXIDE AND HYDROGEN MIXTURE, COMPRESSED** | 2600 | **CHLORATE AND BORATE MIXTURES, SOLUTION** | 1458 |
| *Carbon oxysulphide, see* | 2204 | | |

| Substance | UN Number |
|---|---|
| **CHLORATE AND MAGNESIUM CHLORIDE MIXTURES, SOLUTION** | 1459 |
| **CHLORATES, INORGANIC, N.O.S.** | 1461 |
| **CHLORATES, INORGANIC, AQUEOUS SOLUTION, N.O.S.** | 3210 |
| **CHLORIC ACID AQUEOUS SOLUTION,** *with not more than 10 per cent chloric acid* | 2626 |
| **CHLORINE** | 1017 |
| **CHLORINE PENTAFLUORIDE** | 2548 |
| **CHLORINE TRIFLUORIDE** | 1749 |
| **CHLORITES, INORGANIC, N.O.S.** | 1462 |
| **CHLORITE SOLUTION** | 1908 |
| *Chloroacetaldehyde, see* | 2232 |
| **CHLOROACETIC ACID SOLUTION** | 1750 |
| **CHLOROACETIC ACID, MOLTEN** | 3250 |
| **CHLOROACETIC ACID, SOLID** | 1751 |
| **CHLOROACETONE, STABILISED** | 1695 |
| **CHLOROACETONITRILE** | 2668 |
| **CHLOROACETOPHENONE** | 1697 |
| **CHLOROACETYL CHLORIDE** | 1752 |
| **CHLOROANILINES, LIQUID** | 2019 |
| **CHLOROANILINES, SOLID** | 2018 |
| **CCHLOROANISIDINES** | 2233 |
| **CHLOROBENZENE** | 1134 |
| **CHLOROBENZOTRIFLUORIDES** | 2234 |
| **CHLOROBENZYLCHLORIDES** | 2235 |
| *1-Chlorobutane, see* | 1127 |
| *2-Chlorobutane, see* | 1127 |
| **CHLOROBUTANES** | 1127 |

| Substance | UN Number |
|---|---|
| **CHLOROCRESOLS** | 2669 |
| **CHLORODIFLUORO-BROMOMETHANE** | 1974 |
| **1-CHLORO-1, 1-DIFLUOROETHANE** | 2517 |
| **CHLORODIFLUOROMETHANE** | 1018 |
| **CHLORODIFLUOROMETHANE AND CHLOROPENTAFLUORO-ETHANE MIXTURE,** *with fixed boiling point with appropriately 49 per cent of chlorodifluoromethane* | 1973 |
| *3-Chloro-1,2-dihydroxypropane, see* | 2689 |
| *Chlorodimethyl ether, see* | 1239 |
| **CHLORODINITROBENZENES** | 1577 |
| **2-CHLOROETHANAL** | 2232 |
| *Chloroethane, see* | 1037 |
| *Chloroethane nitrile, see* | 2668 |
| *2-Chloroethanol, see* | 1135 |
| **CHLOROFORM** | 1888 |
| **CHLOROFORMATES, TOXIC CORROSIVE, FLAMMABLE, N.O.S.** | 2742 |
| **CHLOROFORMATES, TOXIC, CORROSIVE, N.O.S.** | 3277 |
| *Chloromethane, see* | 1063 |
| *1-Chloro-3-methylbutane, see* | 1107 |
| *2-Chloro-2-methylbutane, see* | 1107 |
| **CHLOROMETHYL CHLOROFORMATE** | 2745 |
| *Chloromethyl cyanide, see* | 2668 |
| **CHLOROMETHYL ETHYL ETHER** | 2354 |
| *Chloromethyl methyl ether, see* | 1239 |

| Substance | UN Number |
|---|---|
| **3-CHLORO-4-METHYL PHENYLISOCYANATE** | 2236 |
| *1-Chloro-2-methylpropane, see* | 1127 |
| *2-Chloro-2-methylpropane, see* | 1127 |
| *Chloromethylpropanes, see* | 1127 |
| *3-Chloro-2-methylprop-1-ene, see* | 2554 |
| **CHLORONITROANILINES** | 2237 |
| **CHLORONITROBENZENES** | 1578 |
| **CHLORONITROTOLUENES** | 2433 |
| **4-CHLORO-ORTHO-TOLUIDINE HYDROCHLORIDE** | 1579 |
| **CHLOROPENTAFLUOROETHANE** | 1020 |
| **CHLOROPHENOLATES, LIQUID** | 2904 |
| **CHLOROPHENOLATES, SOLID** | 2905 |
| **CHLOROPHENOLS, LIQUID** | 2021 |
| **CHLOROPHENOLS, SOLID** | 2020 |
| **CHLOROPHENYL-TRICHLOROSILANE** | 1753 |
| **CHLOROPICRIN** | 1580 |
| **CHLOROPICRIN AND METHYL BROMIDE MIXTURE** | 1581 |
| **CHLOROPICRIN AND METHYL CHLORIDE MIXTURE** | 1582 |
| **CHLOROPICRIN MIXTURE, N.O.S.** | 1583 |
| **CHLOROPLATINIC ACID, SOLID** | 2507 |
| **CHLOROPRENE, INHIBITED** | 1991 |
| **2-CHLOROPROPANE** | 2356 |
| *3-Chloro-propanediol-1,2 see* | 2689 |
| *Chloropropanol, see* | 2611 |
| *2-Chloro-1-propanol, see* | 2611 |

| Substance | UN Number |
|---|---|
| **3-CHLOROPROPANOL-1** | 2849 |
| **2-CHLOROPROPENE** | 2456 |
| *3-Chloropropene, see* | 1100 |
| *3-Chloroprop-1-ene, see* | 1100 |
| **2-CHLOROPROPIONIC ACID** | 2511 |
| **2-CHLOROPYRIDINE** | 2822 |
| **CHLOROSILANES, FLAMMABLE, CORROSIVE, N.O.S.** | 2985 |
| **CHLOROSILANES, CORROSIVE, N.O.S.** | 2987 |
| **CHLOROSILANES, CORROSIVE, FLAMMABLE, N.O.S.** | 2986 |
| **CHLOROSILANES, WATER REACTIVE, FLAMMABLE, CORROSIVE, N.O.S.** | 2988 |
| **CHLOROSULPHONIC ACID,** *(with or without sulphur trioxide)* | 1754 |
| **1-CHLORO-1,2,2,2-TETRAFLUORO- ETHANE** | 1021 |
| **CHLOROTOLUENES** | 2238 |
| **CHLOROTOLUIDINES** | 2239 |
| **1-CHLORO-2,2,2,-TRIFLUORO-ETHANE** | 1983 |
| *Chlorotrifluoroethylene, see* | 1082 |
| **CHLOROTRIFLUOROMETHANE** | 1022 |
| **CHLOROTRIFLUOROMETHANE AND TRIFLUOROMETHANE AZEOTROPIC MIXTURE,** *with approximately 60 per cent chlorotrifluoromethane* | 2599 |
| *Chromic acid, solid, see* | 1463 |
| **CHROMIC ACID SOLUTION** | 1755 |
| **CHROMIC FLUORIDE, SOLID** | 1756 |
| **CHROMIC FLUORIDE SOLUTION** | 1757 |

| Substance | UN Number | Substance | UN Number |
|---|---|---|---|
| CHROMIUM NITRATE | 2720 | COMPRESSED GAS, TOXIC, FLAMMABLE, N.O.S. | 1953 |
| CHROMIUM OXYCHLORIDE | 1758 | COMPRESSED GAS, TOXIC, N.O.S. | 1955 |
| CHROMIUM TRIOXIDE, ANHYDROUS | 1463 | COMPRESSED GAS, TOXIC, OXIDISING, CORROSIVE, N.O.S. | 3306 |
| CHROMOSULPHURIC ACID | 2240 | COMPRESSED GAS, TOXIC, OXIDISING, N.O.S. | 3303 |
| Chysotile, see | 2590 | COPPER ACETOARSENITE | 1585 |
| Cinene, see | 2052 | COPPER ARSENITE | 1586 |
| Cinnamene, see | 2055 | COPPER BASED PESTICIDE, LIQUID, FLAMMABLE, TOXIC, flash point less than 23°C | 2776 |
| Cinnamol, see | 2055 | | |
| CLINICAL WASTE, UNSPECIFIED, N.O.S. | 3291 | COPPER BASED PESTICIDE, LIQUID, TOXIC, FLAMMABLE, flash point 23°C or above | 3009 |
| COAL GAS, COMPRESSED | 1023 | | |
| COAL TAR DISTILLATES, flammable | 1136 | COPPER BASED PESTICIDE, LIQUID, TOXIC | 3010 |
| Coal tar oil, see | 1136 | COPPER BASED PESTICIDE, SOLID, TOXIC | 2775 |
| COATING SOLUTION | 1139 | COPPER CHLORATE | 2721 |
| COBALT NAPHTHENATES, POWDER | 2001 | COPPER CHLORIDE | 2802 |
| COBALT RESINATE, PRECIPITATED | 1318 | COPPER CYANIDE | 1587 |
| Collodion cottons, see | 2059 2555 2556 2557 | Copper selenate, see | 2630 |
| | | Copper selenite, see | 2630 |
| | | COPRA | 1363 |
| COMPRESSED GAS, FLAMMABLE, N.O.S. | 1954 | CORROSIVE LIQUID, ACIDIC, INORGANIC, N.O.S. | 3264 |
| COMPRESSED GAS, N.O.S. | 1956 | CORROSIVE LIQUID, ACIDIC, ORGANIC, N.O.S. | 3265 |
| COMPRESSED GAS, OXIDISING, N.O.S. | 3156 | CORROSIVE LIQUID, BASIC, INORGANIC, N.O.S. | 3266 |
| COMPRESSED GAS, TOXIC, CORROSIVE, N.O.S. | 3304 | CORROSIVE LIQUID, BASIC, ORGANIC, N.O.S. | 3267 |
| COMPRESSED GAS, TOXIC, FLAMMABLE, CORROSIVE, N.O.S. | 3305 | CORROSIVE LIQUID, FLAMMABLE, N.O.S. | 2920 |

| Substance | UN Number | Substance | UN Number |
|---|---|---|---|
| CORROSIVE LIQUID, N.O.S. | 1760 | COUMARIN DERIVATIVE PESTICIDE, LIQUID, TOXIC | 3026 |
| CORROSIVE LIQUID, OXIDISING, N.O.S. | 3093 | COUMARIN DERIVATIVE PESTICIDE, SOLID, TOXIC | 3027 |
| CORROSIVE LIQUID, SELF-HEATING, N.O.S. | 3301 | Creosote, see | 2810 |
| CORROSIVE LIQUID, TOXIC, N.O.S. | 2922 | Creosote salts, see | 1334 |
| CORROSIVE LIQUID, WATER-REACTIVE, N.O.S. | 3094 | CRESOLS | 2076 |
| CORROSIVE SOLID, FLAMMABLE, N.O.S. | 2921 | CRESYLIC ACID | 2022 |
| CORROSIVE SOLID, ACIDIC, INORGANIC, N.O.S. | 3260 | Crocidolite, see | 2212 |
| CORROSIVE SOLID, ACIDIC, ORGANIC, N.O.S. | 3261 | CROTONALDEHYDE, STABILISED | 1143 |
| CORROSIVE SOLID, BASIC, INORGANIC, N.O.S. | 3262 | CROTONIC ACID | 2823 |
| | | Crotonic aldehyde, see | 1143 |
| CORROSIVE SOLID, BASIC, ORGANIC, N.O.S. | 3263 | CROTONYLENE | 1144 |
| CORROSIVE SOLID, N.O.S. | 1759 | Cumene, see | 1918 |
| CORROSIVE SOLID, OXIDISING, N.O.S. | 3084 | CUPRIETHYLENEDIAMINE SOLUTION | 1761 |
| CORROSIVE SOLID, TOXIC, N.O.S. | 2923 | CYANIDE SOLUTION, N.O.S. | 1935 |
| CORROSIVE SOLID, SELF-HEATING, N.O.S. | 3095 | CYANIDES, INORGANIC, SOLID, TOXIC N.O.S. | 1588 |
| | | Cyanoacetonitrile, see | 2647 |
| CORROSIVE SOLID, WATER-REACTIVE, N.O.S. | 3096 | CYANOGEN BROMIDE | 1889 |
| COTTON WASTE, OILY | 1364 | CYANOGEN CHLORIDE, INHIBITED | 1589 |
| COTTON, WET | 1365 | CYANOGEN | 1026 |
| COUMARIN DERIVATIVE PESTICIDE, LIQUID, FLAMMABLE, TOXIC, flash point less than 23°C | 3024 | CYANURIC CHLORIDE | 2670 |
| | | CYCLOBUTANE | 2601 |
| | | CYCLOBUTYL CHLOROFORMATE | 2744 |
| | | 1,5,9-CYCLODODECATRIENE | 2518 |
| COUMARIN DERIVATIVE PESTICIDE, LIQUID, TOXIC, FLAMMABLE, flash point 23°C or above | 3025 | CYCLOHEPTANE | 2241 |
| | | CYCLOHEPTATRIENE | 2603 |

| Substance | UN Number | Substance | UN Number |
|---|---|---|---|
| *1,3,5-Cyloheptatriene, see* | 2603 | **n-DECANE** | 2247 |
| **CYCLOHEPTENE** | 2242 | **DEUTERIUM, COMPRESSED** | 1957 |
| *1,4-Cyclohexadienedione, see* | 2587 | **DEVICES, SMALL, HYDROCARBON GAS POWERED** *or* **HYDROCARBON GAS REFILLS FOR SMALL DEVICES,** *with release device* | 3150 |
| **CYCLOHEXANE** | 1145 | | |
| *Cyclohexanethiol, see* | 3054 | | |
| **CYCLOHEXANONE** | 1915 | **DIACETONE ALCOHOL** | 1148 |
| **CYCLOHEXENE** | 2256 | **DIALLYLAMINE** | 2359 |
| **CYCLOHEXENYLTRI-CHLOROSILANE** | 1762 | **DIALLYL ETHER** | 2360 |
| **CYCLOHEXYL ACETATE** | 2243 | **4,4'-DIAMINODIPHENYL-METHANE** | 2651 |
| **CYCLOHEXYLAMINE** | 2357 | *1,2-Diaminoethane, see* | 1604 |
| **CYCLOHEXYL ISOCYANATE** | 2488 | *Diaminopropylamine, see* | 2269 |
| **CYCLOHEXYL MERCAPTAN** | 3054 | **DI-n-AMYLAMINE** | 2841 |
| **CYCLOHEXYL TRICHLOROSILANE** | 1763 | *Dibenzopyridine, see* | 2713 |
| *Cyclooctadiene phosphines, see* | 2940 | **DIBENZYLDICHLOROSILANE** | 2434 |
| **CYCLOOCTADIENES** | 2520 | **DIBORANE, COMPRESSED** | 1911 |
| **CYCLOOCTATETRAENE** | 2358 | **1,2-DIBROMOBUTAN-3-ONE** | 2648 |
| **CYCLOPENTANE** | 1146 | **DIBROMOCHLOROPROPANES** | 2872 |
| **CYCLOPENTANOL** | 2244 | *1,2-Dibromo-3-chloropropane, see* | 2872 |
| **CYCLOPENTANONE** | 2245 | **DIBROMODIFLUOROMETHANE** | 1941 |
| **CYCLOPENTENE** | 2246 | **DIBROMOMETHANE** | 2664 |
| **CYCLOPROPANE** | 1027 | **DI-n-BUTYLAMINE** | 2248 |
| **CYMENES** | 2046 | **DIBUTYLAMINOETHANOL** | 2873 |
| *Cymol, see* | 2046 | *N,N-Di-n-butylaminoethanol, see* | 2873 |
| *Deanol, see* | 2051 | **DIBUTYL ETHERS** | 1149 |
| **DECABORANE** | 1868 | **DICHLOROACETIC ACID** | 1764 |
| **DECAHYDRONAPHTHALENE** | 1147 | **1,3-DICHLOROACETONE** | 2649 |
| *Decalin, see* | 1147 | **DICHLOROACETYL CHLORIDE** | 1765 |

| Substance | UN Number | Substance | UN Number |
|---|---|---|---|
| DICHLOROANILINES | 1590 | DICHLOROSILANE | 2189 |
| o-DICHLOROBENZENE | 1591 | 1,2-DICHLORO-1,1,2,2-TETRAFLUOROETHANE | 1958 |
| 2,2'-DICHLORODIETHYL ETHER | 1916 | | |
| DICHLORODIFLUOROMETHANE | 1028 | 3,5-DICHLORO-2,4,6-TRIFLUOROPYRIDINE | 2810 |
| DICHLORODIFLUOROMETHANE AND DIFLUOROETHANE AZEOTROPIC MIXTURE with approximately 74 per cent dichlorodifluoromethane | 2602 | 1,4-Dicyanobutane, see | 2205 |
| | | Dicycloheptadiene, see | 2251 |
| | | DICYCLOHEXYLAMINE | 2565 |
| Dichlorodifluoromethane and ethylene oxide mixtures, see | 3070 | Dicyclohexylamine nitrite, see | 2687 |
| 1,1-DICHLOROETHANE | 2362 | DICYCLOHEXYLAMMONIUM NITRITE | 2687 |
| 1,2-Dichloroethane, see | 1184 | DICYCLOPENTADIENE | 2048 |
| 1,2-DICHLOROETHYLENE | 1150 | 1,2-DI-(DIMETHYLAMINO) ETHANE | 2372 |
| DICHLOROFLUOROMETHANE | 1029 | DIDYMIUM NITRATE | 1465 |
| alpha-Dichlorohydrin, see | 2750 | DIESEL FUEL | 1202 |
| DICHLOROISOCYANURIC ACID, DRY or DICHLOROISOCYANURIC ACID SALTS | 2465 | 1,2-Diethoxyethane, see | 1153 |
| | | DIETHOXYMETHANE | 2373 |
| DICHLOROISOPROPYL ETHER | 2490 | 3,3-DIETHOXYPROPENE | 2374 |
| DICHLOROMETHANE | 1593 | DIETHYLAMINE | 1154 |
| 1,1-DICHLORO-1-NITROETHANE | 2650 | 2-DIETHYLAMINOETHANOL | 2686 |
| DICHLOROPENTANES | 1152 | DIETHYLAMINOPROPYLAMINE | 2684 |
| Dichlorophenols, see | 2020 2021 | N,N-DIETHYLANILINE | 2432 |
| DICHLOROPHENYL ISOCYANATES | 2250 | DIETHYLBENZENES | 2049 |
| | | Diethylcarbinol, see | 1105 |
| DICHLOROPHENYLTRI-CHLOROSILANE | 1766 | DIETHYL CARBONATE | 2366 |
| 1,2-DICHLOROPROPANE | 1279 | DIETHYLDICHLOROSILANE | 1767 |
| 1,3-Dichloro-2-propanone, see | 2649 | Diethylenediamine, see | 2579 |
| 1,3-DICHLOROPROPANOL-2 | 2750 | Diethyleneglycol Chloroformate, See | 2742 |
| DICHLOROPROPENES | 2047 | DIETHYLENETRIAMINE | 2079 |

| Substance | UN Number | Substance | UN Number |
|---|---|---|---|
| *N,N-Diethylethanolamine, see* | 2686 | **1,2-DIMETHOXYETHANE** | 2252 |
| **DIETHYL ETHER** | 1155 | *Dimethoxystrychnine, see* | 1570 |
| **N,N-DIETHYLETHYLENEDIAMINE** | 2685 | **DIMETHYLAMINE ANHYDROUS** | 1032 |
| *Di-(2-ethylhexyl) phosphoric acid, see* | 1902 | **DIMETHYLAMINE SOLUTION** | 1160 |
| **DIETHYL KETONE** | 1156 | **2-DIMETHYLAMINO-ACETONITRILE** | 2378 |
| **DIETHYL SULPHATE** | 1594 | **2-DIMETHYLAMINOETHANOL** | 2051 |
| **DIETHYL SULPHIDE** | 2375 | **2-DIMETHYLAMINOETHYL ACRYLATE** | 3302 |
| **DIETHYL THIOPHOSPHORYL CHLORIDE** | 2751 | **2-DIMETHYLAMINOETHYL METHACRYLATE** | 2522 |
| **DIETHYL ZINC** | 1366 | **N,N-DIMETHYLANILINE** | 2253 |
| *2-4-Difluoroaniline, see* | 2941 | *Dimethylarsenic acid, see* | 1572 |
| **1,1-DIFLUOROETHANE** | 1030 | *N,N-Dimethylbenzylamine, see* | 2619 |
| **1,1-DIFLUOROETHYLENE** | 1959 | **2,3-DIMETHYLBUTANE** | 2457 |
| **DIFLUOROMETHANE** | 3252 | **1,3-DIMETHYLBUTYLAMINE** | 2379 |
| **DIFLUOROPHOSPHORIC ACID, ANHYDROUS** | 1768 | **DIMETHYLCARBAMOYL CHLORIDE** | 2262 |
| **2,3-DIHYDROPYRAN** | 2376 | **DIMETHYL CARBONATE** | 1161 |
| *p-Dihydroxybenzene, see* | 2662 | **DIMETHYLCYCLOHEXANES** | 2263 |
| **DIISOBUTYLAMINE** | 2361 | **DIMETHYLCYCLOHEXYLAMINE** | 2264 |
| **DIISOBUTYLENE, ISOMERIC COMPOUNDS** | 2050 | **DIMETHYLDICHLOROSILANE** | 1162 |
| *alpha-Diisobutylene, see* | 2050 | **DIMETHYLDIETHOXYSILANE** | 2380 |
| *beta-Diisobutylene, see* | 2050 | *2,5-Dimethyl-1,4-dioxane, see* | 2707 |
| **ISOBUTYL KETONE** | 1157 | *4,4-Dimethyldioxane-1,3, see* | 2707 |
| **DIISOOCTYL ACID PHOSPHATE** | 1902 | **DIMETHYLDIOXANES** | 2707 |
| **DIISOPROPYLAMINE** | 1158 | **DIMETHYL DISULPHIDE** | 2381 |
| **DIISOPROPYL ETHER** | 1159 | **DIMETHYL ETHER** | 1033 |
| **DIKETENE, INHIBITED** | 2521 | **N,N-DIMETHYLFORMAMIDE** | 2265 |
| **1,1-DIMETHOXYETHANE** | 2377 | | |

| Substance | UN Number | Substance | UN Number |
|---|---|---|---|
| DIMETHYLHYDRAZINE, SYMMETRICAL | 2382 | DIPHENYLCHLOROARSINE | 1699 |
| | | DIPHENYLDICHLOROSILANE | 1769 |
| DIMETHYLHYDRAZINE, UNSYMMETRICAL | 1163 | DIPHENYLMETHYL BROMIDE | 1770 |
| 2,2-DIMETHYLPROPANE | 2044 | DIPICRYL SULPHIDE, WETTED *with not less than 10 per cent water, by mass* | 2852 |
| DIMETHYL-N-PROPYLAMINE | 2266 | | |
| DIMETHYL SULPHATE | 1595 | DIPROPYLAMINE | 2383 |
| DIMETHYL SULPHIDE | 1164 | *Dipropylene triamine, see* | 2269 |
| DIMETHYL THIOPHOSPHORYL CHLORIDE | 2267 | DI-n-PROPYL ETHER | 2384 |
| | | DIPROPYL KETONE | 2710 |
| DIMETHYL ZINC | 1370 | DIQUAT, *solution* | 3016 |
| DINITROANILINES | 1596 | DIQUAT, *solution in flammable liquid* | 2782 3015 |
| DINITROBENZENES | 1597 | | |
| *Dinitrochlorobenzene, see* | 1577 | DISINFECTANT, LIQUID, CORROSIVE, N.O.S. | 1903 |
| DINITROGEN TETROXIDE | 1067 | DISINFECTANT, LIQUID, TOXIC, N.O.S | 3142 |
| DINITRO-ORTHO-CRESOL | 1598 | | |
| DINITROPHENOL SOLUTION | 1599 | DISINFECTANT, SOLID, TOXIC, N.O.S. | 1601 |
| DINITROPHENOL, WETTED *with not less than 15 per cent water, by mass* | 1320 | DISODIUM TRIOXOSILICATE PENTAHYDRATE | 3253 |
| DINITROPHENOLATES, WETTED *with not less than 15 per cent water, by mass* | 1321 | DISPERSION, WATER-REACTIVE | 3027 |
| DINITRORESORCINOL, WETTED *with not less than 15 per cent water, by mass* | 1322 | DIVINYL ETHER, INHIBITED | 1167 |
| | | DODECYLTRICHLOROSILANE | 1771 |
| DINITROTOLUENES, MOLTEN | 1600 | DYE INTERMEDIATE, LIQUID, CORROSIVE, N.O.S. | 2801 |
| DINITROTOLUENES | 2038 | DYE INTERMEDIATE, LIQUID, TOXIC, N.O.S. | 1602 |
| DIOXANE | 1165 | | |
| DIOXOLANE | 1166 | DYE INTERMEDIATE, SOLID, TOXIC, N.O.S. | 3143 |
| DIPENTENE | 2052 | DYE INTERMEDIATE, SOLID, CORROSIVE, N.O.S. | 3147 |
| DIPHENYLAMINE CHLORO-ARSINE | 1698 | DYE, LIQUID, CORROSIVE, N.O.S. | 2801 |

| Substance | UN Number | Substance | UN Number |
|---|---|---|---|
| **DYE, LIQUID, TOXIC, N.O.S.** | 1602 | **ETHANOLAMINE** *or* **ETHANOLAMINE SOLUTION** | 2491 |
| **DYE, SOLID, TOXIC, N.O.S.** | 3143 | *Ether, see* | 1155 |
| **DYE, SOLID, CORROSIVE, N.O.S.** | 3147 | **ETHERS, N.O.S.** | 3271 |
| *Electric storage, batteries, see* | 2794 | *2-Ethoxyethanol, see* | 1171 |
| | 2795 | | |
| | 2800 | *2-Ethoxyethyl acetate, see* | 1171 |
| | 3028 | | |
| | | *Ethoxy propane-1, see* | 2615 |
| *Electrolyte (acid or alkaline) for batteries, see* | 2796 | **ETHYL ACETATE** | 1173 |
| | 2797 | | |
| **ELEVATED TEMPERATURE LIQUID, N.O.S.,** *with flash point above 61°C, at or above its flash point* | 3256 | **ETHYL ACETYLENE, INHIBITED** | 2452 |
| | | **ETHYL ACRYLATE, INHIBITED** | 1917 |
| **ELEVATED TEMPERATURE LIQUID, N.O.S.,** *at or above 100°C and below its flash point* | 3257 | **ETHYL ALCOHOL** | 1170 |
| | | **ETHYLAMINE** | 1036 |
| **ELEVATED TEMPERATURE SOLID, N.O.S.,** *at or above 240°C* | 3258 | **ETHYLAMINE, AQUEOUS SOLUTION,** *with not less than 50 per cent but not more than 70 per cent ethylamine* | 2270 |
| **ENVIRONMENTALLY HAZARDOUS SUBSTANCE, LIQUID, N.O.S.** | 3082 | | |
| **ENVIRONMENTALLY HAZARDOUS SUBSTANCE, SOLID, N.O.S.** | 3077 | **ETHYL AMYL KETONE** | 2271 |
| **EPIBROMOHYDRIN** | 2558 | **N-ETHYLANILINE** | 2272 |
| **EPICHLOROHYDRIN** | 2023 | **2-ETHYLANILINE** | 2273 |
| *1,2-Epoxybutane, see* | 3022 | **ETHYLBENZENE** | 1175 |
| *Epoxyethane, see* | 1040 | **N-ETHYL-N-BENZYLANILINE** | 2274 |
| **1,2-EPOXY-3-ETHOXYPROPANE** | 2752 | **N-ETHYLBENZYLTOLUIDINES** | 2753 |
| *2,3-Epoxy-1-propanal, see* | 2622 | **ETHYL BORATE** | 1176 |
| *2,3-Epoxypropyl ethyl ether, see* | 2752 | **ETHYL BROMIDE** | 1891 |
| **ESTERS, N.O.S.** | 3272 | **ETHYL BROMOACETATE** | 1603 |
| **ETHANE** | 1035 | **2-ETHYLBUTANOL** | 2275 |
| **ETHANE, REFRIGERATED LIQUID** | 1961 | **ETHYLBUTYL ACETATE** | 1177 |
| *Ethanethiol, see* | 2363 | **ETHYL BUTYL ETHER** | 1179 |
| | | **2-ETHYLBUTYRALDEHYDE** | 1178 |
| **ETHANOL** *or* **ETHANOL SOLUTION** | 1170 | **ETHYL BUTYRATE** | 1180 |

| Substance | UN Number | Substance | UN Number |
|---|---|---|---|
| **ETHYL CHLORIDE** | 1037 | **ETHYLENEIMINE, INHIBITED** | 1185 |
| **ETHYL CHLOROACETATE** | 1181 | **ETHYLENE OXIDE** | 1040 |
| *Ethyl chlorocarbonate, see* | 1182 | **ETHYLENE OXIDE AND CARBON DIOXIDE MIXTURE,** *with more than 87% ethylene oxide* | 3300 |
| **ETHYL CHLOROFORMATE** | 1182 | **ETHYLENE OXIDE AND CARBON DIOXIDE MIXTURE,** *with more than 9 per cent but not more than 87 per cent ethylene oxide* | 1041 |
| **ETHYL-2-CHLOROPROPIONATE** | 2935 | | |
| *Ethyl-alpha-chloropropionate, see* | 2935 | | |
| **ETHYL CHLOROTHIOFORMATE** | 2826 | **ETHYLENE OXIDE AND CARBON DIOXIDE MIXTURE,** *with not more than 9 per cent ethylene oxide* | 1952 |
| **ETHYL CROTONATE** | 1862 | | |
| **ETHYLDICHLOROARSINE** | 1892 | **ETHYLENE OXIDE AND CHLOROTETRAFLUOROETHANE MIXTURE,** *with not more than 8.8% ethylene oxide* | 3297 |
| **ETHYLDICHLOROSILANE** | 1183 | | |
| **ETHYLENE, ACETYLENE AND PROPYLENE IN MIXTURE, REFRIGERATED LIQUID,** *containing at least 71.5 per cent ethylene with not more than 22.5 per cent acetylene and not more than 6 per cent propylene* | 3138 | **ETHYLENE OXIDE AND DICHLORODIFLUORO-METHANE MIXTURE,** *with not more than 12.5 per cent ethylene oxide* | 3070 |
| | | **ETHYLENE OXIDE AND PENTAFLUOROETHANE MIXTURE,** *with not more than 7.9% ethylene oxide* | 3298 |
| **ETHYLENE CHLOROHYDRIN** | 1135 | | |
| **ETHYLENE, COMPRESSED** | 1962 | **ETHYLENE OXIDE AND PROPYLENE OXIDE MIXTURE,** *with not more than 30 per cent ethylene oxide* | 2983 |
| **ETHYLENEDIAMINE** | 1604 | | |
| **ETHYLENE DIBROMIDE** | 1605 | | |
| *Ethylene dibromide and methyl bromide, liquid mixtures, see* | 1647 | **ETHYLENE OXIDE AND TETRA-FLUOROETHANE MIXTURE,** *with not more than 5.6% ethylene oxide* | 3299 |
| **ETHYLENE DICHLORIDE** | 1184 | | |
| **ETHYLENE GLYCOL DIETHYL ETHER** | 1153 | **ETHYLENE OXIDE WITH NITROGEN** *up to a total pressure of 1MPa (10bar) at 50ºC* | 1040 |
| **ETHYLENE GLYCOL MONO-ETHYL ETHER** | 1171 | **ETHYLENE, REFRIGERATED LIQUID** | 1038 |
| **ETHYLENE GLYCOL MONO-ETHYL ETHER ACETATE** | 1172 | **ETHYL ETHER** | 1155 |
| **ETHYLENE GLYCOL MONO-METHYL ETHER** | 1188 | **ETHYL FLUORIDE** | 2453 |
| | | **ETHYL FORMATE** | 1190 |
| **ETHYLENE GLYCOL MONO-METHYL ETHER ACETATE** | 1189 | **2-ETHYLHEXYLAMINE** | 2276 |

| Substance | UN Number | Substance | UN Number |
|---|---|---|---|
| 2-ETHYLHEXYL CHLOROFORMATE | 2748 | FERRIC NITRATE | 1466 |
| Ethylidene chloride, see | 2362 | FERROCERIUM | 1323 |
| ETHYL ISOBUTYRATE | 2385 | FERROSILICON, with 30 per cent or more but less than 90 per cent silicon | 1408 |
| ETHYL ISOCYANATE | 2481 | FERROUS ARSENATE | 1608 |
| ETHYL LACTATE | 1192 | FERROUS METAL BORINGS, SHAVINGS, TURNINGS, or CUTTINGS, in a form liable to self-heating | 2793 |
| ETHYL MERCAPTAN | 2363 | | |
| ETHYL METHACRYLATE | 2277 | | |
| ETHYL METHYL ETHER | 1039 | FERTILISER AMMONIATING SOLUTION, with free ammonia | 1043 |
| ETHYL METHYL KETONE | 1193 | Fertilisers with ammonium nitrate, n.o.s., see | 2072 |
| ETHYL NITRITE SOLUTION | 1194 | | |
| ETHYL ORTHOFORMATE | 2524 | FIBRES or FABRICS, ANIMAL or VEGETABLE or SYNTHETIC, N.O.S., with oil | 1373 |
| ETHYL OXALATE | 2525 | | |
| ETHYLPHENYLDICHLOROSILANE | 2435 | FIBRES or FABRICS, IMPREG-NATED WITH WEAKLY NITRATED NITROCELLULOSE, N.O.S. | 1353 |
| 1-ETHYLPIPERIDINE | 2386 | | |
| ETHYL PROPIONATE | 1195 | | |
| ETHYL PROPYL ETHER | 2615 | Films from which gelatine has been removed, film scrap, see | 2002 |
| Ethyl silicate, see | 1292 | FILMS, NITROCELLULOSE BASE, gelatin coated, except scrap | 1324 |
| Ethyl sulphate, see | 1594 | FIRE EXTINGUISHER CHARGES, corrosive liquid | 1774 |
| N-ETHYLTOLUIDINES | 2754 | | |
| ETHYLTRICHLOROSILANE | 1196 | FIRE EXTINGUISHERS, with compressed or liquefied gas | 1044 |
| EXTRACTS, AROMATIC, LIQUID | 1169 | FIRELIGHTERS, SOLID, with flammable liquid | 2623 |
| EXTRACTS, FLAVOURING, LIQUID | 1197 | | |
| Fabrics, see | 1353 1373 | FIRST AID KIT | 3316 |
| FERRIC ARSENATE | 1606 | Fischer Tropsch gas, see | 2600 |
| FERRIC ARSENITE | 1607 | FISH MEAL, UNSTABILISED | 1374 |
| FERRIC CHLORIDE, ANHYDROUS | 1773 | FISH SCRAP | 1374 |
| FERRIC CHLORIDE SOLUTION | 2582 | Flammable gas in lighters | 1057 |

| Substance | UN Number | Substance | UN Number |
|---|---|---|---|
| FLAMMABLE LIQUID, CORROSIVE, N.O.S. | 2924 | FLUOROBENZENE | 2387 |
| FLAMMABLE LIQUID, N.O.S. | 1993 | *Fluoroethane, see* | 2453 |
| FLAMMABLE LIQUID, TOXIC, CORROSIVE, N.O.S. | 3286 | *Fluoroform, see* | 1984 |
| | | *Fluoromethane, see* | 2454 |
| FLAMMABLE LIQUID, TOXIC, N.O.S. | 1992 | FLUOROPHOSPHORIC ACID, ANHYDROUS | 1776 |
| FLAMMABLE SOLID, INORGANIC, N.O.S. | 3178 | FLUOROSILICATES, N.O.S. | 2856 |
| FLAMMABLE SOLID, CORROSIVE, INORGANIC, N.O.S. | 3180 | FLUOROSULPHONIC ACID | 1777 |
| | | FLUOROTOLUENES | 2388 |
| FLAMMABLE SOLID, TOXIC, INORGANIC, N.O.S. | 3179 | FLUOROSILICIC ACID | 1778 |
| FLAMMABLE SOLID, ORGANIC, N.O.S. | 1325 | FORMALDEHYDE SOLUTION *with not less than 25 per cent formaldehyde* | 2209 |
| FLAMMABLE SOLID, ORGANIC, CORROSIVE, N.O.S. | 2925 | FORMALDEHYDE SOLUTION, FLAMMABLE | 1198 |
| FLAMMABLE SOLID, ORGANIC, MOLTEN, N.O.S. | 3176 | *Formalin, see* | 1198 2209 |
| FLAMMABLE SOLID, OXIDISING, N.O.S. | 3097 | FORMIC ACID | 1779 |
| FLAMMABLE SOLID, ORGANIC, TOXIC, N.O.S. | 2926 | *Formic aldehyde, see* | 1198 2209 |
| *Flue dusts, toxic, see* | 1562 | *2-Formyl-3,4-dihydro-2H-pyran, see* | 2607 |
| FLUOROBORIC ACID | 1775 | FUEL, AVIATION, TURBINE ENGINE | 1863 |
| *Fluoric acid, see* | 1790 | FUMARYL CHLORIDE | 1780 |
| FLUORINE, COMPRESSED | 1045 | FURAN | 2389 |
| FLUOROACETIC ACID | 2642 | FURFURALDEHYDES | 1199 |
| FLUOROANILINES | 2941 | FURFURYL ALCOHOL | 2874 |
| *2-Fluoroaniline, see* | 2941 | FURFURYLAMINE | 2526 |
| *4-Fluoroaniline, see* | 2941 | *Furyl carbinol, see* | 2874 |
| *o-Fluoroaniline, see* | 2941 | FUSEL OIL | 1201 |
| *p-Fluoroaniline, see* | 2941 | GALLIUM | 2803 |

| Substance | UN Number | Substance | UN Number |
|---|---|---|---|
| GAS, REFRIGERATED LIQUID, FLAMMABLE, N.O.S. | 3312 | Heavy Hydrogen, see | 1957 |
| GAS, REFRIGERATED LIQUID, N.O.S. | 3158 | HELIUM, COMPRESSED | 1046 |
| | | HELIUM, REFRIGERATED LIQUID | 1963 |
| GAS, REFRIGERATED LIQUID, OXIDISING, N.O.S. | 3311 | HEPTAFLUOROPROPANE | 3296 |
| GAS CARTRIDGES | 2037 | n-HEPTALDEHYDE | 3056 |
| GAS SAMPLE, NON-PRESSURISED, FLAMMABLE, N.O.S., not refrigerated liquid | 3167 | n-Heptanal, see | 3056 |
| | | HEPTANES | 1206 |
| GAS SAMPLE, NON-PRESSURISED, TOXIC, N.O.S., not refrigerated liquid | 3169 | 4-Heptanone, see | 2710 |
| | | n-HEPTENE | 2278 |
| GAS SAMPLE, NON-PRESSURISED, TOXIC, FLAMMABLE, N.O.S., not refrigerated liquid | 3168 | HEXACHLOROACETONE | 2661 |
| | | HEXACHLOROBENZENE | 2729 |
| GAS OIL | 1202 | HEXACHLOROBUTADIENE | 2279 |
| GASOLINE | 1203 | HEXACHLOROCYCLO-PENTADIENE | 2646 |
| GENETICALLY MODIFIED MICRO-ORGANISMS | 3245 | HEXACHLOROPHENE | 2875 |
| GERMANE | 2192 | Hexachloro-2-propanone, see | 2661 |
| Germanium hydride, see | 2192 | HEXADECYLTRICHLOROSILANE | 1781 |
| Glycerol-1, 3-dichlorohydrin, see | 2750 | HEXADIENE | 2458 |
| GYLCEROL alpha-MONO-CHLOROHYDRIN | 2689 | HEXAETHYL TETRAPHOSPHATE | 1611 |
| Glyceryl trinitrate, see | 1204 | HEXAETHYL TETRAPHOSPHATE AND COMPRESSED GAS MIXTURE | 1612 |
| GLYCIDALDEHYDE | 2622 | | |
| GUANIDINE NITRATE | 1467 | HEXAFLUOROACETONE | 2420 |
| HAFNIUM POWDER, DRY | 2545 | HEXAFLUOROACETONE HYDRATE | 2552 |
| HAFNIUM POWDER, WETTED with not less than 25 per cent water (a visible excess of water must be present) (a) mechanically produced, particle size less than 53 microns; (b) chemically produced, particle size less than 840 microns | 1326 | HEXAFLUOROETHANE, COMPRESSED | 2193 |
| | | HEXAFLUOROPHOSPHORIC ACID | 1782 |
| | | HEXAFLUOROPROPYLENE | 1858 |
| HEATING OIL, LIGHT | 1202 | Hexahydrocresol, see | 2617 |

| Substance | UN Number | Substance | UN Number |
|---|---|---|---|
| *Hexahydromethyl phenol, see* | 2617 | **HYDROCHLORIC ACID, SOLUTION** | 1789 |
| **HEXALDEHYDE** | 1207 | **HYDROCYANIC ACID, AQUEOUS SOLUTIONS,** *with not more than 20 per cent hydrogen cyanide* | 1613 |
| **HEXAMETHYLENEDIAMINE, SOLID** | 2280 | | |
| **HEXAMETHYLENEDIAMINE SOLUTION** | 1783 | *Hydrofluoboric acid, see* | 1775 |
| **HEXAMETHYLENE DIISOCYANATE** | 2281 | **HYDROFLUORIC ACID SOLUTION** | 1790 |
| **HEXAMETHYLENEIMINE** | 2493 | **HYDROFLUORIC ACID AND SULPHURIC ACID MIXTURE** | 1786 |
| **HEXAMETHYLENETETRAMINE** | 1328 | *Hydrofluosilicic acid, see* | 1778 |
| *Hexamine, see* | 1328 | *Hydrogen arsenide, see* | 2188 |
| **HEXANES** | 1208 | **HYDROGEN BROMIDE, ANHYDROUS** | 1048 |
| *Hexanoic acid, see* | 2829 | *Hydrogen bromide solution, see* | 1788 |
| **HEXANOLS** | 2282 | | |
| **1-HEXENE** | 2370 | **HYDROGEN CHLORIDE, ANHYDROUS** | 1050 |
| **HEXYLTRICHLOROSILANE** | 1784 | **HYDROGEN CHLORIDE, REFRIGERATED LIQUID** | 2186 |
| **HYDRAZINE, ANHYDROUS** | 2029 | **HYDROGEN, COMPRESSED** | 1049 |
| **HYDRAZINE, AQUEOUS SOLUTION** *with not less than 37 per cent but not more than 64 per cent hydrazine, by mass* | 2030 | **HYDROGEN CYANIDE, AQUEOUS SOLUTION** | 1613 |
| | | **HYDROGEN CYANIDE, SOLUTION ALCOHOL** *with not more than 45% hydrogen cyanide* | 3294 |
| **HYDRAZINE, AQUEOUS SOLUTION** *with not more than 37% hydrazine, by mass* | 3293 | **HYDROGEN CYANIDE, STABILISED,** *containing less than 3% water* | 1051 |
| **HYDRAZINE HYDRATE** | 2030 | **HYDROGEN CYANIDE, STABILISED,** *containing less than 3% material* | 1614 |
| **HYDRIODIC ACID, SOLUTION** | 1787 | | |
| *Hydriodic acid, anhydrous, see* | 2197 | **HYDROGEN DIFLUORIDES, N.O.S.** | 1740 |
| **HYDROBROMIC ACID, SOLUTION** | 1788 | **HYDROGEN FLUORIDE, ANHYDROUS** | 1052 |
| **HYDROCARBON GAS MIXTURE, COMPRESSED, N.O.S.** | 1964 | *Hydrogen fluoride solution, see* | 1790 |
| **HYDROCARBON GAS MIXTURE, LIQUEFIED, N.O.S.** | 1965 | **HYDROGEN IODIDE, ANHYDROUS** | 2197 |
| **HYDROCARBONS, LIQUID N.O.S.** | 3295 | | |

| Substance | UN Number | Substance | UN Number |
|---|---|---|---|
| *Hydrogen iodide solution, see* | 1787 | **HYPOCHLORITES, INORGANIC, N.O.S.** | 3212 |
| **HYDROGEN AND METHANE MIXTURE, COMPRESSED** | 2034 | **3,3-IMINODIPROPYLAMINE** | 2269 |
| **HYDROGEN PEROXIDE AND PEROXYACETIC ACID MIXTURE, STABILISED** *with acid(s), water and not more than 5 per cent peroxyacetic acid* | 3149 | *India rubber, see* | 1287 |
| | | **INFECTIOUS SUBSTANCE, AFFECTING HUMANS** | 2814 |
| **HYDROGEN PEROXIDE, AQUEOUS SOLUTION,** *with not less than 8 per cent but less than 20 per cent hydrogen peroxide (stabilised as necessary)* | 2984 | **INFECTIOUS SUBSTANCE, AFFECTING ANIMALS,** *only* | 2990 |
| | | *INK, printer's, flammable. see* | 1210 |
| | | **INSECTICIDE GAS, N.O.S.** | 1968 |
| **HYDROGEN PEROXIDE, AQUEOUS SOLUTION,** *with not less than 20 per cent but not more than 60 per cent hydrogen peroxide (stabilised as necessary)* | 2014 | **INSECTICIDE GAS, FLAMMABLE, N.O.S.** | 3354 |
| | | **INSECTICIDE GAS, TOXIC, N.O.S.** | 1967 |
| **HYDROGEN PEROXIDE, STABALISED** *or* **HYDROGEN PEROXIDE AQUEOUS SOLUTION, STABILISED,** *with more than 60 per cent hydrogen peroxide* | 2015 | **INSECTICIDE GAS, TOXIC, FLAMMABLE, N.O.S.** | 3355 |
| | | **IODINE MONOCHLORIDE** | 1792 |
| **HYDROGEN, REFRIGERATED LIQUID** | 1966 | **IODINE PENTAFLUORIDE** | 2495 |
| | | **2-IODOBUTANE** | 2390 |
| **HYDROGEN SELENIDE, ANHYDROUS** | 2202 | *Iodomethane, see* | 2644 |
| *Hydrogen silicide, see* | 2203 | **IODOMETHYL PROPANES** | 2391 |
| **HYDROGEN SULPHIDE** | 1054 | **IODOPROPANES** | 2392 |
| *Hydroquinol, see* | 2662 | *alpha-Iodotoluene, see* | 2653 |
| **HYDROQUINONE** | 2662 | **IPDI** | 2290 |
| *Hydroselenic acid, see* | 2202 | *Iron chloride, see* | 1773 |
| *Hydrosilicofluoric acid, see* | 1778 | *Iron chloride solution, see* | 2582 |
| *3-Hydroxybutan-2-one, see* | 2621 | **IRON OXIDE, SPENT** | 1376 |
| **HYDROXYLAMINE SULPHATE** | 2865 | **IRON PENTACARBONYL** | 1994 |
| *1-Hydroxy-3-methyl-2-penten-4-yne, see* | 2705 | *Iron perchloride, see* | 1773 |
| *3-Hydroxyphenol, see* | 2876 | *Iron powder, pyrophoric, see* | 1383 |
| **HYPOCHLORITE SOLUTION** | 1791 | *Iron sesquichloride, see* | 1773 |

| Substance | UN Number | Substance | UN Number |
|---|---|---|---|
| IRON SPONGE, SPENT *(obtained from coal gas purification)* | 1376 | ISOCYANATES, TOXIC, FLAMMABLE, N.O.S. *or* ISOCYANATE SOLUTION, TOXIC, FLAMMABLE, N.O.S. | 3080 |
| *Iron swarf, see* | 2793 | ISOCYANATOBENZOTRI-FLUORIDES | 2285 |
| ISOBUTANE | 1969 | | |
| ISOBUTANOL | 1212 | *Isododecane, see* | 2286 |
| *Isobutene, see* | 1055 | ISOHEPTENE | 2287 |
| ISOBUTYL ACETATE | 1213 | ISOHEXENE | 2288 |
| ISOBUTYL ACRYLATE, INHIBITED | 2527 | ISOOCTANE | 1262 |
| ISOBUTYL ALCOHOL | 1212 | ISOOCTENE | 1216 |
| ISOBUTYL ALDEHYDE | 2045 | *Isopentane, see* | 1265 |
| ISOBUTYLAMINE | 1214 | ISOPENTENES | 2371 |
| ISOBUTYLENE | 1055 | *Isopentylamine, see* | 1106 |
| ISOBUTYL FORMATE | 2393 | *Isopentyl nitrite, see* | 1113 |
| ISOBUTYL ISOBUTYRATE | 2528 | ISOPHORONEDIAMINE | 2289 |
| ISOBUTYL ISOCYANATE | 2486 | ISOPHORONE DIISOCYANATE | 2290 |
| ISOBUTYL METHACRYLATE, INHIBITED | 2283 | ISOPRENE, INHIBITED | 1218 |
| ISOBUTYL PROPIONATE | 2394 | ISOPROPANOL | 1219 |
| ISOBUTYRALDEHYDE | 2045 | ISOPROPENYL ACETATE | 2403 |
| ISOBUTYRIC ACID | 2529 | ISOPROPENYL BENZENE | 2303 |
| ISOBUTYRIC ANHYDRIDE | 2530 | ISOPROPYL ACETATE | 1220 |
| ISOBUTYRONITRILE | 2284 | ISOPROPYL ACID PHOSPHATE | 1793 |
| ISOBUTYRYL CHLORIDE | 2395 | ISOPROPYL ALCOHOL | 1219 |
| ISOCYANATES, FLAMMABLE, TOXIC, N.O.S., *or* ISOCYANATE SOLUTION, FLAMMABLE, TOXIC, N.O.S. | 2478 | ISOPROPYLAMINE | 1221 |
| | | ISOPROPYL BENZENE | 1918 |
| | | *Isopropyl bromide, see* | 2344 |
| ISOCYANATES, TOXIC, N.O.S., *or* ISOCYANATE SOLUTION, TOXIC, N.O.S. | 2206 | ISOPROPYL BUTYRATE | 2405 |
| | | *Isopropyl chloride, see* | 2356 |

| Substance | UN Number | Substance | UN Number |
|---|---|---|---|
| **ISOPROPYL CHLOROACETATE** | 2947 | *Lamp black, see* | 1361 |
| **ISOPROPYL CHLOROFORMATE** | 2407 | **LEAD ACETATE** | 1616 |
| **ISOPROPYL 2-CHLOROPROPIONATE** | 2934 | **LEAD ARSENATES** | 1617 |
| | | **LEAD ARSENITES** | 1618 |
| *Isopropyl-alpha-chloropropionate, see* | 2394 | *Lead chloride, solid, see* | 2291 |
| *Isopropyl ether, see* | 1159 | **LEAD COMPOUND, SOLUBLE, N.O.S.** | 2291 |
| *Isopropylethylene, see* | 2561 | | |
| *Isopropyl formate, see* | 1281 | **LEAD CYANIDE** | 1620 |
| **ISOPROPYL ISOBUTYRATE** | 2406 | **LEAD DIOXIDE** | 1872 |
| **ISOPROPYL ISOCYANATE** | 2483 | **LEAD NITRATE** | 1469 |
| *Isopropyl mercaptan, see* | 2402 | **LEAD PERCHLORATE** | 1470 |
| **ISOPROPYL NITRATE** | 1222 | *Lead peroxide, see* | 1872 |
| **ISOPROPYL PROPIONATE** | 2409 | **LEAD PHOSPHITE, DIBASIC** | 2989 |
| *Isopropyltoluene, see* | 2046 | **LEAD SULPHATE,** *with more than 3 per cent free acid* | 1794 |
| *Isopropyltoluol, see* | 2046 | | |
| **ISOSORBIDE-5-MONONITRATE** | 3251 | *Lead tetraethyl, see* | 1649 |
| | | *Lead tetramethyl, see* | 1649 |
| **ISOSORBIDE DINITRATE MIXTURE** *with not less than 60 per cent lactose, mannose, starch, or calcium hydrogen phosphate* | 2907 | **LIFE-SAVING APPLIANCES NOT SELF-INFLATING,** *containing dangerous goods as equipment* | 3072 |
| *Isovaleraldehyde, see* | 2058 | **LIFE-SAVING APPLIANCES, SELF-INFLATING** | 2990 |
| **KEROSENE** | 1223 | | |
| **KETONES, LIQUID, N.O.S.** | 1224 | **LIGHTERS** *or* **LIGHTER REFILLS (CIGARETTES),** *containing flammable gas* | 1057 |
| **KRYPTON, COMPRESSED** | 1056 | | |
| **KRYPTON, REFRIGERATED LIQUID** | 1970 | *Limonene, inactive, see* | 2052 |
| | | **LIQUEFIED GAS, N.O.S.** | 3163 |
| *Lacquer base or lacquer chips, nitrocellulose, dry, see* | 2557 | **LIQUEFIED GAS, FLAMMABLE, N.O.S.** | 3161 |
| *Lacquer base or lacquer chips, plastic, wet with alcohol or solvent, see* | 1263 2059 2555 2556 | **LIQUEFIED GAS, OXIDISING, N.O.S.** | 3157 |
| | | **LIQUEFIED GAS, TOXIC, N.O.S.** | 3162 |

| Substance | UN Number | Substance | UN Number |
|---|---|---|---|
| LIQUEFIED GAS, TOXIC, CORROSIVE, N.O.S. | 3308 | LITHIUM HYPOCHLORITE, DRY or LITHIUM HYPOCHLORITE MIXTURE | 1471 |
| LIQUEFIED GAS, TOXIC, FLAMMABLE, CORROSIVE, N.O.S. | 3309 | Lithium in cartouches, see | 1415 |
| LIQUEFIED GAS, TOXIC, OXIDISING, CORROSIVE, N.O.S. | 3310 | LITHIUM NITRATE | 2722 |
| LIQUEFIED GAS, TOXIC, OXIDISING, N.O.S. | 3307 | LITHIUM NITRIDE | 2806 |
|  |  | LITHIUM PEROXIDE | 1472 |
| LIQUEFIED GAS, TOXIC, FLAMMABLE, N.O.S. | 3160 | Lithium silicide, see | 1417 |
| LIQUEFIED GASES, non-flammable, charged with nitrogen, carbon dioxide or air | 1058 | LITHIUM SILICON | 1417 |
|  |  | LNG | 1972 |
| Liquefied natural gas, see | 1972 | LONDON PURPLE | 1621 |
| Liquefied petroleum gas, see | 1075 | LPG | 1075 |
| LITHIUM | 1415 | Lye, see | 1823 |
| LITHIUM ALKYLS | 2445 | M86 fuel, see | 3165 |
| LITHIUM ALUMINIUM HYDRIDE | 1410 | MAGNESIUM or MAGNESIUM ALLOYS, with more than 50 per cent magnesium in pellets, turnings or ribbons | 1869 |
| LITHIUM ALUMINIUM HYDRIDE, ETHEREAL | 1411 | MAGNESIUM ALKYLS | 3053 |
| LITHIUM BATTERIES | 3090 | MAGNESIUM ALLOYS, POWDER | 1418 |
| LITHIUM BATTERIES CONTAINED IN EQUIPMENT | 3091 | MAGNESIUM ALUMINIUM PHOSPHIDE | 1419 |
| LITHIUM BATTERIES PACKED WITH EQUIPMENT | 3091 | MAGNESIUM ARSENATE | 1622 |
| LITHIUM BOROHYDRIDE | 1413 | Magnesium bisulphite solution, see | 2693 |
| LITHIUM FERROSILICON | 2830 | MAGNESIUM BROMATE | 1473 |
| LITHIUM HYDRIDE | 1414 | MAGNESIUM CHLORATE | 2723 |
| LITHIUM HYDRIDE, FUSED SOLID | 2805 | Magnesium chloride and chlorate mixtures, see | 1459 |
| LITHIUM HYDROXIDE MONOHYDRATE | 2680 | MAGNESIUM DIAMIDE | 2004 |
|  |  | MAGNESIUM DIPHENYL | 2005 |
| LITHIUM HYDROXIDE SOLUTION | 2679 | MAGNESIUM FLUOROSILICATE | 2853 |

| Substance | UN Number | Substance | UN Number |
|---|---|---|---|
| **MAGNESIUM GRANULES, COATED,** *particle size not less than 149 microns* | 2950 | **(BIO) MEDICAL WASTE, N.O.S.** | 3291 |
| **MAGNESIUM HYDRIDE** | 2010 | **MEDICINE, LIQUID, FLAMMABLE, TOXIC, N.O.S.** | 3248 |
| **MAGNESIUM NITRATE** | 1474 | **MEDICINE, LIQUID, TOXIC, N.O.S.** | 1851 |
| **MAGNESIUM PERCHLORATE** | 1475 | **MEDICINE, SOLID, TOXIC, N.O.S.** | 3249 |
| **MAGNESIUM PEROXIDE** | 1476 | *Di-p-Mentha-1,8-diene, see* | 2052 |
| **MAGNESIUM PHOSPHIDE** | 2011 | **MERCAPTANS, LIQUID, FLAMMABLE, TOXIC, N.O.S.,** *or* **MERCAPTAN MIXTURE, LIQUID, FLAMMABLE, TOXIC, N.O.S.** | 1228 |
| **MAGNESIUM POWDER** | 1418 | | |
| *Magnesium scrap, see* | 1869 | **MERCAPTANS, LIQUID, FLAMMABLE** | 3336 |
| **MAGNESIUM SILICIDE** | 2624 | **MERCAPTANS, LIQUID, TOXIC, FLAMMABLE, N.O.S.,** *or* **MERCAPTAN MIXTURE, LIQUID, TOXIC, FLAMMABLE, N.O.S.** | 3071 |
| *Magnesium silicofluoride, see* | 2853 | | |
| **MALEIC ANHYDRIDE** | 2215 | | |
| *Malonic dinitrile, see* | 2647 | *2-Mercaptoethanol, see* | 2966 |
| *Malonic ethyl ester nitrile, see* | 2666 | *2-Mercaptopropionic acid, see* | 2936 |
| **MALONONITRILE** | 2647 | **MERCURIC ARSENATE** | 1623 |
| **MANEB, STABILISED** *or* **MANEB PREPARATIONS, STABILISED** *against self-heating* | 2968 | **MERCURIC CHLORIDE** | 1624 |
| | | **MERCURIC NITRATE** | 1625 |
| **MANEB** *or* **MANEB PREPARATIONS** *with not less than 60 per cent maneb* | 2210 | **MERCURIC POTASSIUM CYANIDE** | 1626 |
| *Manganese ethylene-di-dithiocarbamate, see* | 2210 | *Mercurol, see* | 1639 |
| *Manganese ethylene-1,2-di-dithiocarbamate, see* | 2210 | **MERCUROUS NITRATE** | 1627 |
| | | **MERCURY** | 2809 |
| **MANGANESE NITRATE** | 2724 | **MERCURY ACETATE** | 1629 |
| **MANGANESE RESINATE** | 1330 | **MERCURY AMMONIUM CHLORIDE** | 1630 |
| **MATCHES, FUSEE** | 2254 | **MERCURY BASED PESTICIDE, LIQUID, FLAMMABLE, TOXIC,** *flash point less than 23°C* | 2778 |
| **MATCHES, SAFETY,** *(book, card or strike on box)* | 1944 | | |
| **MATCHES, "STRIKE ANYWHERE"** | 1331 | **MERCURY BASED PESTICIDE, LIQUID, TOXIC, FLAMMABLE,** *flash point 23°C or above* | 3011 |
| **MATCHES, WAX "VESTA"** | 1945 | | |

| Substance | UN Number | Substance | UN Number |
|---|---|---|---|
| MERCURY BASED PESTICIDE, LIQUID, TOXIC | 3012 | METAL CARBONYLS, TOXIC, N.O.S. | 3281 |
| MERCURY BASED PESTICIDE, SOLID, TOXIC | 2777 | METAL CATALYST, DRY | 2881 |
| MERCURY BENZOATE | 1631 | METAL CATALYST, WETTED *with a visible excess of liquid* | 1378 |
| *Mercury bichloride, see* | 1624 | METALDEHYDE | 1332 |
| MERCURY BROMIDES | 1634 | METAL HYDRIDES, FLAMMABLE, N.O.S. | 3182 |
| MERCURY COMPOUND, LIQUID, TOXIC, N.O.S. | 2024 | METAL HYDRIDES, WATER-REACTIVE, N.O.S. | 1409 |
| MERCURY COMPOUND, SOLID, TOXIC, N.O.S. | 2025 | METAL POWDER, FLAMMABLE, N.O.S. | 3089 |
| MERCURY CYANIDE | 1636 | METAL POWDER, SELF-HEATING, N.O.S. | 3189 |
| MERCURY GLUCONATE | 1637 | METAL SALTS OF ORGANIC COMPOUNDS, FLAMMABLE, N.O.S. | 3181 |
| MERCURY IODIDE | 1638 | METALLIC SUBSTANCE, WATER-REACTIVE, N.O.S. | 3208 |
| MERCURY NUCLEATE | 1639 | | |
| MERCURY OLEATE | 1640 | METALLIC SUBSTANCE, WATER-REACTIVE, SELF-HEATING, N.O.S. | 3209 |
| MERCURY OXIDE | 1641 | | |
| MERCURY OXYCYANIDE, DESENSITISED | 1642 | METHACRYLALDEHYDE, INHIBITED | 2396 |
| MERCURY POTASSIUM IODIDE | 1643 | METHACRYLIC ACID, INHIBITED | 2531 |
| MERCURY SALICYLATE | 1644 | METHACRYLONITRILE, INHIBITED | 3079 |
| MERCURY SULPHATE | 1645 | METHALLYL ALCOHOL | 2614 |
| MERCURY THIOCYANATE | 1646 | | |
| *Mesitylene, see* | 2325 | *Methanal, see* | 1198 2209 |
| MESITYL OXIDE | 1229 | *Methane and hydrogen mixtures, see* | 2034 |
| METAL ALKYL HALIDES, N.O.S. *or* METAL ARYL HALIDES, N.O.S. | 3049 | METHANE, COMPRESSED *or* NATURAL GAS, COMPRESSED *(with high methane content)* | 1971 |
| METAL ALKYL HYDRIDES, N.O.S. *or* METAL ARYL HYDRIDES, N.O.S. | 3050 | METHANE, REFRIGERATED LIQUID *or* NATURAL GAS, REFRIGERATED LIQUID *(with high methane content)* | 1972 |
| METAL ALKYLS, N.O.S. *or* METAL ARYLS, N.O.S. | 2003 | | |

| Substance | UN Number | Substance | UN Number |
|---|---|---|---|
| METHANESULPHONYL CHLORIDE | 3246 | METHYL BROMIDE | 1062 |
| METHANOL | 1230 | Methyl bromide and chloropicrin mixtures, see | 1581 |
| 2-Methoxyethyl acetate, see | 1189 | METHYL BROMIDE AND ETHYLENE DIBROMIDE MIXTURE, LIQUID | 1647 |
| METHOXYMETHYL ISOCYANATE | 2605 | | |
| 4-METHOXY-4-METHYL-PENTAN-2-ONE | 2293 | METHYL BROMOACETATE | 2643 |
| 1-Methoxy-2-nitrobenzene, see | 2730 | 3-METHYLBUTAN-2-ONE | 2397 |
| 1-Methoxy-3-nitrobenzene, see | 2730 | 2-METHYL-1-BUTENE | 2459 |
| 1-Methoxy-4-nitrobenzene, see | 2730 | 2-METHYL-2-BUTENE | 2460 |
| 1-METHOXY-2-PROPANOL | 3092 | 3-METHYL-1-BUTENE | 2561 |
| METHYL ACETATE | 1231 | N-METHYLBUTYLAMINE | 2945 |
| METHYL ACETYLENE AND PROPADIENE MIXTURE, STABILISED | 1060 | METHYL tert-BUTYL ETHER | 2398 |
| | | METHYL BUTYRATE | 1237 |
| beta-Methyl acrolein, see | 1143 | METHYL CHLORIDE | 1063 |
| METHYL ACRYLATE, INHIBITED | 1919 | Methyl chloride and chloropicrin mixtures, see | 1582 |
| METHYLAL | 1234 | | |
| METHYL ALCOHOL | 1230 | METHYL CHLORIDE AND METHYLENE CHLORIDE MIXTURE | 1912 |
| Methylallyl alcohol, see | 2614 | | |
| METHYL ALLYL CHLORIDE | 2554 | METHYL CHLOROACETATE | 2295 |
| METHYLAMINE, ANHYDROUS | 1061 | Methyl chlorocarbonate, see | 1238 |
| METHYLAMINE, AQUEOUS SOLUTION | 1235 | Methyl chloroform, see | 2831 |
| | | METHYL CHLOROFORMATE | 1238 |
| METHYL AMYL ACETATE | 1233 | METHYL CHLOROMETHYL ETHER | 1239 |
| Methyl amyl alcohol, see | 2053 | METHYL 2-CHLOROPROPIONATE | 2933 |
| Methyl amyl ketone, see | 1110 | Methyl alpha-chloropropionate, see | 2933 |
| N-METHYLANILINE | 2294 | METHYL CHLOROSILANE | 2534 |
| Methylated spirit, see | 1986 1987 | Methyl cyanide, see | 1648 |
| alpha-METHYLBENZYL ALCOHOL | 2937 | METHYLCYCLOHEXANE | 2296 |

| Substance | UN Number | Substance | UN Number |
|---|---|---|---|
| **METHYLCYCLOHEXANOLS,** *flammable* | 2617 | **METHYL ISOPROPENYL KETONE, INHIBITED** | 1246 |
| **METHYCYCLOHEXANONE** | 2297 | **METHYL ISOTHIOCYANATE** | 2477 |
| **METHYLCYCLOPENTANE** | 2298 | **METHYL ISOVALERATE** | 2400 |
| **METHYL DICHLOROACETATE** | 2299 | **METHYL MAGNESIUM BROMIDE in ETHYL ETHER** | 1928 |
| **METHYLDICHLOROSILANE** | 1242 | | |
| *Methylene bromide, see* | 2664 | **METHYL MERCAPTAN** | 1064 |
| *Methylene chloride, see* | 1593 | *Methyl mercaptopropionaldehyde, see* | 2785 |
| *Methylene chloride and methyl chloride mixtures, see* | 1912 | **METHYL METHACRYLATE MONOMER, INHIBITED** | 1247 |
| *Methylene cyanide, see* | 2647 | **4-METHYLMORPHOLINE (n-METHYLMORPHOLINE)** | 2535 |
| *p,p' - Methylene dianiline, see* | 2651 | | |
| *Methylene dibromide, see* | 2664 | **METHYL ORTHOSILICATE** | 2606 |
| *2,2'-Methylene-di-(3,4,6-trichlorophenol) see* | 2875 | **METHYL PENTADIENE** | 2461 |
| | | *Methyl pentanes, see* | 1208 |
| *Methyl ethyl ether, see* | 1039 | **2-METHYLPENTAN-2-OL** | 2560 |
| **METHYL ETHYL KETONE** | 1193 | *4-Methylpentan-2-ol, see* | 2053 |
| **2-METHYL-5-ETHYLPYRIDINE** | 2300 | *3-Methyl-2-penten-4-yne-ol, see* | 2705 |
| **METHYL FLUORIDE** | 2454 | **METHYL PHENYLDICHLORO-SILANE** | 2437 |
| **METHYL FORMATE** | 1243 | | |
| **2-METHYLFURAN** | 2301 | *2-Methyl-2-phenylpropane, see* | 2709 |
| *Methyl glycol, see* | 1188 | **1-METHYL PIPERIDINE** | 2399 |
| *Methyl glycol acetate, see* | 1189 | **METHYL PROPIONATE** | 1248 |
| **2-METHYL-HEPTANETHIOL** | 3023 | *Methyl propylbenzene, see* | 2046 |
| **5-METHYL HEXAN-2-ONE** | 2302 | **METHYL PROPYL ETHER** | 2612 |
| **METHYL HYDRAZINE** | 1244 | **METHYL PROPYL KETONE** | 1249 |
| **METHYL IODIDE** | 2644 | *Methyl pyridines, see* | 2313 |
| **METHYL ISOBUTYL CARBINOL** | 2053 | *Methylstyrene, see* | 2618 |
| **METHYL ISOBUTYL KETONE** | 1245 | *alpha-Methylstyrene, see* | 2303 |
| **METHYL ISOCYANATE** | 2480 | *Methyl sulphate, see* | 1595 |

| Substance | UN Number | Substance | UN Number |
|---|---|---|---|
| *Methyl sulphide, see* | 1164 | **NAPHTHALENE, CRUDE** | 1334 |
| **METHYL TETRAHYDROFURAN** | 2536 | **NAPHTHALENE, MOLTEN** | 2304 |
| **METHYL TRICHLOROACETATE** | 2533 | **NAPHTHALENE, REFINED** | 1334 |
| **METHYL TRICHLOROSILANE** | 1250 | **alpha-NAPHTHYLAMINE** | 2077 |
| **alpha-METHYL VALERALDEHYDE** | 2367 | **beta-NAPHTHYLAMINE** | 1650 |
| *Methyl vinyl benzene, see* | 2613 | **NAPHTHYLTHIOUREA** | 1651 |
| **METHYL VINYL KETONE, STABILISED** | 1251 | **NAPHTHYLUREA** | 1652 |
| *m.i.b.c.* | 2053 | **NATURAL GASES** *(with high methane content), see* | 1971 1972 |
| *Mirbane oil, see* | 1662 | *Neohexane, see* | 1208 |
| *Misch metal, see* | 1333 | **NEON, COMPRESSED** | 1065 |
| **MOLYBDENUM PENTACHLORIDE** | 2508 | **NEON, REFRIGERATED LIQUID** | 1913 |
| *Monochloroacetic acid, see* | 1750 | *Neopentane, see* | 2044 |
| *Monochlorodifluoromethane, see* | 1018 | *Neothyl, see* | 2612 |
| *Monochlorodifluoromethane and monochloropentafluoroethane mixture with fixed boiling point, with approximately 49 per cent monochlorodifluoromethane, see* | 1973 | **NICKEL CARBONYL** | 1259 |
| | | **NICKEL CYANIDE** | 1653 |
| *Monochlorodifluoromonobromomethane, see* | 1974 | **NICKEL NITRATE** | 2725 |
| | | **NICKEL NITRITE** | 2726 |
| *Monochloropentafluoroethane and monochlorodifluoromethane mixture, see* | *1973* | **NICOTINE** | 1654 |
| *Monoethylamine, see* | 1036 | **NICOTINE COMPOUND, LIQUID, N.O.S.** *or* **NICOTINE PREPARA- TION, LIQUID, N.O.S.** | 3144 |
| *Monopropylamine, see* | 1277 | | |
| **MORPHOLINE** | 2054 | **NICOTINE COMPOUND, SOLID, N.O.S.** *or* **NICOTINE PREPARATION, SOLD, N.O.S.** | 1655 |
| **MOTOR FUEL ANTI-KNOCK MIXTURE** | 1649 | **NICOTINE HYDROCHLORIDE** *or* **NICOTINE HYDROCHLORIDE SOLUTION** | 1656 |
| **MOTOR SPIRIT** | 1203 | | |
| *Muriatic acid, see* | 1789 | **NICOTINE SALICYLATE** | 1657 |
| **MUSK XYLENE** | 2956 | **NICOTINE SULPHATE, SOLID** | 1658 |
| *Mysorite, see* | 2212 | **NICOTINE SULPHATE SOLUTION** | 1658 |

| Substance | UN Number | Substance | UN Number |
|-----------|-----------|-----------|-----------|
| **NICOTINE TARTRATE** | 1659 | **NITRO CELLULOSE SOLUTIONS, FLAMMABLE,** *with not more than 12.6 per cent nitrogen, by mass, and not more than 55 per cent nitrocellulose* | 2059 |
| **NITRATES, INORGANIC, N.O.S.** | 1477 | **NITROCELLULOSE MEMBRANE FILTERS** | 3270 |
| **NITRATES, INORGANIC, AQUEOUS SOLUTION, N.O.S.** | 3218 | **NITROCELLULOSE, WITH ALCOHOL,** *not less than 25 per cent alcohol by mass and not more than 12.6 per cent nitrogen by dry mass* | 2556 |
| **NITRATING ACID, MIXTURE** | 1796 | | |
| **NITRATING ACID, MIXTURE, SPENT** | 1826 | **NITROCELLULOSE,** *with not more than 12.6 per cent nitrogen, by dry mass,* **MIXTURE, WITH** *or* **WITHOUT PLASTICISER, WITH** *or* **WITHOUT PIGMENT** | 2557 |
| **NITRIC ACID,** *other than red fuming nitric acid* | 2031 | | |
| **NITRIC ACID, RED FUMING** | 2032 | **NITROCELLULOSE WITH WATER,** *not less than 25 per cent water by mass* | |
| **NITRIC OXIDE, COMPRESSED** | 1660 | | |
| **NITRIC OXIDE AND DINITROGEN TETROXIDE MIXTURES** | 1975 | *Nitrochlorobenzene, see* | 1578 |
| **NITRIC OXIDE AND NITROGEN DIOXIDE, MIXTURE** | 1975 | **3-NITRO-4-CHLOROBENZO-TRIFLUORIDE** | 2307 |
| **NITRILES, FLAMMABLE, TOXIC, N.O.S.** | 3273 | **NITROCRESOLS** | 2446 |
| **NITRILES, TOXIC, FLAMMABLE, N.O.S.** | 3275 | **NITROETHANE** | 2842 |
| **NITRILES, TOXIC, N.O.S.** | 3276 | **NITROGEN, COMPRESSED** | 1066 |
| **NITRITES, INORGANIC, N.O.S.** | 2627 | *Nitrogen dioxide, see* | 1067 |
| **NITRITES, INORGANIC, AQUEOUS SOLUTION, N.O.S.** | 3219 | *Nitrogen mixtures with rare gases, see* | 1981 |
| **NITROANILINES (o-,m-,p-)** | 1661 | **NITROGEN, REFRIGERATED LIQUID** | 1977 |
| **NITROANISOLE** | 2730 | *Nitrogen tetroxide, see* | 1067 |
| **NITROBENZENE** | 1662 | *Nitrogen tetroxide and nitric oxide mixtures, see* | 1975 |
| *Nitrobenzene bromide, see* | 2732 | | |
| **NITROBENZENE SULPHONIC ACID** | 2305 | **NITROGLYCERIN MIXTURE,** *with more than 2% but not more than 10% nitro-glycerine, by mass, desensitised* | 3319 |
| *Nitrobenzol, see* | 1662 | **NITROGLYCERINE MIXTURE, DESENSITIZED, LIQUID, FLAMMABLE** | 3343 |
| **NITROBENZOTRIFLUORIDES** | 2306 | | |
| **NITROBROMOBENZENE** | 2732 | | |

| Substance | UN Number | Substance | UN Number |
|---|---|---|---|
| NITROGLYCERIN SOLUTION IN ALCOHOL, *with not more than 1 per cent nitroglycerin* | 1204 | 2,5-NORBORNADIENE, INHIBITED | 2251 |
| | | OCTADECYLTRICHLOROSILANE | 1800 |
| NITROGLYCERIN, SOLUTION, IN ALCOHOL, *with more than 1 per cent but not more than 5 per cent nitroglycerin* | 3064 | OCTADIENE | 2309 |
| | | OCTAFLUOROBUT-2-ENE | 2422 |
| | | OCTAFLUOROCYCLOBUTANE | 1976 |
| NITROGUANIDINE, WETTED *with not less than 20 per cent water, by mass* | 1336 | OCTAFLUOROPROPANE | 2424 |
| NITROHYDROCHLORIC ACID | 1798 | OCTANES | 1262 |
| NITROMETHANE | 1261 | OCTYL ALDEHYDES, *flammable* | 1191 |
| *Nitromuriatic acid, see* | 1798 | tert-OCTYL MERCAPTAN | 3023 |
| NITRONAPHTHALENE | 2538 | OCTYLTRICHLOROSILANE | 1801 |
| NITROPHENOLS (o-,m-,p-) | 1663 | *Oenanthol, see* | 3056 |
| NITROPROPANES | 2608 | OIL GAS, COMPRESSED | 1071 |
| p-NITROSODIMETHYLANILINE | 1369 | *Oleum, see* | 1831 |
| NITROSTARCH, WETTED, *with not less than 20 per cent water, by mass* | 1337 | ORGANIC PEROXIDE TYPE B, LIQUID | 3101 |
| NITROSYL CHLORIDE | 1069 | ORGANIC PEROXIDE TYPE B, LIQUID, TEMPERATURE CONTROLLED | 3111 |
| NITROSYL SULPHURIC ACID | 2308 | |  |
| NITROTOLUENES (o-,m-,p-) | 1664 | ORGANIC PEROXIDE TYPE B, SOLID | 3102 |
| NITROTOLUIDINES (mono) | 2660 | ORGANIC PEROXIDE TYPE B, SOLID, TEMPERATURE CONTROLLED | 3112 |
| *Nitrous oxide and carbon dioxide mixtures, see* | 1015 | |  |
| NITROUS OXIDE | 1070 | ORGANIC PEROXIDE TYPE C, LIQUID | 3103 |
| NITROUS OXIDE, REFRIGERATED LIQUID | 2201 | ORGANIC PEROXIDE TYPE C, LIQUID, TEMPERATURE CONTROLLED | 3113 |
| NITROXYLENES (o-,m-,p-) | 1665 | |  |
| *Non-activated carbon, see* | 1361 | ORGANIC PEROXIDE TYPE C, SOLID | 3104 |
| *Non-activated charcoal, see* | 1361 | ORGANIC PEROXIDE TYPE C, SOLID, TEMPERATURE CONTROLLED | 3114 |
| NONANES | 1920 | |  |
| NONYLTRICHLOROSILANE | 1799 | |  |

| Substance | UN Number | Substance | UN Number |
|---|---|---|---|
| ORGANIC PEROXIDE TYPE D, LIQUID | 3105 | ORGANOCHLORINE PESTICIDE, LIQUID, TOXIC | 2996 |
| ORGANIC PEROXIDE TYPE D, LIQUID, TEMPERATURE CONTROLLED | 3115 | ORGANOCHLORINE PESTICIDE, SOLID, TOXIC | 2761 |
| ORGANIC PEROXIDE TYPE D, SOLID | 3106 | ORGANOMETALLIC COMPOUND, or SOLUTION, or DISPERSION, WATER-REACTIVE, FLAMMABLE, N.O.S. | 3207 |
| ORGANIC PEROXIDE TYPE D, SOLID, TEMPERATURE CONTROLLED | 3116 | ORGANOMETALLIC COMPOUNDS, TOXIC, N.O.S. | 3282 |
| ORGANIC PEROXIDE TYPE E, LIQUID | 3107 | ORGANOPHOSPHORUS COMPOUNDS, TOXIC, FLAMMABLE, N.O.S. | 3279 |
| ORGANIC PEROXIDE TYPE E, LIQUID, TEMPERATURE CONTROLLED | 3117 | ORGANOPHOSPHORUS COMPOUNDS, TOXIC | 3278 |
| ORGANIC PEROXIDE TYPE E, SOLID | 3108 | ORGANOPHOSPHOROUS PESTICIDE, LIQUID, FLAMMABLE, TOXIC, *flash point less than 23°C* | 2784 |
| ORGANIC PEROXIDE TYPE E, SOLID, TEMPERATURE CONTROLLED | 3118 | ORGANOPHOSPHORUS PESTICIDE, LIQUID, TOXIC, FLAMMABLE, *flash point 23°C or above* | 3017 |
| ORGANIC PEROXIDE TYPE F, LIQUID | 3109 | ORGANOPHOSPHORUS PESTICIDE, LIQUID, TOXIC | 3018 |
| ORGANIC PEROXIDE TYPE F, LIQUID, TEMPERATURE CONTROLLED | 3119 | ORGANOPHOSPHORUS PESTICIDE, SOLID, TOXIC | 2783 |
| ORGANIC PEROXIDE TYPE F, SOLID | 3110 | ORGANOTIN COMPOUND, LIQUID, TOXIC, N.O.S. | 2788 |
| ORGANIC PEROXIDE TYPE F, SOLID, TEMPERATURE CONTROLLED | 3120 | ORGANOTIN COMPOUND, SOLID, TOXIC, N.O.S. | 3146 |
| ORGANIC PIGMENTS SELF-HEATING | 3313 | ORGANOTIN PESTICIDE, LIQUID, FLAMMABLE, TOXIC, *flash point less than 23°C* | 2787 |
| ORGANOARSENIC COMPOUNDS, TOXIC, N.O.S. | 3280 | ORGANOTIN PESTICIDE, LIQUID, TOXIC, FLAMMABLE, *flash point 23°C or above* | 3019 |
| ORGANOCHLORINE PESTICIDE, LIQUID, FLAMMABLE, TOXIC, *flash point less than 23°C* | 2762 | ORGANOTIN PESTICIDE, LIQUID, TOXIC | 3020 |
| ORGANOCHLORINE PESTICIDE, LIQUID, TOXIC, FLAMMABLE, *flash point 23°C or above* | 2995 | ORGANOTIN PESTICIDE, SOLID, TOXIC | 2786 |

| Substance | UN Number | Substance | UN Number |
|---|---|---|---|
| *Orthophosphoric acid, see* | 1805 | *Paraquat, solution* | 3016 |
| **OSMIUM TETROXIDE** | 2471 | *Paraquat, solution in flammable liquid* | 2782 3015 |
| **OXIDISING LIQUID, CORROSIVE, N.O.S.** | 3098 | *pcb's* | 2315 |
| **OXIDISING LIQUID, N.O.S.** | 3139 | **PENTABORANE** | 1380 |
| **OXIDISING LIQUID, TOXIC, N.O.S.** | 3099 | **PENTACHLOROETHANE** | 1669 |
| **OXIDISING SOLID, CORROSIVE, N.O.S.** | 3085 | **PENTACHLOROPHENOL** | 3155 |
| **OXIDISING SOLID, N.O.S.** | 1479 | **PENTAERYTHRITE TETRANITRATE MIXTURE, DESENSITIZED, SOLID** | 3344 |
| **OXIDISING SOLID, TOXIC, N.O.S.** | 3087 | **PENTAMETHYLHEPTANE** | 2286 |
| *Oxirane, see* | 1040 | *Pentanal, see* | 2058 |
| *Oxygen and carbon dioxide mixtures, see* | 1014 | **PENTANE-2,4-DIONE** | 2310 |
| **OXYGEN, COMPRESSED** | 1072 | **PENTAFLUOROETHANE** | 3220 |
| **OXYGEN DIFLUORIDE, COMPRESSED** | 2190 | **PENTANES,** *liquid* | 1265 |
| **OXYGEN GENERATOR** | 3356 | *3-Pentanol, see* | 1105 |
| *Oxygen, mixtures with rare gases, see* | 1980 | **PENTANOLS** | 1105 |
| **OXYGEN, REFRIGERATED LIQUID** | 1073 | **1-PENTENE** | 1108 |
| *1-Oxy-4-nitrobenzene, see* | 1663 | **1-PENTOL** | 2705 |
| **PAINT** *(including paint, lacquer, enamel, stain, shellac, varnish, polish, liquid filler and liquid lacquer base)* | 1263 3066 | *Pentyl nitrite, see* | 1113 |
| | | **PERCHLORATES, INORGANIC, N.O.S.** | 1481 |
| **PAINT RELATED MATERIAL** *(including paint thinning or reducing compound)* | 1263 3066 | **PERCHLORATES, INORGANIC, AQUEOUS SOLUTION, N.O.S.** | 3211 |
| **PAPER, UNSATURATED OIL TREATED,** *incompletely dried (includes carbon paper)* | 1379 | **PERCHLORIC ACID,** *with more than 50 per cent and not more than 72 per cent acid, by mass* | 1873 |
| | | **PERCHLORIC ACID,** *with not more than 50 per cent acid, by mass* | 1802 |
| *Paraffin, see* | 1223 | *Perchlorobenzene, see* | 2729 |
| **PARAFORMALDEHYDE** | 2213 | *Perchlorocyclopentadiene, see* | 2646 |
| **PARALDEHYDE** | 1264 | | |

| Substance | UN Number | Substance | UN Number |
|---|---|---|---|
| *Perchloroethylene, see* | 1897 | **PETROLEUM GASES, LIQUEFIED** | 1075 |
| **PERCHLOROMETHYL MERCAPTAN** | 1670 | **PETROLEUM PRODUCTS, N.O.S.** | 1268 |
| **PERCHLORYL FLUORIDE** | 3083 | *Petroleum raffinate, see* | 1268 |
| *Perfluoroacetylchloride, see* | 3057 | **PHENACYL BROMIDE** | 2645 |
| **PERFLUORO (ETHYL VINYL ETHER)** | 3154 | **PHENETIDINES** | 2311 |
| | | **PHENOL, MOLTEN** | 2312 |
| **PERFLUORO (METHYL VINYL ETHER)** | 3153 | **PHENOL, SOLID** | 1671 |
| | | **PHENOL SOLUTION** | 2821 |
| *Perfluoropropane, see* | 2424 | **PHENOLATES, LIQUID** | 2904 |
| **PERFUMERY PRODUCTS,** *with flammable solvents.* | 1266 | **PHENOLATES, SOLID** | 2905 |
| **PERMANGANATES, INORGANIC, N.O.S.** | 1482 | **PHENOL SULPHONIC ACID, LIQUID** | 1803 |
| **PERMANGANATES, INORGANIC, AQUEOUS SOLUTION, N.O.S.** | 3214 | **PHENOXYACETIC ACID DERIVATIVE PESTICIDE, LIQUID, FLAMMABLE, TOXIC** | 3346 |
| **PEROXIDES, INORGANIC, N.O.S.** | 1483 | **PHENOXYACETIC ACID DERIVATIVE PESTICIDE, LIQUID, TOXIC** | 3348 |
| **PERSULPHATES, INORGANIC, N.O.S.** | 3215 | |  |
| **PERSULPHATES, INORGANIC, AQUEOUS SOLUTION, N.O.S.** | 3216 | **PHENOXYACETIC ACID DERIVATIVE PESTICIDE, LIQUID, TOXIC, FLAMMABLE** | 3347 |
| **PESTICIDE, LIQUID, FLAMMABLE, TOXIC, N.O.S.** *flash point less than 23°C* | 3021 | **PHENOXYACETIC ACID DERIVATIVE PESTICIDE, SOLID, TOXIC** | 3345 |
| **PESTICIDE, LIQUID, TOXIC, FLAMMABLE, N.O.S.,** *flash point 23°C or above* | 2903 | **PHENYLACETONITRILE LIQUID** | 2470 |
| | | **PHENYLACETYL CHLORIDE** | 2577 |
| **PESTICIDE, LIQUID, TOXIC, N.O.S** | 2902 | *Phenylamine, see* | 1547 |
| **PESTICIDE, SOLID, TOXIC, N.O.S.** | 2588 | *1-Phenylbutane, see* | 2709 |
| *Pesticides, toxic, under compressed gas, n.o.s., see* | 1950 | *2-Phenylbutane, see* | 2709 |
| *petn* | 3344 | **PHENYLCARBYLAMINE CHLORIDE** | 1672 |
| **PETROL** | 1203 | | |
| **PETROLEUM CRUDE OIL** | 1267 | **PHENYL CHLOROFORMATE** | 2746 |

| Substance | UN Number | Substance | UN Number |
|---|---|---|---|
| *Phenyl cyanide, see* | 2224 | PHOSPHORUS OXYBROMIDE, MOLTEN | 2576 |
| PHENYLENEDIAMINES(o-,m-,p) | 1673 | PHOSPHORUS OXYCHLORIDE | 1810 |
| *Phenylethylene, see* | 2055 | PHOSPHORUS PENTABROMIDE | 2691 |
| PHENYLHYDRAZINE | 2572 | PHOSPHORUS PENTACHLORIDE | 1806 |
| PHENYL ISOCYANATE | 2487 | PHOSPHORUS PENTAFLUORIDE, COMPRESSED | 2198 |
| PHENYL MERCAPTAN | 2337 | PHOSPHORUS PENTASULPHIDE, *free from yellow and white phosphorus* | 1340 |
| PHENYL MERCURIC ACETATE | 1674 | | |
| PHENYL MERCURIC COMPOUND, TOXIC, N.O.S. | 2026 | PHOSPHORUS PENTOXIDE | 1807 |
| PHENYL MERCURIC HYDROXIDE | 1894 | PHOSPHORUS SESQUISULPHIDE, *free from yellow and white phosphorus* | 1341 |
| PHENYL MERCURIC NITRATE | 1895 | *Phosphorus sulphochloride, see* | 1837 |
| PHENYL PHOSPHORUS DICHLORIDE | 2798 | PHOSPHORUS TRIBROMIDE | 1808 |
| PHENYL PHOSPHORUS THIODICHLORIDE | 2799 | PHOSPHORUS TRICHLORIDE | 1809 |
| | | PHOSPHORUS TRIOXIDE | 2578 |
| *2-Phenylpropene, see* | 2303 | PHOSPHORUS TRISULPHIDE, *free from yellow and white phosphorus* | 1343 |
| PHENYLTRICHLOROSILANE | 1804 | | |
| PHOSGENE | 1076 | PHOSPHORUS, WHITE , MOLTEN | 2447 |
| 9-PHOSPHABICYCLONONANES | 2940 | PHOSPHORUS, WHITE *or* YELLOW, DRY *or* UNDER WATER *or* IN SOLUTION | 1391 |
| PHOSPHINE | 2199 | | |
| *Phosphoretted hydrogen, see* | 2199 | *Phosphoryl chloride, see* | 1810 |
| PHOSPHORIC ACID | 1805 | PHTHALIC ANHYDRIDE, *with more than 0.05 per cent maleic anhydride* | 2214 |
| *Phosphoric acid, anhydrous, see* | 1807 | | |
| PHOSPHORUS ACID | 2834 | PICOLINES | 2313 |
| PHOSPHORUS, AMORPHOUS | 1338 | PICRITE | 1336 |
| *Phosphorus bromide, see* | 1808 | alpha-PINENE | 2368 |
| *Phosphorus chloride, see* | 1809 | PINE OIL | 1272 |
| PHOSPHORUS HEPTASULPHIDE, *free from yellow and white phosphorus* | 1339 | PIPERAZINE | 2579 |
| | | PIPERIDINE | 2401 |
| PHOSPHORUS OXYBROMIDE | 1939 | *Privaloyl chloride, see* | 2438 |

| Substance | UN Number | Substance | UN Number |
|---|---|---|---|
| **PLASTICS MOULDING COMPOUND,** *in dough, sheet or extruded rope form evolving flammable vapour* | 3314 | **POLYMERIC BEADS EXPANDABLE,** *evolving flammable vapour* | 2211 |
| | | **POTASSIUM** | 2257 |
| **PLASTICS, NITROCELLULOSE-BASED, SELF-HEATING, N.O.S.** | 2006 | **POTASSIUM ARSENATE** | 1677 |
| | | **POTASSIUM ARSENITE** | 1678 |
| *Poisonous liquid, corrosive, n.o.s., see* | 2927 | **POTASSIUM HYDROGEN DIFLUORIDE** | 1811 |
| *Poisonous liquid, flammable, n.o.s., see* | 2929 | | |
| *Poisonous liquid, organic, n.o.s. see* | 2810 | *Potassium bisulphate, see* | 2509 |
| *Poisonous liquid, oxidising, n.o.s., see* | 3122 | *Potassium bisulphate solution, see* | 2693 |
| *Poisonous liquid, water-reactive, n.o.s., see* | 3123 | **POTASSIUM BOROHYDRIDE** | 1870 |
| | | **POTASSIUM BROMATE** | 1484 |
| *Poisonous solid, corrosive, n.o.s., see* | 2928 | **POTASSIUM CHLORATE** | 1485 |
| *Poisonous solid, flammable, n.o.s., see* | 2930 | **POTASSIUM CHLORATE, AQUEOUS SOLUTION** | 2427 |
| *Poisonous solid, organic, n.o.s., see* | 2811 | **POTASSIUM CUPROCYANIDE** | 1679 |
| *Poisonous solid, oxidising, n.o.s., see* | 3086 | **POTASSIUM CYANIDE** | 1680 |
| *Poisonous solid, self-heating, n.o.s., see* | 3124 | **POTASSIUM DITHIONITE** | 1929 |
| *Poisonous solid, water-reactive, n.o.s., see* | 3125 | **POTASSIUM FLUORIDE** | 1812 |
| **POLYAMINES, FLAMMABLE, CORROSIVE, N.O.S.** | 2733 | **POTASSIUM FLUOROACETATE** | 2628 |
| **POLYAMINES, LIQUID, CORROSIVE, N.O.S.** | 2735 | **POTASSIUM FLUOROSILICATE** | 2655 |
| | | *Potassium hydrate, see* | 1814 |
| **POLYAMINES, LIQUID, CORROSIVE, FLAMMABLE, N.O.S.** | 2734 | **POTASSIUM HYDROGEN SULPHATE** | 2509 |
| **POLYAMINES, SOLID, CORROSIVE N.O.S.** | 3259 | **POTASSIUM HYDROSULPHITE** | 1929 |
| **POLYCHLORINATED BIPHENYLS** | 2315 | *Potassium hydroxide, liquid, see* | 1814 |
| **POLYESTER RESIN KIT** | 3269 | **POTASSIUM HYDROXIDE, SOLID** | 1813 |
| **POLYHALOGENATED BIPHENYLS, LIQUID** *or* **POLYHALOGENATED TERPHENYLS, LIQUID** | 3151 | **POTASSIUM HYDROXIDE SOLUTION** | 1814 |
| **POLYHALOGENATED BIPHENYLS, SOLID** *or* **POLYHALOGENATED TERPHENYLS, SOLID** | 3152 | **POTASSIUM METAL ALLOYS** | 1420 |
| | | **POTASSIUM METAVANADATE** | 2864 |

| Substance | UN Number | Substance | UN Number |
|-----------|-----------|-----------|-----------|
| **POTASSIUM  MONOXIDE** | 2033 | **PROPIONALDEHYDE** | 1275 |
| **POTASSIUM NITRATE** | 1486 | **PROPIONALDEHYDE** | 1275 |
| **POTASSIUM NITRATE AND  SODIUM NITRATE MIXTURE** | 1487 | **PROPIONIC ACID** | 1848 |
| **POTASSIUM NITRITE** | 1488 | **PROPIONIC ANHYDRIDE** | 2496 |
| **POTASSIUM PERCHLORATE** | 1489 | **PROPIONITRILE** | 2404 |
| **POTASSIUM PERMANGANATE** | 1490 | **PROPIONYL CHLORIDE** | 1815 |
| **POTASSIUM PEROXIDE** | 1491 | **n-PROPYL ACETATE** | 1276 |
| **POTASSIUM PERSULPHATE** | 1492 | *Propyl alcohol, normal* | 1274 |
| **POTASSIUM PHOSPHIDE** | 2012 | **PROPYLAMINE** | 1277 |
| *Potassium selenate, see* | 2630 | **n-PROPYLBENZENE** | 2364 |
| *Potassium selenite, see* | 2630 | **PROPYL CHLORIDE** | 1278 |
| *Potassium sllicofluoride, see* | 2655 | **n-PROPYL CHLOROFORMATE** | 2740 |
| **POTASSIUM SODIUM ALLOYS** | 1422 | **PROPYLENE** | 1077 |
| **POTASSIUM SULPHIDE,  ANHYDROUS** *or* **POTASSIUM  SULPHIDE,** *with less than 30 per  cent water crystallisation* | 1382 | **PROPYLENE CHLOROHYDRIN** | 2611 |
| | | **1,2-PROPYLENEDIAMINE** | 2258 |
| | | *Propylene dichloride* | 1279 |
| **POTASSIUM SULPHIDE,  HYDRATED,** *with not less than 30  per cent water of crystallisation* | 1847 | **PROPYLENEIMINE, INHIBITED** | 1921 |
| | | **PROPYLENE OXIDE** | 1280 |
| **POTASSIUM SUPEROXIDE** | 2466  3164 | **PROPYLENE TETRAMER** | 2850 |
| | | *Propylene trimer, see* | 2057 |
| *Pressurised articles, see* | | **PROPYL FORMATES** | 1281 |
| **PRINTING INK,** *flammable* | 1210 | **n-PROPYL ISOCYANATE** | 2482 |
| **PROPADIENE, INHIBITED** | 2200 | *Propyl mercaptan, see* | 2402 |
| *Propadiene and methyl acetylene  mixtures, see* | 1060 | **n-PROPYL NITRATE** | 1865 |
| **PROPANE** | 1978 | **PROPYLTRICHLOROSILANE** | 1816 |
| **PROPANETHIOLS** | 2402 | *Pyrazine hexahydride, see* | 2579 |
| **n-PROPANOL** | 1274 | **PYRETHROID PESTICIDE,  LIQUID,  FLAMMABLE, TOXIC** | 3350 |
| *Propene, see* | 1077 | | |

| Substance | UN Number | Substance | UN Number |
|---|---|---|---|
| **PYRETHROID PESTICIDE, LIQUID, TOXIC** | 3352 | *R21, see* | 1029 |
| | | *R22, see* | 1018 |
| **PYRETHROID PESTICIDE, LIQUID, TOXIC, FLAMMABLE** | 3351 | *R23, see* | 1984 |
| **PYRETHROID PESTICIDE, SOLID, TOXIC** | 3349 | *R40, see* | 1063 |
| | | *R41, see* | 2454 |
| **PYRIDINE** | 1282 | *R114, see* | 1958 |
| **PYROPHORIC ALLOY, N.O.S.** | 1383 | *R115, see* | 1020 |
| **PYROPHORIC LIQUID, ORGANIC, N.O.S.** | 2845 | *R116, see* | 1021 |
| **PYROPHORIC LIQUID, INORGANIC, N.O.S.** | 3194 | *R124, see* | 3220 |
| | | *R125, see* | 1983 |
| **PYROPHORIC METAL, N.O.S. PYROPHORIC** | 1383 | *R133a, see* | 3159 |
| **ORGANOMETALLIC COMPOUND N.O.S.** | 3203 | *R134a. see* | 2035 |
| | | *R143a, see* | 2035 |
| **PYROPHORIC SOLID, ORGANIC N.O.S.** | 2846 | *R152a, see* | 1030 |
| **PYROPHORIC SOLID, INORGANIC, N.O.S.** | 3200 | *R161, see* | 2453 |
| | | *R161, see* | 2453 |
| **PYROSULPHURYL CHLORIDE** | 1817 | *R218, see* | 2424 |
| *Pyroxylin solution, see* | 2059 | *R227, see* | 3296 |
| **PYRROLIDINE** | 1922 | *R404A* | 3337 |
| *Quinol, see* | 2662 | *R407A* | 3338 |
| **QUINOLINE** | 2656 | *R407B* | 3339 |
| *Quinone, see* | 2587 | *R407C* | 334 |
| *RC318* | 1976 | *R500, see* | 2602 |
| *R12, see* | 1028 | *R503, see* | 2599 |
| *R12B1, see* | 1974 | *R1132a, see* | 1959 |
| *R13, see* | 1022 | *R1216, see* | 1858 |
| *R13B1, see* | 1009 | *R1318, see* | 2422 |
| *R14, see* | 1982 | | |

| Substance | UN Number | Substance | UN Number |
|---|---|---|---|
| *R1426, see* | 2517 | *not exceeding 840 microns and rubber content exceeding 45%* | 1345 |
| **RADIOACTIVE MATERIAL, FISSILE, N.O.S.** | 2918 | **RUBBER SOLUTION** | 1287 |
| **RADIOACTIVE MATERIAL, EXCEPTED PACKAGE** | 2910 | **RUBIDIUM** | 1423 |
| **RADIOACTIVE MATERIAL, LOW SPECIFIC ACTIVITY (LSA) N.O.S.** | 2912 | **RUBIDIUM HYDROXIDE** | 2678 |
| **RADIOACTIVE MATERIAL, N.O.S.** | 2982 | **RUBIDIUM HYDROXIDE SOLUTION** | 2677 |
| **RADIOACTIVE MATERIAL SPECIAL FORM, N.O.S.** | 2974 | *Saltpetre, see* | 1486 |
| **RADIOACTIVE MATERIAL SURFACE CONTAMINATED OBJECTS (SCO)** | 2913 | *Sand acid, see* | 1778 |
| **RARE GASES MIXTURE, COMPRESSED** | 1979 | **SEAT-BELT PRETENSIONERS** | 3268 3353 |
| **RARE GASES AND NITROGEN MIXTURE, COMPRESSED** | 1981 | **SEED CAKE,** *with more than 1.5 per cent oil and not more than 11 per cent moisture* | 1386 |
| **RARE GASES AND OXYGEN MIXTURE, COMPRESSED** | 1980 | **SEED CAKE,** *with not more than 1.5 per cent oil and not more than 11 per cent moisture* | 2217 |
| **RECEPTACLES, SMALL, CONTAINING GAS** *without release device, not refillable* | 2037 | *See expellers, see* | 2217 1386 |
| *Red phosphorus, see* | 1338 | **SELENATES** | 2630 |
| **REFRIGERANT GAS, N.O.S.** | 1078 | **SELENIC ACID** | 1905 |
| | | **SELENITES** | 2630 |
| **REFRIGERATING MACHINES,** *containing non-flammable, non-toxic, liquid liquefied gas or ammonia solutions (UN 2672)* | 2857 | **SELENIUM COMPOUNDS, TOXIC, N.O.S.** | 3283 |
| **REGULATED MEDICAL WASTE, N.O.S.** | 3291 | **SELENIUM DISULPHIDE** | 2657 |
| | | **SELENIUM HEXAFLUORIDE** | 2194 |
| | | **SELENIUM OXYCHLORIDE** | 2879 |
| **RESIN SOLUTION, FLAMMABLE** | 1866 | **SELF-HEATING LIQUID, INORGANIC, N.O.S.** | 3186 |
| *Resorcin, see* | 2876 | | |
| **RESORCINOL** | 2876 | **SELF-HEATING LIQUID, CORROSIVE, INORGANIC, N.O.S.** | 3188 |
| **ROSIN OIL** | 1286 | **SELF-HEATING LIQUID, TOXIC, INORGANIC, N.O.S.** | 3187 |
| **RUBBER SCRAP** *or* **RUBBER SHODDY,** *powdered or granulated,* | | | |

| Substance | UN Number | Substance | UN Number |
|---|---|---|---|
| SELF-HEATING LIQUID, ORGANIC, N.O.S. | 3183 | SELF-REACTIVE SOLID TYPE B | 3222 |
| SELF-HEATING LIQUID, ORGANIC, CORROSIVE, N.O.S. | 3185 | SELF-REACTIVE SOLID TYPE B, TEMPERATURE CONTROLLED | 3232 |
| | | SELF-REACTIVE SOLID TYPE C | 3224 |
| SELF-HEATING LIQUID, ORGANIC, TOXIC, N.O.S. | 3184 | SELF-REACTIVE SOLID TYPE C, TEMPERATURE CONTROLLED | 3234 |
| SELF-HEATING SOLID, ORGANIC TOXIC, N.O.S. | 3126 | SELF-REACTIVE SOLID TYPE D | 3226 |
| SELF-HEATING METAL, POWDERS, N.O.S. | 3189 | SELF-REACTIVE SOLID TYPE D TEMPERATURE CONTROLLED | 3236 |
| SELF-HEATING SOLID, INORGANIC, N.O.S. | 3190 | SELF-REACTIVE SOLID TYPE E | 3228 |
| SELF-HEATING SOLID, CORROSIVE, INORGANIC, N.O.S. | 3192 | SELF-REACTIVE SOLID TYPE E, TEMPERATURE CONTROLLED | 3238 |
| SELF-HEATING SOLID, TOXIC, INORGANIC, N.O.S. | 3191 | SELF-REACTIVE SOLID TYPE F | 3230 |
| SELF-HEATING SOLID, ORGANIC, N.O.S. | 3088 | SELF-REACTIVE SOLID TYPE F, TEMPERATURE CONTROLLED | 3240 |
| SELF-HEATING SOLID, ORGANIC, TOXIC, N.O.S. | 3128 | SHALE OIL | 1288 |
| SELF-REACTIVE LIQUID TYPE B | 3221 | SILANE, COMPRESSED | 2203 |
| SELF-REACTIVE LIQUID TYPE B, TEMPERATURE CONTROLLED | 3231 | Silicofluoric acid, see | 1778 |
| SELF-REACTIVE LIQUID TYPE C | 3223 | Silicofluorides, n.o.s., see | 2856 |
| SELF-REACTIVE LIQUID TYPE C, TEMPERATURE CONTROLLED | 3233 | Silicon chloride, see | 1818 |
| SELF-REACTIVE LIQUID TYPE D | 3225 | SILICON POWDER, AMORPHOUS | 1346 |
| SELF-REACTIVE LIQUID TYPE D, TEMPERATURE CONTROLLED | 3235 | SILICON TETRACHLORIDE | 1818 |
| SELF-REACTIVE LIQUID TYPE E, | 3227 | SILICON TETRAFLUORIDE, COMPRESSED | 1859 |
| SELF-REACTIVE LIQUID TYPE E, TEMPERATURE CONTROLLED | 3237 | SILVER ARSENITE | 1683 |
| SELF-REACTIVE LIQUID TYPE F | 3229 | SILVER CYANIDE | 1684 |
| | | SILVER NITRATE | 1493 |
| SELF-REACTIVE LIQUID TYPE F, TEMPERATURE CONTROLLED | 3239 | SILVER PICRATE, WETTED with not less than 30 per cent water, by mass | 1347 |
| | | SLUDGE ACID | 1906 |
| | | Small devices, see | 3150 |

| Substance | UN Number | Substance | UN Number |
|---|---|---|---|
| **SODA LIME,** *with more than 4 per cent sodium hydroxide* | 1907 | **SODIUM CYANIDE SOLUTION** | 1689 |
| **SODIUM** | 1428 | *Sodium dimethylarsenate, see* | 1688 |
| **SODIUM ALUMINATE SOLUTION** | 1819 | **SODIUM DINITRO-ORTHO-CRESOLATE, WETTED** *with not less than 15 per cent water, by mass* | |
| **SODIUM ALUMINIUM HYDRIDE** | 2835 | *Sodium dioxide, see* | 1504 |
| **SODIUM AMMONIUM VANADATE** | 2863 | **SODIUM DITHIONITE** | 1348 |
| **SODIUM ARSANILATE** | 2473 | **SODIUM FLUORIDE** | 1690 |
| **SODIUM ARSENATE** | 1685 | **SODIUM FLUOROACETATE** | 2629 |
| **SODIUM ARSENITE, AQUEOUS SOLUTIONS** | 1686 | **SODIUM FLUOROSILICATE** | 2674 |
| **SODIUM ARSENITE, SOLID** | 2027 | *Sodium hydrate, see* | 1824 |
| **SODIUM AZIDE** | 1687 | **SODIUM HYDRIDE** | 1427 |
| *Sodium bifluoride, see* | 2439 | **SODIUM HYDROGEN DIFLUORIDE** | 2439 |
| *Sodium binoxide, see* | 1504 | *Sodium hydrogen sulphate solution, see* | 2837 |
| *Sodium bisulphite solution, see* | 2693 | **SODIUM HYDROSULPHIDE** *with less than 25 per cent water of crystallisation* | 3218 |
| **SODIUM BOROHYDRIDE** | 1426 | **SODIUM HYDROSULPHIDE** *with not less than 25 per cent water of crystallisation* | 2949 |
| **SODIUM BOROHYDRIDE AND SODIUM HYDROXIDE SOLUTION,** *with not more than 12% sodium borohydride and not more than 40% sodium hydroxide, by mass* | 3320 | **SODIUM HYDROSULPHITE** | 1384 |
| **SODIUM BROMATE** | 1494 | **SODIUM HYDROXIDE, SOLID** | 1838 |
| **SODIUM CACODYLATE** | 1688 | **SODIUM HYDROXIDE SOLUTION** | 1824 |
| **SODIUM CHLORATE** | 1495 | **SODIUM METHYLATE** | 1431 |
| **SODIUM CHLORATE, AQUEOUS SOLUTION** | 2428 | **SODIUM METHYLATE SOLUTION,** *in alcohol* | 1289 |
| **SODIUM CHLORITE** | 1496 | **SODIUM MONOXIDE** | 1825 |
| **SODIUM CHLOROACETATE** | 2659 | **SODIUM NITRATE** | 1498 |
| **SODIUM CUPROCYANIDE SOLID** | 2316 | **SODIUM NITRATE AND POTASSIUM NITRATE MIXTURE** | 1499 |
| **SODIUM CUPROCYANIDE SOLUTION** | 2317 | **SODIUM NITRITE** | 1500 |
| **SODIUM CYANIDE, SOLID** | 1689 | **SODIUM PENTACHLOROPHENATE** | 2567 |

| Substance | UN Number | Substance | UN Number |
|---|---|---|---|
| **SODIUM PERCHLORATE** | 1502 | **STIBINE** | 2676 |
| **SODIUM PERMANGANATE** | 1503 | *Strontium alloys, pyrophoric, see* | 1383 |
| **SODIUM PEROXIDE** | 1504 | **STRONTIUM ARSENITE** | 1691 |
| **SODIUM PEROXOBORATE, ANHYDROUS** | 3247 | **STRONTIUM CHLORATE** | 1506 |
| **SODIUM PERSULPHATE** | 1505 | *Strontium dioxide, see* | 1509 |
| **SODIUM PHOSPHIDE** | 1432 | **STRONTIUM NITRATE** | 1507 |
| **SODIUM PICRAMATE, WETTED** *with not less than 20 per cent water, by mass* | 1349 | **STRONTIUM PERCHLORATE** | 1508 |
| | | **STRONTIUM PEROXIDE** | 1509 |
| *Sodium potassium alloys, solid, see* | 1422 | **STRONTIUM PHOSPHIDE** | 2013 |
| *Sodium selenate, see* | 2630 | **STRYCHNINE** *or* **STRYCHNINE SALTS** | 1692 |
| *Sodium selenite, see* | 2630 | **STYRENE MONOMER, INHIBITED** | 2055 |
| *Sodium silicofluoride, see* | 2674 | *Substances liable to spontaneous combustion, n.o.s., see* | 2845 2846 |
| **SOSODIUM SULPHIDE, ANHYDROUS** *or* **SODIUM SULPHIDE** *with less than 30 per cent water of crystallisation* | 1385 | **SUBSTITUTED NITROPHENOL PESTICIDE, LIQUID, FLAMMABLE, TOXIC,** *flash point less than 23°C* | 2780 |
| **SODIUM SULPHIDE, HYDRATED** *with not less than 30 per cent water* | 1849 | **SUBSTITUTED NITROPHENOL PESTICIDE, LIQUID, TOXIC, FLAMMABLE,** *flash point 23°C or above* | 3013 |
| **SODIUM SUPEROXIDE** | 2547 | **SUBSTITUTED NITROPHENOL PESTICIDE, LIQUID, TOXIC** | 3014 |
| **SOLIDS CONTAINING CORROSIVE LIQUID , N.O.S.** | 3244 | **SUBSTITUTED NITROPHENOL PESTICIDE, SOLID, TOXIC** | 2779 |
| **SOLIDS CONTAINING FLAMMABLE LIQUID, N.O.S.** | 3175 | **SULPHAMIC ACID** | 2967 |
| **SOLIDS CONTAINING TOXIC LIQUID, N.O.S.** | 3243 | **SULPHUR** | 1350 |
| *Solvents, flammable, n.o.s., see* | 1933 | **SULPHUR CHLORIDES** | 1828 |
| *Solvents, flammable, toxic, n.o.s., see* | 1992 | *Sulphur dichloride, see* | 1828 |
| **STANNIC CHLORIDE, ANHYDROUS** | 1827 | **SULPHUR DIOXIDE** | 1079 |
| **STANNIC CHLORIDE PENTAHYDRATE** | 2440 | **SULPHUR HEXAFLUORIDE** | 1080 |
| **STANNIC PHOSPHIDES** | 1433 | **SULPHUR, MOLTEN** | 2448 |
| *Steel swarf, see* | 2793 | | |

| Substance | UN Number | Substance | UN Number |
|---|---|---|---|
| *Sulphur monochloride, see* | 1828 | **TETRACHLOROETHYLENE** | 1897 |
| *Sulphuretted hydrogen, see* | 1053 | **TETRAETHYLDITHIOPYRO-PHOSPHATE** | 1704 |
| **SULPHURIC ACID** *with more than 51% acid* | 1830 | **TETRAETHYLENEPENTAMINE** | 2320 |
| **SULPHURIC ACID** *with not more than 51% acid* | 2796 | *Tetraethyl lead, see* | 1649 |
| | | **TETRAETHYL SILICATE** | 1292 |
| **SULPHURIC ACID, FUMING** | 1831 | *Tetrafluorodichloroethane, see* | 1958 |
| **SULPHURIC ACID, SPENT** | 1832 | **1,1,1,2-TETRAFLUOROETHANE** | 3159 |
| *Sulphuric and hydrofluoric acid mixtures, see* | 1786 | **TETRAFLUOROETHYLENE, INHIBITED** | 1081 |
| **SULPHUROUS ACID** | 1833 | **TETRAFLUOROMETHANE, COMPRESSED** | 1982 |
| **SULPHUR TETRAFLUORIDE** | 2418 | **1,2,3,6-TETRAHYDRO-BENZALDEHYDE** | 2498 |
| **SULPHUR TRIOXIDE, INHIBITED** | 1829 | **TETRAHYDROFURAN** | 2056 |
| **SULPHUR TRIOXIDE, STABILISED** | 1829 | **TETRAHYDROFURFURYLAMINE** | 2943 |
| **SULPHURYL CHLORIDE** | 1834 | *Tetrahydro-1, 4-oxazine, see* | 2045 |
| **SULPHURYL FLUORIDE** | 2191 | **TETRAHYDROPHTHALIC ANHYDRIDES,** *with more than 0.05 per cent of maleic anhydride* | 2698 |
| *Synthesis gas, see* | 2600 | **1,2,3,6-TERTRAHYDROPYRIDINE** | 2410 |
| **TARS, LIQUID, INCLUDING ROAD ASPHALT AND OILS, BITUMEN AND CUTBACKS** | 1999 | **TETRAHYDROTHIOPHENE** | 2412 |
| *Tartar emetic, see* | 1551 | *Tetramethoxysilane, see* | 2606 |
| **TEAR GAS CANDLES** | 1700 | **TETRAMETHYL AMMONIUM HYDROXIDE SOLUTION** | 1835 |
| **TEAR GAS SUBSTANCE, LIQUID** *or* **SOLID, N.O.S.** | 1693 | *Tetramethylene, see* | 2601 |
| **TELLURIUM COMPOUNDS, TOXIC, N.O.S.** | 3284 | *Tetramethylene cyanide* | 2205 |
| | | *Tetramethyl lead, see* | 1649 |
| **TELLURIUM HEXAFLUORIDE** | 2195 | **TETRAMETHYLSILANE** | 2749 |
| **TERPENE HYDROCARBONS N.O.S.** | 2319 | **TETRANITROMETHANE** | 1510 |
| **TERPINOLENE** | 2541 | **TETRAPROPYL ORTHOTITANATE** | 2413 |
| **TETRABROMOETHANE** | 2504 | **THALLIUM CHLORATE** | 2573 |
| **TETRACHLOROETHANE** | 1702 | | |

| Substance | UN Number | Substance | UN Number |
|---|---|---|---|
| THALLIUM COMPOUND, N.O.S. | 1707 | **TITANIUM POWDER, WETTED** *with not less than 25 per cent water (a visible excess of water must be present) (a) mechanically produced, particle size less than 53 microns; (b) chemically produced, particle size less than 840 microns* | 1352 |
| THALLIUM NITRATE | 2727 | | |
| 4-THIAPENTANAL | 2785 | | |
| THIOACETIC ACID | 2436 | | |
| THIOCARBAMATE PESTICIDE, LIQUID, FLAMMABLE, TOXIC, *flash point less than 23°C* | 2772 | TITANIUM SPONGE GRANULES or **TITANIUM SPONGE POWDERS** | 2878 |
| | | TITANIUM TETRACHLORIDE | 1838 |
| THIOCARBAMATE PESTICIDE, LIQUID, TOXIC, FLAMMABLE, *flash point 23°C or above* | 3005 | TITANIUM TRICHLORIDE MIXTURES | 2869 |
| THIOCARBAMATE PESTICIDE, LIQUID, TOXIC | 3006 | TITANIUM TRICHLORIDE, PYROPHORIC | 2441 |
| THIOCARBAMATE PESTICIDE, SOLID, TOXIC | 2771 | TITANIUM TRICHLORIDE MIXTURE, PYROPHORIC | 2441 |
| THIOGLYCOL | 2966 | TNT, *see* | 1356 |
| THIOGLYCOLIC ACID | 1940 | TOLUENE | 1294 |
| THIOLACTIC ACID | 2936 | TOLUENE DI-ISOCYANATE | 2078 |
| THIONYL CHLORIDE | 1836 | TOLUENE SULPHONIC ACID | 2583 2584 2585 2586 |
| THIOPHENE | 2414 | | |
| Thiophenol, *see* | 2337 | TOLUIDINES | 1708 |
| THIOPHOSGENE | 2474 | Toluol, *see* | 1294 |
| THIOPHOSPHORYL CHLORIDE | 1837 | Toluylene diisocyanate, *see* | 2078 |
| THIOUREA DIOXIDE | 3341 | 2,4-TOLUYLENEDIAMINE | 1709 |
| THORIUM METAL, PYROPHORIC | 2975 | Tolyene diisocyanate, *see* | 2078 |
| THORIUM NITRATE , SOLID | 2976 | Tolylethylene, *see* | 2618 |
| TINCTURES, MEDICINAL | 1293 | TOXIC LIQUID, CORROSIVE, INORGANIC, N.O.S. | 3289 |
| Tin tetrachloride, *see* | 1827 | | |
| TITANIUM DISULPHIDE | 3174 | TOXIC LIQUID, CORROSIVE, ORGANIC, N.O.S. | 2927 |
| TITANIUM HYDRIDE | 1871 | TOXIC LIQUID, FLAMMABLE, ORGANIC, N.O.S. | 2929 |
| TITANIUM POWDER, DRY | 2546 | | |

| Substance | UN Number | Substance | UN Number |
|---|---|---|---|
| TOXIC LIQUID , INORGANIC, N.O.S. | 3287 | TRIBUTYL PHOSPHANE | 3254 |
| TOXIC LIQUID, ORGANIC, N.O.S. | 2810 | *Trichloroacetaldehyde, see* | 2075 |
| TOXIC LIQUID, OXIDISING, N.O.S. | 3122 | TRICHLOROACETIC ACID | 1839 |
| TOXIC LIQUID, WATER-REACTIVE, N.O.S. | 3123 | TRICHLOROACETIC ACID SOLUTION | 2564 |
| TOXIC SOLID, CORROSIVE, INORGANIC, N.O.S. | 3290 | *Trichloroaceticaldehyde, see* | 2075 |
| TOXIC SOLID, CORROSIVE, ORGANIC, N.O.S. | 2928 | TRICHLOROACETYL CHLORIDE | 2442 |
| TOXIC SOLID, FLAMMABLE, ORGANIC, N.O.S. | 2930 | TRICHLOROBENZENES, LIQUID | 2321 |
| | | TRICHLOROBUTENE | 2322 |
| TOXIC SOLID, SELF-HEATING, N.O.S. | 3124 | 1,1,1-TRICHLOROETHANE | 2831 |
| TOXIC SOLID, ORGANIC, N.O.S. | 2811 | TRICHLOROETHYLENE | 1710 |
| TOXIC SOLID, OXIDISING, N.O.S. | 3086 | TRICHLOROISOCYANURIC ACID, DRY | 2468 |
| TOXIC SOLID, WATER-REACTIVE N.O.S. | 3125 | *Trichloronitromethane, see* | 1580 |
| TOXIC, EXTRACTED FROM LIVING SOURCES, TOXIC, N.O.S. | 3172 | TRICHLOROSILANE | 1295 |
| *Tremolite. see* | 2590 | *2,4,6-Trichloro-1,3,5-triazine, see* | 2670 |
| TRIALLYLAMINE | 2610 | TRICRESYL PHOSPHATE, with *more than 3 per cent ortho isomer* | 2574 |
| TRIALLYL BORATE | 2609 | TRIETHYLAMINE | 1296 |
| TRIAZINE PESTICIDE, LIQUID FLAMMABLE, TOXIC, *flash point less than 23°C* | 2764 | *Triethyl borate, see* | 1176 |
| | | TRIETHYLENETETRAMINE | 2259 |
| TRIAZINE PESTICIDE, LIQUID TOXIC, FLAMMABLE, *flash point 23°C or above* | 2997 | *Triethyl orthoformate, see* | 2524 |
| | | TRIETHYL PHOSPHITE | 2323 |
| TRIAZINE PESTICIDE, LIQUID, TOXIC | 2998 | TRIFLUOROACETIC ACID | 2699 |
| | | TRIFLUOROACETYL CHLORIDE | 3057 |
| TRIAZINE PESTICIDE, SOLID, TOXIC | 2763 | *Trifluorobromoemethane, see* | 1009 |
| | | *Trifluorochloroethane, see* | 1983 |
| *Tribromoborane, see* | 2692 | TRIFLUOROCHLOROETHYLENE, INHIBITED | 1082 |
| TRIBUTYLAMINE | 2542 | | |

| Substance | UN Number | Substance | UN Number |
|-----------|-----------|-----------|-----------|
| *Trifluorochloro methane, see* | 1022 | **TRINITROPHENOL, WETTED** *with not less than 30 per cent water, by mass* | 1344 |
| **1,1,1-TRIFLUOROETHANE** | 2035 | | |
| **TRIFLUOROMETHANE** | 1984 | **TRINITROTOLUENE, WETTED** *with not less than 30 per cent water, by mass* | 1356 |
| **TRIFLUOROMETHANE, REFRIGERATED LIQUID** | 3136 | **TRIPROPYLAMINE** | 2260 |
| **2-TRIFLUOROMETHYLANILINE** | 2942 | **TRIPROPYLENE** | 2057 |
| **3-TRIFLUOROMETHYLANILINE** | 2948 | **TRIS-(I-AZINIDINYL) PHOSHINE OXIDE** | 2501 |
| **TRIISOBUTYLENE** | 2324 | *Tropilidene, see* | 2603 |
| **TRIISOPROPYL BORATE** | 2616 | **TUNGSTEN HEXAFLUORIDE** | 2196 |
| **TRIMETHYLACETYL CHLORIDE** | 2438 | **TURPENTINE** | 1299 |
| **TRIMETHYLAMINE, ANHYDROUS** | 1083 | **TURPENTINE SUBSTITUTE** | 1300 |
| **TRIMETHYLAMINE, AQUEOUS SOLUTION,** *not more than 50 per cent trimethylamine by mass* | 1297 | **UNDECANE** | 2330 |
| **1,3,5-TRIMETHYLBENZENE** | 2325 | **URANIUM HEXAFLUORIDE, FISSILE,** *containing more than 1.0 per cent Uranium-235* | 2977 |
| **TRIMETHYL BORATE** | 2416 | **URANIUM HEXAFLUORIDE,** *fissile excepted or no-fissile* | 2978 |
| **TRIMETHYLCHLOROSILANE** | 1298 | **URANIUM METAL, PYROPHORIC** | 2979 |
| **TRIMETHYLCYCLOHEXYLAMINE** | 2326 | **URANYL NITRATE HEXAHYDRATE SOLUTION** | 2980 |
| *Trimethylene chlorobromide, see* | 2688 | **URANYL NITRATE, SOLID** | 2981 |
| **TRIMETHYLHEXA-METHYLENEDIAMINES** | 2327 | **UREA HYDROGEN PEROXIDE** | 1511 |
| **TRIMETHYLHEXAMETHYLENE DIISOCYANATE** | 2328 | **UREA NITRATE, WETTED** *with not less than 20 per cent water, by mass* | 1357 |
| *2,4,4-Trimethyl pentene-1, see* | 2050 | *Valeral, see* | 2058 |
| *2,4,4-Trimethyl pentene-2, see* | 2050 | **VALERALDEHYDE** | 2058 |
| **TRIMETHYL PHOSPHITE** | 2329 | *n-Valeraldehyde, see* | 2058 |
| **TRINITROBENZENE, WETTED** *with not less than 30 per cent water, by mass* | 1453 | *Valeric aldehyde, see* | 2058 |
| **TRINITROBENZOIC ACID, WETTED** *with not less than 30 per cent water, by mass* | 1355 | **VALERYL CHLORIDE** | 2502 |
| | | **VANADIUM COMPOUNDS, TOXIC, N.O.S.** | 3285 |

| Substance | UN Number | Substance | UN Number |
|---|---|---|---|
| *Vanadium oxysulphate, see* | 2931 | WATER-REACTIVE LIQUID, CORROSIVE, N.O.S. | 3129 |
| VANADIUM PENTOXIDE, *non-fused form* | 2862 | WATER-REACTIVE LIQUID, N.O.S. | 3148 |
| VANADIUM TETRACHLORIDE | 2444 | WATER-REACTIVE LIQUID, TOXIC, N.O.S. | 3130 |
| VANADIUM TRICHLORIDE | 2475 | WATER-REACTIVE SOLID CORROSIVE, N.O.S. | 3131 |
| VANADYL SULPHATE | 2931 | WATER-REACTIVE SOLID, FLAMMABLE, N.O.S. | 3132 |
| *Viliaumite, see* | 1690 | | |
| VINYL ACETATE, INHIBITED | 1301 | WATER-REACTIVE SOLID, N.O.S. | 2813 |
| *Vinylbenzene, see* | 2055 | WATER-REACTIVE SOLID, TOXIC, N.O.S. | 3134 |
| VINYL BROMIDE, INHIBITED | 1085 | | |
| VINYL BUTYRATE, INHIBITED | 2838 | WATER-REACTIVE SOLID, SELF-HEATING, N.O.S. | 3135 |
| VINYL CHLORIDE, INHIBITED *or* VINYL CHLORIDE, STABILISED | 1086 | *Wheelchair, electric, see* | 3171 |
| VINYL CHLOROACETATE | 2589 | *White arsenic, see* | 1561 |
| VINYL ETHYL ETHER, INHIBITED | 1302 | WHITE ASBESTOS *(chrysotile, actinolite, anthophyllite, tremolite)* | 2590 |
| VINYL ETHYL ETHER, INHIBITED | 1302 | *White spirit, see* | 1300 |
| VINYL FLUORIDE, INHIBITED | 1860 | WOOD PRESERVATIVES, LIQUID | 1306 |
| VINYLIDENE CHLORIDE, INHIBITED | 1303 | XANTHATES | 3342 |
| VINYL ISOBUTYL ETHER, INHIBITED | 1304 | XENON, COMPRESSED | 2036 |
| VINYL METHYL ETHER INHIBITED | 1087 | XENON, REFRIGERATED LIQUID | 2591 |
| | | XYLENES | 1307 |
| VINYL PYRIDINES, INHIBITED | 3073 | XYLENOLS | 2261 |
| VINYLTOLUENES, INHIBITED | 2618 | XYLIDINES | 1711 |
| | | *Xylols, see* | 1307 |
| VINYLTRICHLOROSILANE, INHIBITED | 1305 | XYLYL BROMIDE | 1701 |
| *Water gas, see* | 2600 | ZINC AMMONIUM NITRATE | 1512 |
| *Water reactive substances, n.o.s. see* | 2813 | ZINC ARSENATE | 1712 |

| Substance | UN Number | Substance | UN Number |
|---|---|---|---|
| **ZINC ARSENITE** | 1712 | **ZIRCONIUM POWDER, DRY** | 2008 |
| **ZINC ARSENATE AND ZINC ARSENITE MIXTURE** | 1712 | **ZIRCONIUM POWDER, WETTED** *with not less than 25 per cent water (a visible excess of water must be present)* *(a) mechanically produced, particle size less than 53 microns; (b) chemically produced, particle size less than 840 microns* | 1358 |
| **ZINC ASHES** | 1435 | | |
| *Zinc bisulphite solution, see* | 2693 | | |
| **ZINC BROMATE** | 2469 | | |
| **ZINC CHLORATE** | 1513 | **ZIRCONIUM NITRATE** | 2728 |
| **ZINC CHLORIDE, ANHYDROUS** | 2331 | **ZIRCONIUM PICRAMATE, WETTED** *with not less than 20 per cent water, by mass* | 1517 |
| **ZINC CHLORIDE SOLUTION** | 1840 | | |
| **ZINC CYANIDE** | 1713 | **ZIRCONIUM SCRAP** | 1932 |
| **ZINC DITHIONITE** | 1931 | **ZIRCONIUM SUSPENDED IN A FLAMMABLE LIQUID** | 1308 |
| **ZINC DUST** | 1436 | | |
| **ZINC FLUOROSILICATE** | 2855 | **ZIRCONIUM TETRACHLORIDE** | 2503 |
| **ZINC HYDROSULPHITE** | 1931 | | |
| **ZINC NITRATE** | 1514 | | |
| **ZING PERMANGANATE** | 1515 | | |
| **ZINC PEROXIDE** | 1516 | | |
| **ZINC PHOSPHIDE** | 1714 | | |
| **ZINC POWDER** | 1436 | | |
| **ZINC RESINATE** | 2714 | | |
| *Zinc selenate, see* | 2630 | | |
| *Zinc selenite, see* | 2630 | | |
| *Zinc silicofluoride, see* | 2855 | | |
| **ZIRCONIUM HYDRIDE** | 1437 | | |
| **ZIRCONIUM, DRY,** *coiled wire, finished metal sheets, strip (thinner than 254 microns but not thinner than 18 microns)* | 2858 | | |
| **ZIRCONIUM, DRY,** *finished sheets, strip or coiled wire* | 2009 | | |

Produced by the Home Office Hazchem Committee, consisting of representatives from the following organisations:-

Chemical Industries Association

Department of Environment Transport and the Regions

Environment Agency

Health and Safety Executive

Home Office, Fire & Emergency Planning Directorate

Independent Consultant

London Fire and Civil Defence Authority

National Chemical Emergency Centre

Scottish Office, Home Department

Stanger Science and Environment

Water Services Association